D1351073

THE REACTIVE INTERMEDIATES
OF ORGANIC CHEMISTRY

THE REACTIVE INTERMEDIATES
OF ORGANIC CHEMISTRY

JOHN E. LEFFLER
Florida State University
Tallahassee, Florida

INTERSCIENCE PUBLISHERS, INC., NEW YORK
1956   Interscience Publishers Ltd., London

Interscience Publishers, Inc.,
250 Fifth Avenue, New York 1, N. Y.
For Great Britain and Northern Ireland:
Interscience Publishers Ltd.,
88/90 Chancery Lane, London, W.C. 2
PRINTED IN THE NETHERLANDS

Preface

The reaction mechanisms available to the organic chemist today are both useful and self-consistent. They are aids to the prediction of by-products and in the improvement of reaction conditions. And yet they very often assume intermediates which have not been isolable for direct experimental study. The physical reality of such intermediates depends not only on the self-consistency of the mechanisms which use them but also on their relation to similar substances that do happen to be stable enough to study directly. It is the additional relationships to things directly accessible that constitute our reasons for believing in the physical reality of the unstable intermediates.[1]

As an example of the insufficiency of present usefulness and self-consistency as grounds for belief in a scientific construct, it may be in order to recall some scientific history. In our own field we have the familiar example of phlogiston and in astronomy the example of epicycles. By the use of epicycle superimposed on epicycle, the geocentric theory was able to give a self-consistent, popular, and accurate description of apparent planetary motions. The epicycle treatment is analogous to a Fourier analysis of the motions and its accuracy did not guarantee the physical reality of epicycles.

It is fortunate that in many cases we are able to show that there are stable substances (radicals, ions, etc.) of the same type as the hypothetical intermediate and that these more stable or more accessible substances actually have the chemical properties required of the hypothetical ones. Observable radicals and ions have a great variety of degrees of stability, depending on their structures. The extrapolation to the properties of the hypothetical intermediate is therefore a continuous one.

The objectives of the present book are to provide some of the background of information about stable radicals and ions needed by those

[1] H. Margenau, *The Nature of Physical Reality*, McGraw-Hill, New York, 1950.

v

interested in organic reaction mechanisms, to point out some of the pitfalls awaiting the unwary,[2] and to show some of the criteria for preferring one type of intermediate over another.

Since there is no sharp boundary line between fact and theory, it is proper for the reader to be skeptical even of some of the facts in this moderately skeptical book. Some of them have been included for their interest and importance if true, rather than from a conviction of their truth. The reader will also note and perhaps help to close some rather alarming gaps in our fundamental information about ions and radicals, especially in quantitative information. The strength of the methods so ably applied by our predecessors has lain in the continuous confrontation of theory with experiment. It is not at all likely that we have reached a stage where we can afford to rely on either theory or experiment alone to the neglect of the other.

The author would like to acknowledge that whatever merit this book may possess is primarily due to his colleagues and teachers. If credit is not always given for specific ideas, it is because of the tendency for ideas born in conversation or elsewhere to be resurrected long after the source is forgotten. I am particularly indebted to my students and to Professors P. D. Bartlett and L. P. Hammett.

Tallahassee, Florida   J. E. L.
January 1956

[2] "There is something fascinating about science. One gets such wholesale returns of conjecture out of such a trifling investment of fact." Mark Twain, *Life on the Mississippi*, Chapter XVII.

Contents

CHAPTER I

Triarylmethyl Radicals

A free radical is best defined as an atom or molecule containing one or more unpaired electrons, or in the illuminating expression of our French colleagues, *électrons célibataires*.[1] The unpaired electron exists alone in an orbital and therefore has a spin and resulting magnetic moment uncompensated by the oppositely directed spin and magnetic moment of another electron. This has certain physical and chemical consequences which serve to show the presence of a free radical. But it must be emphasized that unusual reactivity alone (the chemical consequences) is never conclusive proof that a substance is a free radical.

Physical Properties of Radicals

The effects of an uncompensated electron are: (*1*) to split the molecule's spectral lines into doublets, or in the case of certain diradicals, into triplets, (*2*) to make the molecule paramagnetic, (*3*) to catalyze the conversion of para and ortho hydrogen molecules, and (*4*) to cause paramagnetic resonance absorption.

The splitting of spectral lines is obscured in organic molecules by the complexity of their spectra.

The paramagnetism, which here refers to the tendency to be drawn into magnetic fields rather than to the resonance absorption, has been measured for a large number of radicals. It is a fairly reliable qualitative test when the radicals are present in considerable concentration and has also been used to estimate the degree of dissociation of compounds in a state of equilibrium with radicals. Unfortunately, the

---

[1] The reader may prefer to attach a reservation to this definition, making an exception of atoms in which the unpaired electron occupies an inner shell as in transition series elements.

calculation of the paramagnetic susceptibility requires a correction for the underlying and opposing diamagnetic susceptibility. It used to be thought that the diamagnetic susceptibility could be calculated accurately enough from Pascal's constants. Diamagnetism, or the tendency to be thrust out of an applied magnetic field, is due to the effect of the field on the moving electrons: their velocities are changed in such a way as to generate a new field in opposition to the old one. The diamagnetic polarization is equal to the sum of the Pascal constants corresponding to the atoms constituting the molecule plus a correction due to the type of bonding. It is enhanced by resonance. The contribution due to resonance is unknown in the case of organic free radicals, and it should be considerable if the unpaired electron is appreciably free to move in response to the applied magnetic field. Because of the uncertainty in the diamagnetic correction, the paramagnetic susceptibility of organic molecules can be estimated only approximately. Radical dissociation constants determined by this method are therefore uncertain and disagree with those obtained in other ways.[2] For example, the para to ortho hydrogen conversion is catalysed by Chichibabin's hydrocarbon to an extent indicating 10% of the diradical form whereas the paramagnetism indicates only 2% or less and the paramagnetic resonance method 4%.[3,5] The quantitative interpretation of the hydrogen conversion results is also in doubt in many cases.

Chichibabin's Hydrocarbon

In connection with Chichibabin's hydrocarbon it is appropriate to mention that there is little or no resonance between states of different multiplicity.[4] Thus the singlet-triplet transition represented by the covalent and diradical structures of the hydrocarbon is a true equilibrium and not an example of resonance.

[2] P. W. Selwood and R. M. Dobres, *J. Am. Chem. Soc.* **72**, 3860 (1950).

[3] G. Schwab and N. Agliardi, *Ber.*, **73**, 95 (1940).

[4] P. Yuster and S. I. Weissman, *J. Chem. Phys.*, **17**, 1182 (1949).

The method of paramagnetic resonance absorption makes use of the precession of the spinning unpaired electron when it is placed in a magnetic field. This precession gives rise to absorption of radiation in the microwave region. The frequency at which the absorption takes place is given by the expression

$$\nu = g\beta H/h$$

in which g is the gyromagnetic ratio, β is the Bohr magneton, H is the field strength and h is Planck's constant. A common technique is to hold the frequency of the applied electromagnetic radiation constant and measure the intensity of the absorption while the magnetic field is modulated. The width of the absorption band is therefore measured in oersteds or other magnetic unit rather than in units of frequency. The area under the absorption curve, or integrated absorption, is directly proportional to the concentration of radicals and permits the calculation of dissociation constants. The method is accurate since it requires no correction for diamagnetism. The proportion of diradical in the Chichibabin hydrocarbon (I) is found to be 4% by this method.[5] Other examples will be found in the following chapters.

The First Radical

The first organic free radical to be discovered was triphenylmethyl, the result of the effort of Gomberg to prepare hexaphenylethane.[6] In geographical exploration, isolated white spaces on the map rarely contain anything strikingly different from the neighboring explored regions; chemical exploration leads to all sorts of surprises.

Treatment of triphenylmethyl chloride with silver gave not the expected hydrocarbon but an oxygen-containing compound later found to be the peroxide. The reaction run in an inert atmosphere did give a hydrocarbon, but one with unusual properties. It reacted rapidly with oxygen, chlorine, and bromine, and was quite different from tetraphenylmethane or what was expected of hexaphenylethane. Gomberg

[5] C. A. Hutchison, Jr., A. Kowalsky, R. C. Pastor, and G. Wheland, *J. Chem. Phys.*, **20**, 1485 (1952).
[6] M. Gomberg, *J. Am. Chem. Soc.*, **22**, 757 (1900); *Ber.*, **33**, 3150 (1900).

tested the hypothesis that the product was a free radical by showing that the molecular weight in solution was intermediate between that of triphenylmethyl and that of hexaphenylethane, suggesting an equilibrium between the two.

$$\phi_3CCl + Ag \longrightarrow AgCl + \phi_3C\bullet$$

$$2\phi_3C\bullet \rightleftharpoons \phi_3C-C\phi_3$$

<table>
<tr><td>Yellow and
paramagnetic</td><td>Colorless and
diamagnetic</td></tr>
</table>

The reaction with oxygen has been used to measure the rate of dissociation of the ethane.[7]

$$\phi_3C\bullet + O_2 \longrightarrow \phi_3C-O-O\bullet \longrightarrow \phi_3C-OO-C\phi_3$$

The dissociation is the slow step that fixes the rate of the over-all oxidation reaction, but only if an inhibitor is added to remove the intermediate triphenylmethylperoxy radicals. Otherwise they contribute to the disappearance of the ethane by attacking it directly rather than waiting for additional free triphenylmethyl radicals.

$$\phi_3COO\bullet + \phi_3C-C\phi_3 \longrightarrow \phi_3C-OO-C\phi_3 + \phi_3C\bullet$$

$$\underset{\text{(inhibitor)}}{\phi_3COO\bullet + HO-\underset{}{\overset{\text{HO OH}}{\bigcirc}}} \longrightarrow \text{(less reactive radical)}$$

The initial product of the inhibition step is not known in this case and may be a molecular complex.[8] The direct reaction of the ethane with the peroxy radical is an example of a covalent compound giving a reaction resembling that of a related free radical. The molecular weight determination by Gomberg was therefore a necessary part of the proof that he was dealing with radicals and not merely an unusually reactive hydrocarbon. The presence of free radicals has since been confirmed by measurements of the paramagnetic susceptibility and the paramagnetic resonance absorption.[9, 10] The latter evidence also rules out an alter-

---

[7] K. Ziegler, L. Ewald, and P. Orth, *Ann.*, 479, 277 (1930).

[8] C. E. Boozer and G. S. Hammond, *J. Am. Chem. Soc.*, **76**, 3861 (1954).

[9] E. Müller and I. Müller-Rodloff, *Ann.*, **521**, 89 (1936).

[10] S. I. Weissman and J. C. Sowden, *J. Am. Chem. Soc.*, **75**, 503 (1953).

native explanation of the observed molecular weight and reactivity in terms of ionization:

$$\phi_3C\!-\!C\phi_3 \;\rightleftharpoons\; 2\phi_3C\bullet \qquad\qquad \phi_3C\!-\!C\phi_3 \;\rightleftharpoons\; \phi_3C^{(+)} + \phi_3C^{(-)}$$

$$\phi_3C\bullet + Br_2 \;\rightleftharpoons\; \phi_3CBr + Br\bullet \qquad \phi_3C^{(-)} + Br_2 \;\rightarrow\; \phi_3CBr + Br^{(-)}$$

$$Br\bullet + \phi_3C\bullet \;\rightarrow\; \phi_3CBr \qquad\qquad Br^{(-)} + \phi_3C^{(+)} \;\rightarrow\; \phi_3CBr$$

As we shall see, triphenyl carbonium ions and carbanions exist, although largely as solvent complexes or pairs with inorganic ions. The fact that the ions are also colored and also very reactive has led to confusion in the early literature. Radicals were once thought of, in the organic nomenclature sense, as fragments of molecules, and the distinction between radicals and ions was not very clear. Some authors talked about free radicals, meaning by this expression a part of a molecule disconnected from the rest, even when the disconnected part with which they were dealing was actually an ion. Still another source of confusion lay in the fact that triphenylmethyl in the presence of various catalysts adds to itself irreversibly to form an isomer of hexaphenylethane. This substance is perfectly stable and has the properties originally expected of hexaphenylethane itself. It was therefore sometimes mistaken for the ethane, and the discrepancy in the properties displayed by the rival hexaphenylethanes was the occasion for considerable controversy.

$$2\phi_3C\bullet \xrightarrow[\text{or Na ether}]{\text{HCl }\phi H} \phi\!-\!\overset{\displaystyle\phi}{\underset{\displaystyle\phi}{C}}\!-\!\!\!\bigcirc\!\!\!-\!\overset{\displaystyle\phi}{\underset{\displaystyle\phi}{C}}\!-\!H$$

$$\text{(II)}$$

The addition product (II) is also called Chichibabin's hydrocarbon and should not be confused with Chichibabin's (diradical) hydrocarbon of formula I.

Measurement of Dissociation

The primary measure of the amount of free radical must depend on those properties unambiguously due to the unpaired electron. In the past the most common method has been the measurement of the paramagnetic susceptibility, now subject to difficulties of quantitative interpretation. The method of paramagnetic resonance absorption is as yet so new that very few such measurements have been published.

Once it has been shown by the primary methods that radicals are present other methods may be applied, especially if a parallelism between the other measured property and the paramagnetic property can be shown. The molecular weight by freezing point depression or boiling point elevation are examples. In the case of highly reactive radicals care must be taken to avoid disproportionation or reaction with the solvent during the measurement. Spectrophotometry affords still another method, but one that is safe only after it has been demonstrated that the color is really associated with the radical. Although the corresponding positive and negative ions and the related quinonoid compounds are also colored, they are not paramagnetic and they have spectra different from those of the radicals.

The color of the quinonoid compounds that may be obtained by disproportionation can be sufficiently like that of the radicals to cause confusion if visual observation or broad-band spectrophotometry is used.[11] For example, Preckel and Selwood, using paramagnetism as a measure of the amount of radical, reported that solutions of triphenyl-methyl derivatives more or less rapidly lost their paramagnetism. The decomposed solutions were still highly colored, but the color was no longer dependent on the temperature as it is in the case of a radical-dimer equilibrium mixture. What is more striking, and an even more subtle and dirtier trick on the part of nature, is the fact that Preckel and Selwood's non-paramagnetic solutions were still rapidly bleached by exposure to the air. It is clear that radical-like reactivity is not a safe criterion for the presence of radicals. It is also clear that the ebullioscopic method is particularly unsatisfactory in view of the excellent chance for decomposition.

The rate of the dissociation has been measured by the uptake of oxygen or nitric oxide.[12,13] In the case of triphenylmethyl the dis-

[11] R. Preckel and P. W. Selwood, *J. Am. Chem. Soc.*, **63**, 3397 (1941); C. S. Marvel, J. Whitson, and H. W. Johnston, *ibid.*, **66**, 415 (1944).

[12] K. Ziegler, L. Ewald, and P. Orth, *Ann.*, **479**, 277 (1930); K. Ziegler, P. Orth, and K. Weber, *ibid.*, **504**, 131 (1933); K. Ziegler, L. Ewald, and A. Seib, *ibid.*, **504**, 182 (1933).

[13] K. Ziegler, A. Seib, F. Knoevenagel, P. Herte, and F. Andreas, *Ann.*, **551**, 150 (1942).

sociation has an activation enthalpy of 19 kcal. and an overall enthalpy change of 11 kcal. The activation enthalpy for the recombination reaction is therefore about 8 kcal. The significance of the non-zero activation enthalpy for the recombination is that the radicals, as they recombine in the transition state, have a geometry rather like that of the ethane. This geometry interferes with some of the resonance stabilization of the free radical which exists in a nearly planar propeller shape. It must also interfere with solvation.

The equilibrium constant of hexaphenylethane dissociation, in striking contrast to the rate constant for dissociation, varies considerably with solvent. The radical with its unpaired electron and nearly planar structure probably complexes with solvents to a considerable extent while the ethane does not. Since the transition state is like the ethane and its solvation is hindered, the dissociation rate constants change very little with solvent.[12,13] From an empirical relationship that happens to exist in this case between the rate and equilibrium constants in a series of solvents, it has been calculated that the transition state resembles the ethane at least four times as much as it resembles the radical. These are the proportions that must be used if the free energy of the transition state in a given solvent is to be expressed as a linear combination of the free energies of the ethane and radical states.[14]

Factors Affecting Stability of Ethane and Radicals

Aside from the interaction of the radical with the solvent there are several factors that can make the ethane unstable or stabilize the resulting free radical. They are the stabilization of the radical by resonance, steric strain in the ethane, and dipole-dipole repulsion in the ethane. Steric inhibition of both resonance and solvation in the radical favor association to the dimer.

We can assume (for the moment) that a carbon free radical is planar with a threefold axis of symmetry as far as the remaining bonds to carbon are concerned. Quantum mechanics predicts that delocaliza-

[14] J. E. Leffler, *Science*, **117**, 340 (1953).

tion of the unpaired electron will stabilize the radical. The resonance method of approximation to the true nature of the molecule represents the electron delocalization in the triphenylmethyl radical by the following and other similar resonance structures:

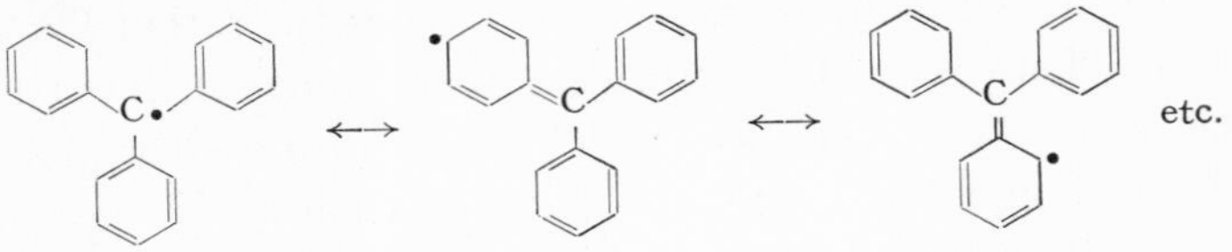

If all of the structures are to contribute to the resonance, the geometry of the radical must be essentially the same as that of each of the structures simultaneously. All of the benzene rings are therefore required to be coplanar in order to get the maximum of resonance stabilization. The molecular orbital approximation makes the same prediction. The unpaired electron may be thought of as occupying a p-orbital of the central carbon atom, perpendicular to the plane of the three sp^2 bonding orbitals. If this central p-orbital is to overlap with the p-orbitals of the adjacent benzene ring carbon atoms to form a molecular orbital, then all of the p-orbitals involved must be parallel. Since the p-orbitals are perpendicular to the rings, the rings have to be coplanar.

A structure that prevents coplanarity prevents resonance stabilization to a corresponding degree. Thus the triptycyl radical has none of the stability of triphenylmethyl and the benzene rings are tied back in a position with the very maximum deviation from coplanarity.[15]

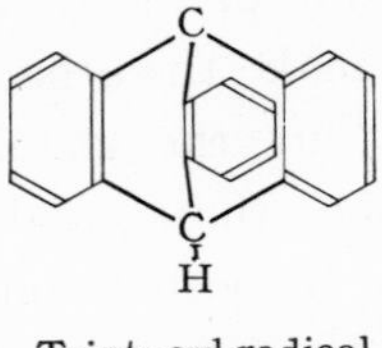

Triptycyl radical

The question then arises as to which is the more responsible for the dissociation of hexaphenylethane, steric strain in the dimer or resonance stabilization in the radical? Because bulky groups in the

[15] P. D. Bartlett, M. J. Ryan, and S. G. Cohen, *J. Am. Chem. Soc.* **64**, 2649 (1942).

ortho position increase the dissociation it is likely that steric strain in the dimer is an important factor. Bulky ortho groups not only exert steric strain in the dimer but also interfere somewhat with the near coplanarity needed for resonance stabilization of the radical. On the other hand, the marked effect of substituents in the para position where they can not exert a steric effect indicates that resonance is also important.

An argument from heats of hydrogenation concludes that resonance is responsible for about two-thirds of the difference in stability between the central bond of hexaphenylethane and normal carbon-carbon bonds. It can be calculated from other thermochemical data that the heat of hydrogenation of ethane to two moles of methane is —13 kcal. In contrast the heat of hydrogenation of hexaphenylethane has been shown to be —35 kcal. per mole.

$$CH_3CH_3 + H_2 \longrightarrow 2CH_4 + 13 \text{ kcal.}$$

$$\phi_3C\!-\!C\phi_3 + H_2 \longrightarrow 2\phi_3C\!-\!H + 35 \text{ kcal.}$$

Since triphenylmethane is not stabilized by any resonance not already present in hexaphenylethane, the difference between the two heats of hydrogenation, or 22 kcal., might be a measure of the steric effect alone. The difference in the heats of dissociation into radicals when ethane and hexaphenylethane are compared is 62 kcal. This leaves about 40 kcal. to be accounted for as resonance stabilization of the radical.[16] This degree of resonance stabilization for the triphenylmethyl radical does not violate quantum mechanical expectations.

If the unpaired electron is stabilized by resonance or is in a molecular orbital extending over the whole molecule, it must sometimes be detectable elsewhere than on the central carbon atom. The radical in which the central carbon atom is the isotope of mass 13 has been prepared. Whereas carbon 12 has a zero nuclear magnetic spin moment, carbon 13 has a nuclear spin of 0.5 and a magnetic moment of 0.7021 nuclear magnetons. The nuclear magnetic spin moment in an external field gives rise to a nuclear magnetic resonance absorption line, in much the same way as does the unpaired electron. If the unpaired electron

---

[16] H. E. Bent and G. R. Cuthbertson, *J. Am. Chem. Soc.*, **58**, 170 (1936).

is near the carbon thirteen nucleus the interaction of its magnetic field with that of the electron, which can be positive or negative, should split the carbon thirteen nuclear magnetic resonance line into two lines. One of these is due to the external field plus that of the electron, the other to the external field minus that of the electron. The separation of the two lines depends on the field strength at the nucleus due to the electron, and hence on the mean distance of the electron from the nucleus.[17] This distance appears to be only 0.7 A. The low value of this average, however, may signify merely that the electron sometimes gets very close to the nucleus and not that it can rarely be found elsewhere. It will be interesting to see the results of a similar experiment in which the isotopic carbon atom is elsewhere in the radical.

Geometry of Triphenylmethyl and
Other Radicals

Although the resonance or delocalization stabilization of triphenylmethyl will be at its maximum only when the radical is completely planar, such a structure involves repulsion by adjacent ortho hydrogen atoms:

The average shape of the radical will therefore be a compromise between strain due to hydrogen-hydrogen repulsion in the completely planar state and torsional strain of the partial double bonds in the skew state. Such a compromise should result in a propeller form in which the blades are slightly feathered out of the plane. It is possible that the radical exists in two isomeric forms, one corresponding to a symmetrical propeller and the other to a propeller in which one of the blades has been tilted the wrong way. Although such isomerism has been ob-

---

[17] S. I. Weissman and J. C. Sowden, *J. Am. Chem. Soc.*, **75**, 503 (1953).

served in ions, there is no evidence of it in the spectrum of triphenyl-methyl free radical.[18]

It will be noted that the non-planar propeller form lacks a plane of symmetry and that the production of optically active products by way of an intermediate radical might therefore be possible. Attempts to make precursory optically active phenylxenyl-α-naphthylmethyl halides failed, but the corresponding active thioglycolic acid has been prepared. It is racemized by the reaction with triphenylmethyl free radicals.[19] Various other reactions believed to involve radical inter-mediates also give inactive products:

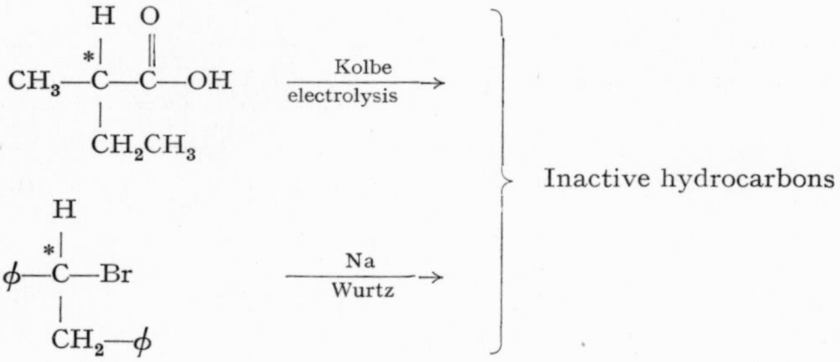

Relation between Structure and Dissociation
Constant in the Hexaarylethane Series

Because of the scarcity of electronic paramagnetic resonance data, and because of the frequent unreliability of the data from para-magnetism, boiling point elevation, spectrophotometry, and ortho-para hydrogen conversion, most published radical dissociation constants can be accepted only with reservations. An error of 50% is not at all improbable in many cases. We are therefore not yet in a position to explain, or rather to test our explanations of, small differences in dissociation constants. Table I shows the values of K corresponding to various hexaarylethanes in benzene at 25°. Because of the order of magnitude differences in Table I, however, it is likely that some of the expected large effects, such as steric and resonance effects, exist.

[18] G. N. Lewis, D. Lipkin, and T. T. Magel, *J. Am. Chem. Soc.*, **66**, 1579 (1944).

[19] E. S. Wallis and F. H. Adams, *J. Am. Chem. Soc.*, **55**, 3838 (1933).

TABLE I
Dissociation of Hexaarylethanes in Benzene, 25°, $K \times 10^3$

Substituent	Number of para substituents in triphenylmethyl		
	1	2	3
H[a]	0.22 (24°)	0.22	0.22
CH_3O[b]	0.81		
Cl[c]	1.1		
CH_3[d]	1.1	1.3	12
tert-butyl[d]	2.4	3.2	
sec-butyl[d]			65
cyclo-hexyl[e]	3.2	3.8 (27°)	20
phenyl[f]	3.8 (26°)	16	37
F[g]			0.60
NO_2			large

Substituent	Number of meta substituents (only one to a ring)		
	1	2	3
H	0.22	0.22	0.22
CH_3O[b]	0.28		
Cl[c]	1.8		
CH_3[d]	1.8	2.1	110
phenyl[f,h]	2.9 (26°)		85

Substituent	Number of ortho substituents (only one to a ring)		
	1	2	3
H	0.22	0.22	0.22
CH_3O[b]	0.60		120
Cl[c]	6.5		
CH_3[d]	33	1500	
Ethyl[d]	65		

[a] E. Müller and I. Müller-Rodloff, *Ann.* **521** 89 (1936).

[b] C. S. Marvel, J. Whitson, and H. W. Johnston, *J. Am. Chem. Soc.* **66,** 415 (1944).

[c] C. S. Marvel, F. C. Dietz, and C. M. Himel, *J. Org. Chem.* **7,** 392 (1942).

[d] C. S. Marvel, J. F. Kaplan, and C. M. Himel, *J. Am. Chem. Soc.* **63,** 1892 (1941).

[e] C. S. Marvel and C. M. Himel, *J. Am. Chem. Soc.* **62,** 1550 (1940).

[f] C. S. Marvel, M. B. Mueller, and E. Ginsberg, *J. Am. Chem. Soc.* **61,** 2008 (1939); C. S. Marvel, J. W. Shackleton, C. M. Himel, and J. Whitson, *ibid.* **64,** 1824 (1942).

[g] C. S. Marvel, H. W. Johnston, J. W. Meier, T. W. Mastin, J. Whitson, and C. M. Himel, *J. Am. Chem. Soc.* **66,** 914 (1944).

[h] C. S. Marvel, E. Ginsberg, and M. B. Mueller, *J. Am. Chem. Soc.* **61,** 77 (1939).

There also seems to be an unexpected effect of meta substituents. Lichtin and Glazer have suggested, since purely radical structures can not involve meta substituents, that combined radical and dipole structures are important:[20]

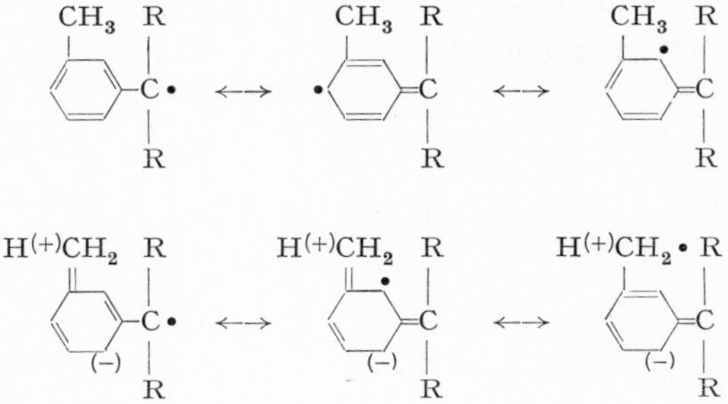

No similar meta substituent effect exists for ions since resonance between a singlet and triplet (diradical) state is prohibited. The dipolar ion theory would suggest that suitably disubstituted radicals should be especially stable, particularly in polar solvents, because of structures like III.

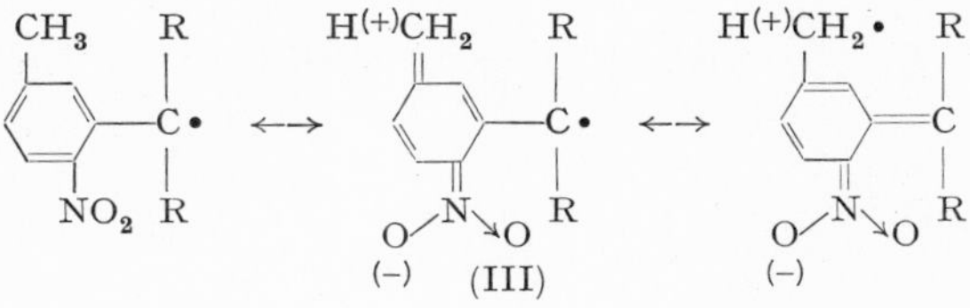

It has been reported that the degree of dissociation of unsymmetrical hexaarylethanes is usually somewhat less than the average of the related symmetrical ethanes.[21,22] Unfortunately, the available ethanes do not include any with extremely electronegative and electropositive substituents in opposite parts of the ethane molecule. A marked difference in electronegativity of the two radicals might increase the strength of the central bond by increasing its ionic character.

[20] N. N. Lichtin and H. Glazer, *J. Am. Chem. Soc.*, **73**, 5537 (1951).
[21] C. S. Marvel and C. M. Himel, *J. Am. Chem. Soc.*, **64**, 2227 (1942).
[22] T. L. Chu and S. I. Weissman, *J. Am. Chem. Soc.*, **73**, 4462 (1951).

Preparation of Triarylmethyl Radicals or the Corresponding Ethanes

In addition to Gomberg's original method using the reaction of the triarylmethyl halide with copper, zinc, or silver amalgam in an inert solvent, a number of other methods have been used. Table II shows some of them. Some of the methods amount to oxidation of a

TABLE II

Formation of Triarylmethyl Radicals

$$K^{(+)}\,{}^{(-)}C(Ar)_2\text{—}Ar + HC(Br)(CH_3)\text{—}CH(Br)(CH_3) \longrightarrow KBr + CH_3CH{=}CHCH_3 + Ar_3C\bullet$$

$$Na^{(+)}\,{}^{(-)}C\phi_3 + \phi_3CCl \longrightarrow NaCl + \phi_3C\text{—}C\phi_3$$

$$\phi_3C\text{—}OH \xrightarrow[VCl_2\,+\,HCl]{\text{acetone}} \phi_3C\text{—}C\phi_3 + VCl_3 + H_2O$$

$$\phi_3C\text{—}Br + NaI \xrightarrow{\text{acetone}} \phi_3C\text{—}I + \underline{NaBr}$$

$$\phi_3C\text{—}I \rightleftharpoons \phi_3C\bullet + I_2$$

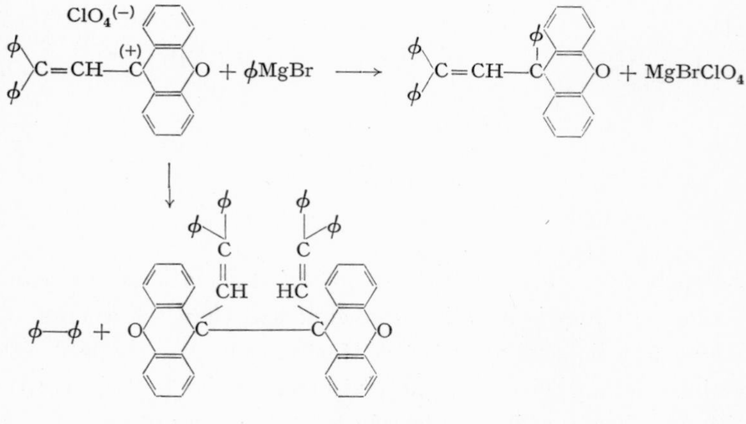

carbanion, others to reduction of a carbonium ion, and the last reaction to formation of an unstable compound by displacement. The reaction of triphenylmethyl bromide with ions other than iodide ion results in simple displacement to give stable and undissociated products.

$$\phi_3C\text{---}Br + S_2O_3^{=} \longrightarrow \phi_3C\text{---}S\text{---}SO_3^- + Br^-$$

$$\phi_3C\text{---}Br + NaO\text{---}\overset{\overset{O}{\|}}{C}\text{---}\phi \xrightarrow{\text{acetone}} \phi_3C\text{---}O\text{---}\overset{\overset{O}{\|}}{C}\text{---}\phi + NaBr$$

But the trinitro-substituted compound seems to give free radicals directly:

$$(p\text{---}NO_2\phi)_3CBr + Na_2S_2O_3 \xrightarrow{\text{acetone}} (p\text{---}O_2N\phi)_3C\bullet + NaBr$$

$$(p\text{---}NO_2\phi)_3CBr + NaO\text{---}\overset{\overset{O}{\|}}{C}\text{---}\phi \xrightarrow{\text{acetone}} (p\text{---}O_2N\phi)_3C\bullet + NaBr$$

Although the reaction with thiosulfate and with iodide ions may be a mere reduction of the halide, the reaction with sodium benzoate would appear to be a radical dissociation induced by the attack of a negative ion. The fate of the benzoate ion is unknown. Tris-(p-nitrophenyl)-methyl benzoate is a stable substance which does not dissociate into radicals.[23]

Reactions of Triarylmethyl Radicals

We have already seen that triphenylmethyl radical reacts both with itself to form Chichibabin's hydrocarbon (formula II, not the diradical) and with halogens and oxygen. The reactions of the stable radical are important because of the expectation that radicals too unstable to isolate will betray their presence by giving similar products.

In contrast with the more reactive radicals, triphenylmethyl reacts only with the alkali metals and not with lead.

$$\phi_3C\bullet + Na \rightleftharpoons \phi_3CNa \xrightarrow{Hg} \phi_3C\bullet + NaHg$$

Sodium amalgam rather than sodium is used in the preparation of triphenylmethyl from the halide; the mercury prevents the formation of sodium triphenylmethyl and of Chichibabin's hydrocarbon.

[23] J. E. Leffler, *J. Am. Chem. Soc.*, **75**, 3598 (1953).

The tendency to add to systems of multiple bonds is illustrated by the following reactions:

$$2\phi_3C\cdot + CH_3 = CH—CH=CH_2 \longrightarrow \phi_3C—CH_2CH=CHCH_2C\phi_3$$

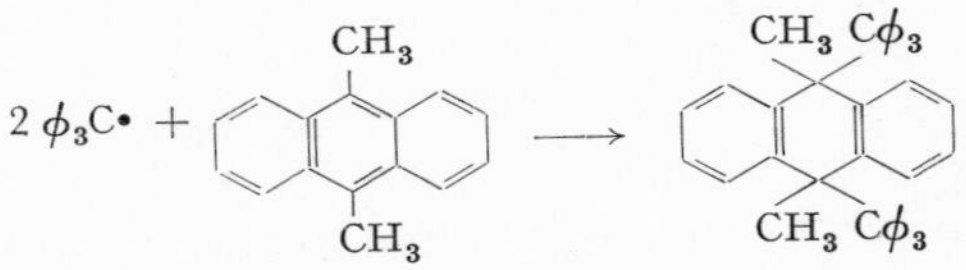

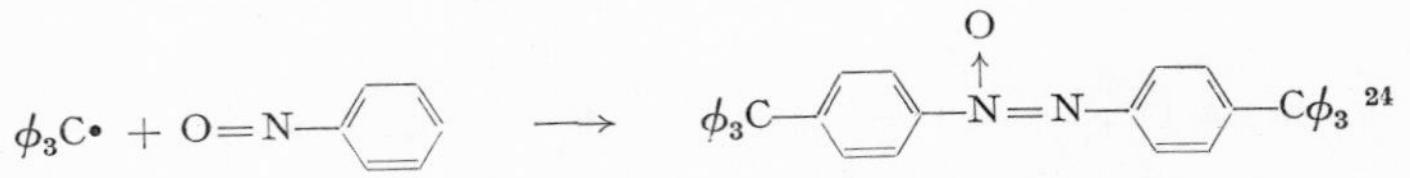

Disproportionation by exchange of hydrogen is another common reaction:

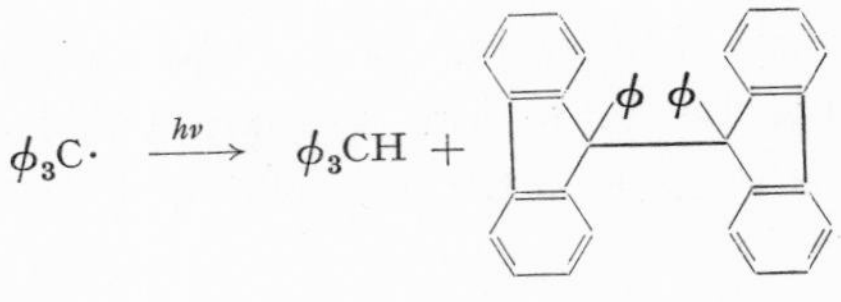

The product of the latter reaction, diphenylbifluorenyl, is almost entirely undissociated in spite of the ease with which the radical is formed in ways other than the dissociation of the ethane.[25]

Solutions of hexaphenylethane in liquid sulfur dioxide conduct electricity, suggesting an ionization into triphenylmethyl positive and negative ions. Since the spectrum of triphenylmethide ion was missing from the spectrum of the solution the following equilibrium was postulated:

$$\phi_3CC\phi_3 + SO_2 \quad \rightleftharpoons \quad \phi_3C^{(+)} + SO_2^{(-)}$$

However, it has recently been shown that the conductivity depends on the presence of oxygen, indicating ionization of the peroxide rather than the ethane.[26] The reader will perhaps be surprised that it has also

[24] S. Goldschmidt and F. Christmann, *Ann.*, **442**, 246 (1925).

[25] G. N. Lewis, D. Lipkin, and T. T. Magel, *J. Am. Chem. Soc.*, **66**, 1579 (1944).

[26] H. P. Leftin and N. N. Lichtin, *J. Am. Chem. Soc.*, **76**, 2593 (1954).

been suggested in various places that hexaphenylethane in ether solution is largely ionized into the triphenylcarbonium ion and carbanion. This suggestion probably stems from a misinterpretation of the work of Anderson[27] who showed that while both radical and carbonium ion spectra somewhat resemble those of quinones, they are nevertheless different from each other. The spectrum of the carbanion (triphenylmethyl sodium) is quite different from that of either the radical or the cation. Ionized hexaphenylethane in ether should resemble the anion since the carbonium ion would undoubtedly be in the from of a colorless etherate ion.

$$\phi_3C-\overset{\diagup\text{Et}}{\underset{\diagdown\text{Et}}{O^{(+)}}}$$

Addition of ether to solutions containing carbonium ions discharges the color.

The redox potential of triphenylmethyl for the oxidation to triphenylcarbonium sulfate in glacial acetic acid has been measured by Conant.[28] The potential could not be measured for the more readily oxidized dimethylamino-substituted triphenylmethyl radicals since these react with acetic acid to give the carbonium ion and the triphenylmethane, a result that suggests ionization in that solvent.[29] The electron affinity of triarylmethyl radicals has been measured by Bent and Keevil using cells of triarylmethyl sodium and hexaarylethane in ether.[30] The free energy change for the reaction sodium plus radical to give sodium triarylmethide averages 1 kcal. for a series of twenty triarylmethyl radicals.

Attempts in the author's laboratory to prepare highly unsymmetrical, and hence possibly ionic, ethanes have been unsuccessful. The electron-releasing substituents needed in one-half of the molecule facilitate various reactions leading to the destruction of the radicals. In any case, no product having the properties to be expected of the

[27] L. C. Anderson, *J. Am. Chem. Soc.*, **57**, 1673 (1935).

[28] J. B. Conant, L. F. Small, and B. S. Taylor, *J. Am. Chem. Soc.*, **47**, 1959 (1925).

[29] J. B. Conant and N. M. Bigelow, *J. Am. Chem. Soc.*, **53**, 676 (1931).

[30] H. E. Bent and N. B. Keevil, *J. Am. Chem. Soc.*, **58**, 1228 (1936).

unsymmetrical ethane or ion complex shown below could be isolated:

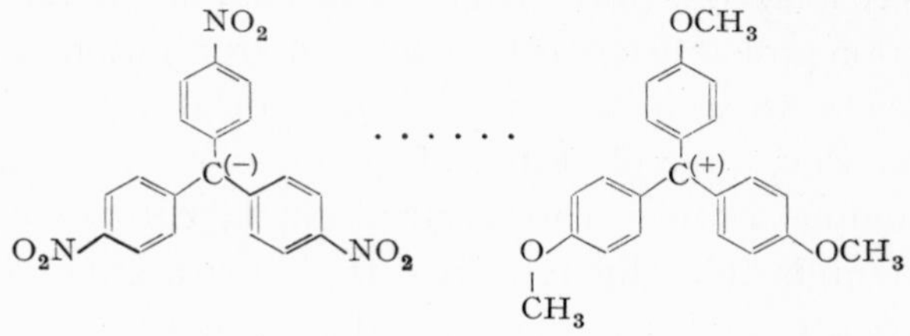

Reaction with other radicals is characteristic of the triarylmethyls and the chain reaction with oxygen has already been discussed. The absorption of the radical nitric oxide is also used as an analytical method for triphenylmethyl.

$$\phi_3 C\bullet + \bullet NO_2 \longrightarrow \phi_3 C\!-\!NO_2 + \phi_3 C\!-\!O\!-\!NO \;^{31}$$

$$\phi_3 C\bullet + \bullet NO \longrightarrow \phi_3 C\!-\!NO$$

Triphenylmethyl reacts with atomic hydrogen and with methyl free radicals when a solution of it is exposed to a gas stream containing the other radicals.[32]

$$\phi_3 C\bullet + H\bullet \longrightarrow \phi_3 C\!-\!H$$

$$\phi_3 C\bullet + CH_3\bullet \longrightarrow \phi_3 C\!-\!CH_3$$

The type of reactivity shown by the formation of Chichibabin's hydrocarbon extends to the activation of substituents other than hydrogen as well. For example, molecular silver will not usually remove fluorine from organic compounds, not even from triphenylmethyl fluoride. Yet the radical parafluorophenyldiphenylmethyl reacts with molecular silver to give silver fluoride.[33]

[31] W. Schlenk, L. Mair, and C. Bornhardt, *Ber.*, **44**, 1169 (1911).
[32] F. Benington, *Symposium on Combustion and Flame and Explosion Phenomena*, Williams and Wilkins, Baltimore, 1949, p. 448.
[33] S. T. Bowden and T. F. Watkins, *J. Chem. Soc.*, **1940**, 1249.

In the similar case of bromine in the para ring position it is known that only one-half is removed by silver. It has been suggested that the bromine is replaced by another radical in the following fashion:

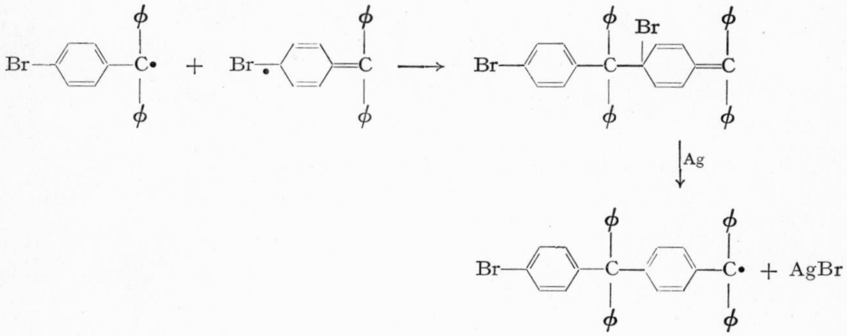

Analogs of Triphenylmethyl

Considerable attention has been paid in recent years to the problem of free radicals in which the central carbon atom of triphenylmethyl has been replaced by another element. For example the compound hexaphenyldisilane has been made.[34] Although some hexa-substituted disilanes are cleaved by sodium or potassium in a reaction suggestive of free radicals, hexaphenyldisilane is diamagnetic. It has been suggested that the instability of triphenylsilyl radicals is due to the high energy of double bonds between carbon and silicon. The half-analog with only one silicon atom is also undissociated.[35]

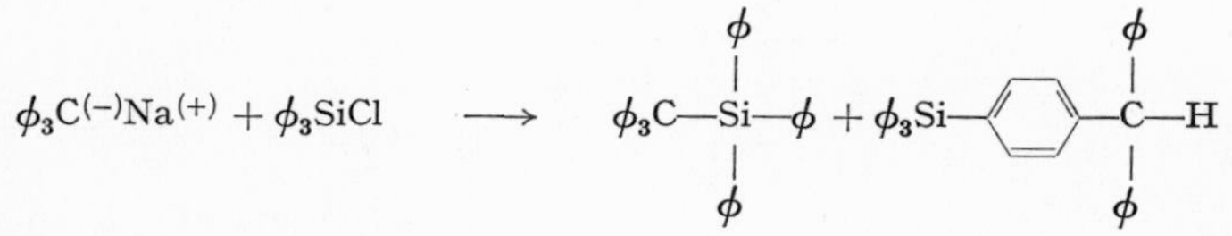

But the hexaphenylethane analog with lead atoms in the place of the central carbon atoms appears to be about 50% dissociated.[36]

[34] H. Gilman and T. C. Wu, *J. Am. Chem. Soc.*, **75**, 3762 (1953).
[35] A. G. Brook, H. Gilman, and L. S. Miller, *J. Am. Chem. Soc.*, **75**, 4759 (1953).
[36] J. C. Bailie, *Iowa State Coll. J. Sci.*, **14**, 8 (1939).

The sodium derivative of triphenylboron gives several radical-like reactions but shows no paramagnetic resonance absorption. It probably exists as the dimer.[37]

$$\phi_3 B^{(\bullet)} Na^{(+)} \quad \underset{\longleftarrow}{\longrightarrow} \quad \phi_3 BB\phi_3{}^{(=)} Na_2{}^{(++)}$$

$$\downarrow I_2$$

$$\phi_3 B + NaI$$

[37] T. L. Chu, *J. Am. Chem. Soc.*, **75**, 1730 (1953).

CHAPTER II

Unstable Carbon Radicals

Relation to Triarylmethyl

When one of the aromatic groups of the triarylmethyl free radical is replaced by an alkyl group, a decrease in stability due to a loss of resonance stabilization is to be expected. The paramagnetism and reactions associated with these less stable radicals will therefore appear only when the ethane is heated well above room temperature, the dissociation being, endothermic. The rate of formation, but not the equilibrium constant, is experimentally accessible for these radicals since the radical once formed is subject to rearrangement, cleavage, and disproportionation reactions:

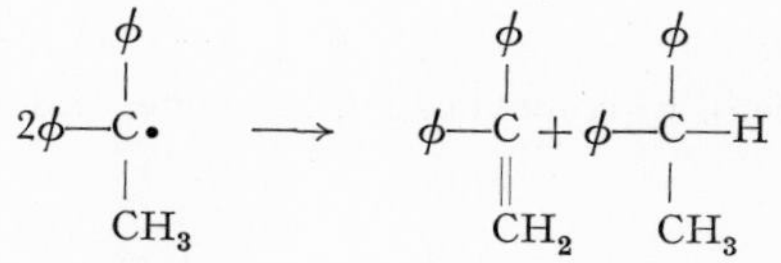

$$2\phi - \overset{\displaystyle \phi}{\underset{\displaystyle CH_3}{\overset{|}{\underset{|}{C}}}} \cdot \quad \longrightarrow \quad \phi - \overset{\displaystyle \phi}{\underset{\displaystyle CH_2}{\overset{|}{\underset{\|}{C}}}} + \phi - \overset{\displaystyle \phi}{\underset{\displaystyle CH_3}{\overset{|}{\underset{|}{C}}}} - H$$

The rate of dissociation has been measured by oxygen uptake in the presence of an inhibitor of chain reactions as in the case of hexaaryl-ethanes. Since the uptake of oxygen obeys the same kinetic law, it is a reasonable extrapolation to suppose that here too the rate-determining step is a dissociation into radicals. When one of the phenyl groups in triphenylmethyl is replaced by a cyclohexyl group, the rate of dissociation of the ethane is reduced by a factor of 170.[38] Some dissociation rate parameters are given in Tables III A and B.

When solutions of ethanes with four aryl groups and two bulky

[38] K. Ziegler, *Ann.*, **551**, 127 (1942).

TABLE III A

Radical Dissociation Rates in Bromobenzene[a]

Ethane	E (kcal.)	PZ (min.$^{-1}$)	Half-life at 20° (min.)
hexaphenylethane	19	3.4×10^{14}	0.4
symmetrical tetraphenyl-1,2-dialkylethanes			
cyclohexyl	25.0	5.4×10^{16}	70.0
isopropyl	25.0	2.5×10^{16}	128.5
cyclopentyl	24.7	2.7×10^{16}	84.6
tert-butyl	–	–	0.83
methyl	30.0	7.8×10^{17}	28000
ethyl	27.2	2.6×10^{19}	6.0
n-propyl	26.7	5.6×10^{19}	1.3
n-amyl	26.6	4.3×10^{19}	1.25
1,2-diphenyl-1,1,2,2-tetracyclohexylethane	21.4	5×10^{13}	40 (at 30°)
10,10'-dialkyl-10,10'-bixanthyls			
methyl	30.1	1.8×10^{19}	1170
ethyl	30.1	2×10^{19}	1006
n-propyl	30.0	11×10^{19}	152
n-butyl	29.3	4×10^{19}	160

[a] K. Ziegler, A. Seib, F. Knoevenagel, P. Herte, and F. Andreas, *Ann.* **551**, 150 (1942).

alkyl groups are exposed to air, they form either the peroxide or the decomposition products to be expected from such a peroxide.[39, 40]

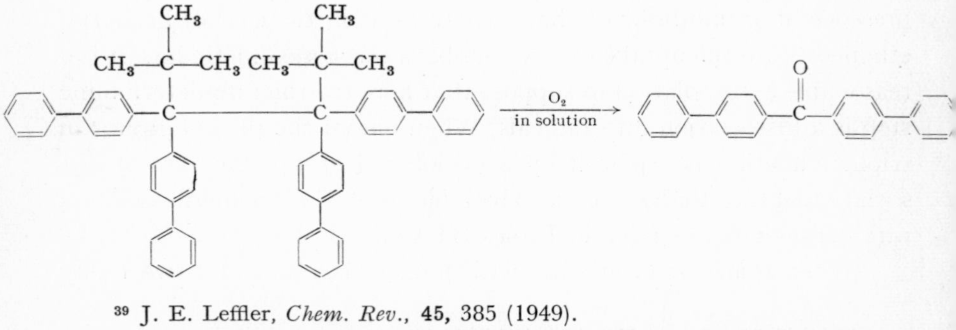

[39] J. E. Leffler, *Chem. Rev.*, **45**, 385 (1949).
[40] J. B. Conant and R. F. Schultz, *J. Am. Chem. Soc.*, **55**, 2098 (1933).

TABLE III B

Radical Dissociation Rates in o-Dichlorobenzene[a]

Ring substituent in the diphenylmethyl part of pentaphenylethane	E (kcal.)	PZ (sec.$^{-1}$)	Half-life at 80° (min.)
none	30.1	10×10^{14}	49
2-methyl	29.2	8×10^{14}	17
3-methyl	31.4	78×10^{14}	39
4-methyl	29.3	3×10^{14}	50
3,3'-dimethyl	28.1	2×10^{14}	33
4,4'-dimethyl	29.7	5×10^{14}	53
2,3-dimethyl	28.2	3×10^{14}	11
2,4-dimethyl	28.3	2×10^{14}	18
2,5-dimethyl	28.1	2×10^{14}	14
3,4-dimethyl	29.2	6×10^{14}	23
3,5-dimethyl	29.4	6×10^{14}	32

[a] J. Coops, H. Galenkamp, T. Haantjies, H. L. Luirink and W. T. Nauta, *Rec. trav. chim.* **67**, 469 (1948); J. Coops, H. Galenkamp, H. L. Luirink, A. N. Balk, and W. T. Nauta, *ibid.* **68**, 160 (1949).

The same thing happens when alkyl halides are treated with silver in the presence of oxygen.[41] The reaction with silver in the absence of oxygen is of course one of the methods used to prepare the stable triarylmethyl free radicals.

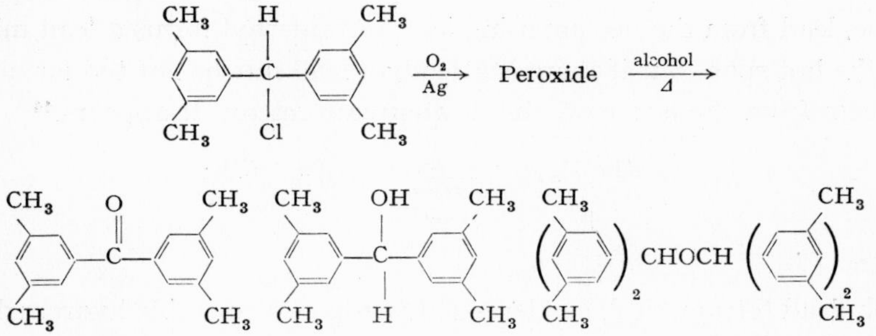

When the nitrile IV is heated it develops color reversibly at 100° and above. Bases, however, cause the formation of a product analogous

[41] W. T. Nauta, M. J. E. Ernsting, and A. C. Faber, *Rec. trav. chim.*, **60** 915 (1941).

to that formed from triphenylmethyl by the action of hydrogen
chloride in benzene or sodium in ether:[42]

$$
\begin{array}{c}
\phi \quad \phi \\
| \quad | \\
\phi\!-\!C\!-\!-\!C\!-\!\phi \\
| \quad | \\
C\!\equiv\!N \; C\!\equiv\!N \\
\text{(IV)}
\end{array}
\;\rightleftharpoons\;
\left[
\begin{array}{c}
\phi \\
| \\
\phi\!-\!C\bullet \\
| \\
C\!\equiv\!N \\
\end{array}
\right]
\;\;\xrightarrow[\text{CHCl}_3,\,50°]{\text{Et}_3\text{N}}\;\;
\begin{array}{c}
\phi \qquad\qquad H \\
| \qquad\qquad | \\
\phi\!-\!C\!-\!\langle\;\;\rangle\!-\!C\!-\!\phi \\
| \qquad\qquad | \\
C\!\equiv\!N \qquad\quad C\!\equiv\!N
\end{array}
$$

Colored

The nitrile IV can be titrated in the presence of the colorless rearrangement product by means of reducing agents. It also reacts
rapidly in the cold with nitrogen dioxide, a typical radical reaction.[43]

$$
\left[
\begin{array}{c}
\phi \\
| \\
\phi\!-\!C\bullet \\
| \\
C\!\equiv\!N \\
\end{array}
\right]
\;\;\xrightarrow{\text{NO}_2}\;\;
\begin{array}{c}
\phi \\
| \\
\phi\!-\!C\!-\!NO_2 \\
| \\
C\!\equiv\!N
\end{array}
$$

Formation of Radicals in the Gas Phase

Radicals still less stable than the ones discussed thus far are
proposed as reaction intermediates. Many of these have been prepared
in the gas phase where they may be detected by the well-known mirror
technique. When a stream of a carrier gas, such as hydrogen or nitrogen
containing lead tetramethyl vapor, is passed over a hot spot in a quartz
tube, lead from the decomposing lead tetramethyl forms a lead mirror
at the hot spot. But if there is already a lead mirror not too far downstream from the hot spot, the downstream mirror disappears.[44]

$$
\text{Pb(CH}_3)_4 \quad \xrightarrow[\text{region}]{\leftarrow\;\text{hot}} \quad \text{Pb} + \text{CH}_3\bullet
$$

cold
region

Only lead tetramethyl, carrier gas, hydrogen, and stable hydrocarbons
issue from the downstream end of the tube, and none of these will
react with lead. Clearly some unstable and reactive intermediate is

[42] G. Wittig and H. Petri, *Ann.*, **513**, 26 (1934).
[43] G. Wittig and U. Pockels, *Ber.*, **69**, 790 (1936).
[44] F. Paneth and W. Hofeditz, *Ber.*, **62**, 1335 (1929).

formed and it is most plausibly a free radical since ions and ion pairs owe a good deal of their stability to interaction with the solvent, absent in this experiment. The radicals react rapidly with one another to form unreactive hydrocarbons, and if the second mirror is too far downstream it is not removed. From the critical distance downstream and the speed of the gas, the half-life for the methyl radical has been calculated to be 6×10^{-3} second.[45] Lead tetraethyl behaves similarly At one time it was believed that lead tetraethyl in gasoline functioned as a detonation inhibitor by providing chain-stopping ethyl radicals. More recently it has been suggested that the anti-knock effect is due instead to a heterogeneous chain-stopping reaction taking place on a fog of lead oxide.[46, 47] Since other sources of free radicals, such as azomethane, actually promote knocking, it is probable that the ethyl radicals start more chains than they stop. The radicals from the decomposition of azomethane are also capable of removing lead mirrors. More complex radicals break down under the same conditions. The isopropyl radicals from azoisopropane, for example, rearrange and decompose to give methyl radicals and hydrocarbons.

Rice has shown that the cracking of hydrocarbons at high temperatures gives free radicals.[48] Only the methyl and ethyl radicals survive long enough to react with mercury to give dialkylmercury. Presumably the others decomposes by a beta cleavage process.

$$CH_3CH_2CH_2 \cdot \quad \underset{\longrightarrow}{\longleftarrow} \quad CH_3 \cdot + CH_2 = CH_2$$

The cleavage reaction is the reverse of the reaction of addition to unsaturated molecules which prevails at lower temperatures.

Photolysis of acetone forms methyl radicals, isolated as dimethylmercury, and acetyl radicals isolated as diacetyl. Photolysis of benzophenone forms phenyl radicals which remove a tellurium mirror to give diphenyltellurium.

[45] Expressing the stability of these gas phase radicals in terms of approximate half-lives is not meant to imply a unimolecular decomposition of the radicals, nor even a strictly first order disappearance.

[46] D. Downs, A. D. Walsh, and R. W. Wheeler, *Trans. Roy. Soc. (London)*, **A 243**, 299 (1951).

[47] A. D. Walsh, *J. Roy. Inst. Chem.*, **75**, 323 (1951).

[48] F. O. Rice, *J. Am. Chem. Soc.*, **53**, 1959 (1931).

Photolysis of diisopropyl ketone in the presence of mercury yields di-*n*-propylmercury, indicating rearrangement of the isopropyl radical.[49] It will be recalled that the radicals from azoisopropane cleaved to methyl radicals, perhaps after rearranging. It is not expected that normal propyl radicals will be more stable than isopropyl radicals, but the apparent rearrangement may merely mean that the normal radical undergoes the final irreversible reaction faster than the isopropyl radical does. In the decomposition of diacyl peroxides the alkyl radical, if it is formed, does not rearrange:[50]

$$CH_3CH_2CH_2-\overset{\overset{O}{\|}}{C}-O-O-\overset{\overset{O}{\|}}{C}-CH_2CH_2CH_3 \xrightarrow[\Delta]{CCl_4} [CH_3CH_2CH_2\cdot] \longrightarrow CH_3CH_2CH_2Cl$$

$$H-\overset{\overset{CH_3}{|}}{\underset{\underset{CH_3}{|}}{C}}-\overset{\overset{O}{\|}}{C}-O-O-\overset{\overset{O}{\|}}{C}-\overset{\overset{CH_3}{|}}{\underset{\underset{CH_3}{|}}{C}}-H \xrightarrow[\Delta]{CCl_4} \left[H-\overset{\overset{CH_3}{|}}{\underset{\underset{CH_3}{|}}{C}}\cdot\right] \longrightarrow H-\overset{\overset{CH_3}{|}}{\underset{\underset{CH_3}{|}}{C}}-Cl$$

Aside from the possibility that these alkyl radicals simply do not rearrange under the conditions used, there are several other possible explanations for the apparent discrepancy. For example, in the case of benzoyl peroxide there is conclusive evidence that the first step in the decomposition is the production of acyloxy radicals alone, rather than acyloxy radicals, phenyl radicals, and carbon dioxide.[51] This of course does not mean that the same thing has to be true of diacyl peroxides in general. But if the carboxy group is still attached to the radical when it reacts, it could explain the difference between the products from the peroxide and the ketone. For example, the acyloxy radical might react directly with carbon tetrachloride to give alkyl chloride, carbon dioxide, and trichloromethyl. A somewhat more plausible path is the formation of an acyl hypochlorite which decomposes by an S_ni process to give alkyl chloride and carbon dioxide. Since his experiments on the decomposition in carbon tetrachloride,

[49] H. H. Glazebrook and T. G. Pearson, *J. Chem. Soc.*, **1936**, 1777.
[50] M. S. Kharasch, S. S. Kane, and H. C. Brown, *J. Am. Chem. Soc.*, **63**, 526 (1941).
[51] G. S. Hammond and L. M. Soffer, *J. Am. Chem. Soc.*, **72**, 4711 (1950).

Kharasch has shown by the decomposition of an optically active peroxide that no alkyl radical involved in the formation of at least one product, the ester, becomes sufficiently free to racemize during the decomposition.[52] In fact, the geometrical result is retention of the original configuration.

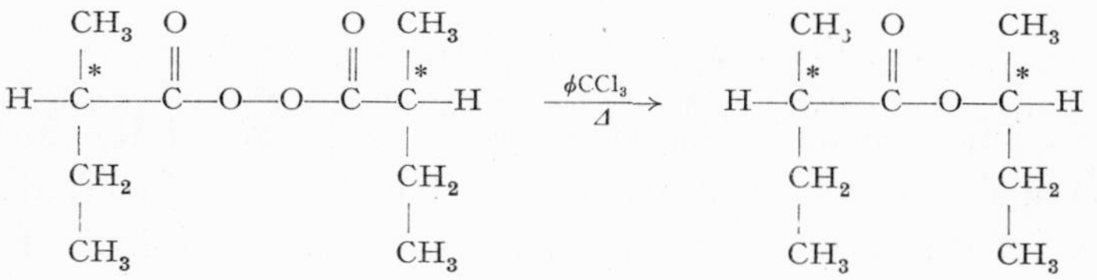

The mechanism of the ester formation would seem to be either an S_ni decomposition of the peroxide to give the ester directly, or a front side reaction between two acyloxy radicals.

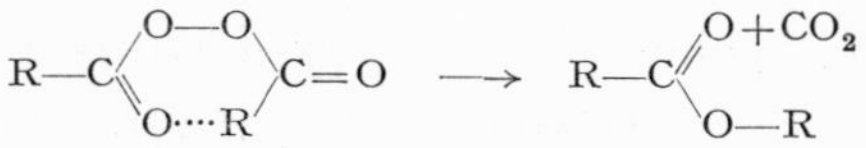

Methyl, ethyl, and phenyl radicals have been detected by mirror removal downstream from an organic halide sodium flame.

Besides the mirror and addition reactions already discussed, gas phase radicals dimerize, disproportionate, transfer hydrogen, and polymerize olefins. Similar reactions in the liquid phase are an indication (but not proof) of free radical intermediates.

$$2R\bullet \longrightarrow R\text{---}R$$

$$2CH_3CH_2\bullet \longrightarrow CH_2{=}CH_2 + CH_3CH_3$$

$$R\bullet + H_2 \longrightarrow R\text{---}H + H\bullet$$

$$R\bullet + R'\text{---}H \longrightarrow RH + R'\bullet$$

$$Hg(CH_2CH_3)_2 \xrightarrow{\Delta} CH_3CH_3\bullet \xrightarrow{CH_2=CH_2} CH_3CH_2CH_2CH_2\bullet \longrightarrow CH_3(CH_2)_nCH_3$$

When a beam of alkyl radicals and hydrocarbons from a furnace in which a lead tetraalkyl is decomposing is crossed with a beam of electrons, the resulting ions can be identified by the mass spectrograph

[52] M. S. Kharasch, J. Kuderna, and W. Nudenberg, *J. Org. Chem.*, **19**, 1283 (1954).

and their appearance potentials determined[53]. The appearance potential gives the minimum energy that the electrons must have to ionize the molecule or radical.

$$CH_3 \bullet \xrightarrow{10.0\ ev} CH_3^{(+)} + e^{(-)}$$

$$CH_4 \xrightarrow{14.4\ ev} CH_3^{(+)} + H \bullet + e^{(-)}$$

$$CH_3CH_2 \bullet \xrightarrow{8.6\ ev} CH_3CH_2^{(+)} + e^{(-)}$$

The difference between the appearance potentials of the ions from methyl and ethyl radicals indicates that hyperconjugation is less effective in stabilizing an unpaired electron than a positive charge.

$$
\begin{array}{ccc}
\quad\ \text{H} \quad\ \text{H} & & \quad\ \text{H} \quad\ \text{H} \\
\quad\ | \quad\ | & & \quad\ | \quad\ | \\
\text{H}-\text{C}=\text{C} & > & \text{H}-\text{C}=\text{C} \\
\quad\ | & & \quad\ | \\
\text{H}^{(+)}\ \text{H} & & \text{H}\cdot\ \text{H}
\end{array}
$$

The results of gas phase chlorination of hydrocarbons suggest that, due to differences in activation energy, tertiary radicals are more readily formed than secondary radicals which in turn are more readily formed than primary radicals.

$$
\begin{array}{ccccc}
\text{CH}_3 & & \text{CH}_3 & \text{H}\cdot & \text{CH}_3 \\
| & & | & & | \\
\text{CH}_3-\text{C}-\text{H} + \text{Cl}\bullet \longrightarrow & \text{HCl} + \text{CH}_3-\text{C}\bullet & \longleftrightarrow & \text{CH}_2=\text{C} \\
| & & | & & | \\
\text{CH}_3 & & \text{CH}_3 & & \text{CH}_3
\end{array}
$$

The activation energies parallel the bond energies with a proportionality factor of about 0.22, that is, 22% of any decrease in bond energy appears as a decrease in activation energy.[54]

Formation of Unstable Radicals in the Liquid Phase

The formation of radicals in the liquid phase is of greater interest to organic chemists than is the corresponding gas phase reaction, because it is not limited to substances of low molecular weight. It takes

[53] J. A. Hipple and D. P. Stevenson, *Phys. Rev.*, **63**, 121 (1943).
[54] H. Steiner and H. R. Watson, *Discussions Faraday Soc.*, No. 2, 88 (1947).

place by the same reactions that occur in the gas phase and by others as well. The radicals subsequently react with the solvent in most cases, giving rather complicated mixtures.

For example, in the decomposition of phenylazotriphenylmethane in benzene, triphenylmethyl peroxide is formed if oxygen is present, indicating a radical reaction. The unstable phenyl radical does not persist long enough to dimerize but reacts instead with the solvent.

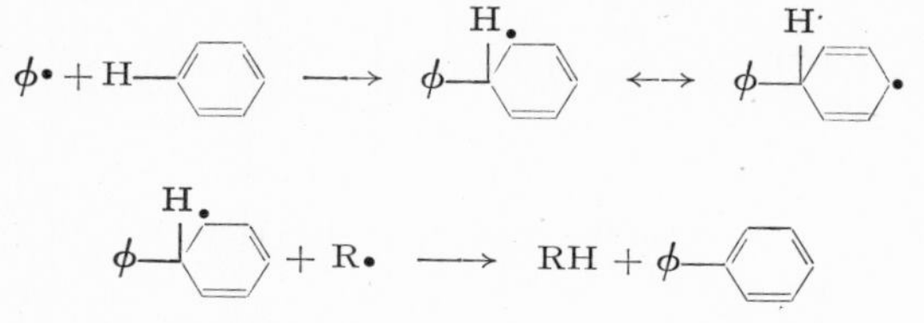

Thus, when the radical generated is p-chlorophenyl, no dichlorobiphenyl is formed but only p-chlorobiphenyl.[55]

The decomposition of aromatic diazonium salts in neutral or alkaline solution generates radicals that attack supernatant benzene.[56]

An intramolecular transfer of hydrogen as well as ring closure occurs with diazonium salts containing a suitably located second aromatic ring.[57] The amount of ring closure by radicals, however, is very much less than the amount that occurs in the corresponding polar reaction.

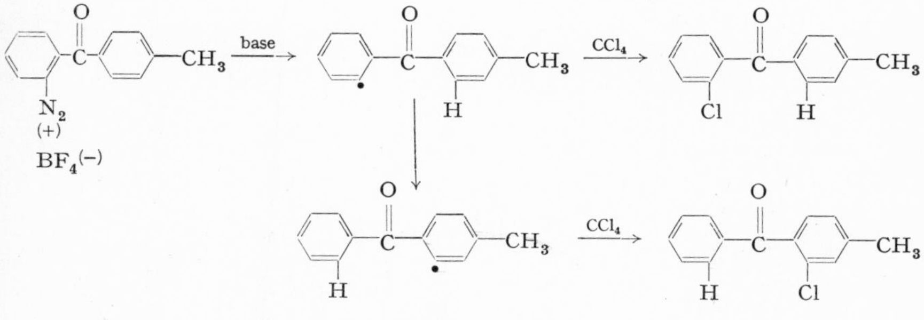

[55] H. Wieland, E. Popper, and H. Seefried, *Ber.*, **55**, 1816 (1922).
[56] W. A. Waters, *J. Chem. Soc.*, **1942**, 266.
[57] D. I. Relyea and D. F. De Tar, *J. Am. Chem. Soc.*, **76**, 1202 (1954).

The substitution reactions of free radicals give considerable para-oriented product even when the substrate molecule bears a meta-directing group.[58] A "meta-directing group" is of course defined by its effect in reactions in which the attacking reagent is a cation or potential cation. Groups that are not able to distribute or stabilize a positive charge can nevertheless distribute the unpaired electron:

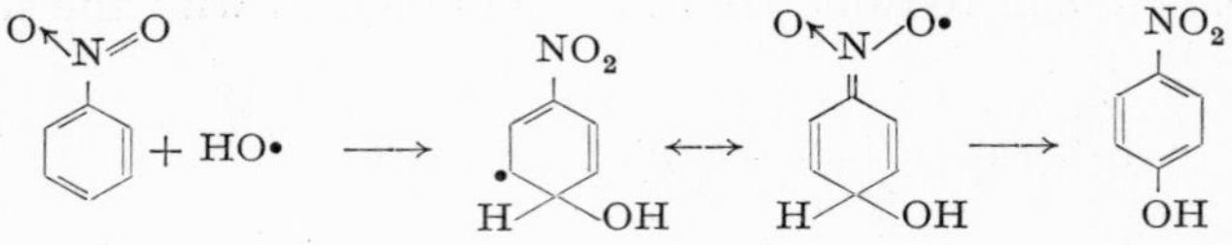

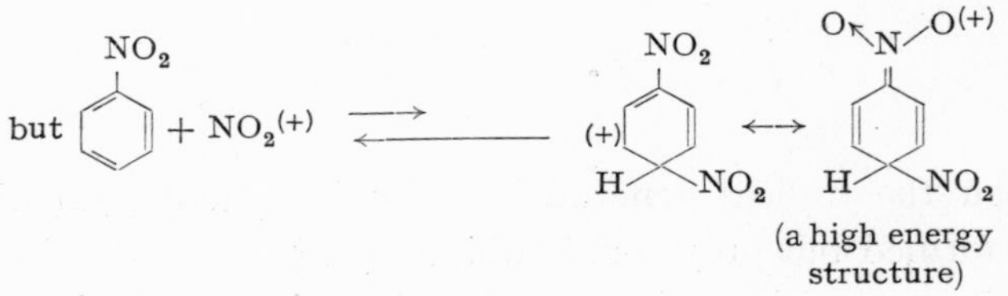

(a high energy structure)

The complexity of the product is one of the better criteria for a mechanism involving unstable free radicals. Being unstable they need relatively little activation energy for any reaction and are therefore not very selective.

The decomposition of azobisnitriles is used to initiate polymerization. In the presence of quinones they give the same kind of addition product that is obtained from triphenylmethyl free radicals, strengthening the hypothesis that the decomposition is a radical one.

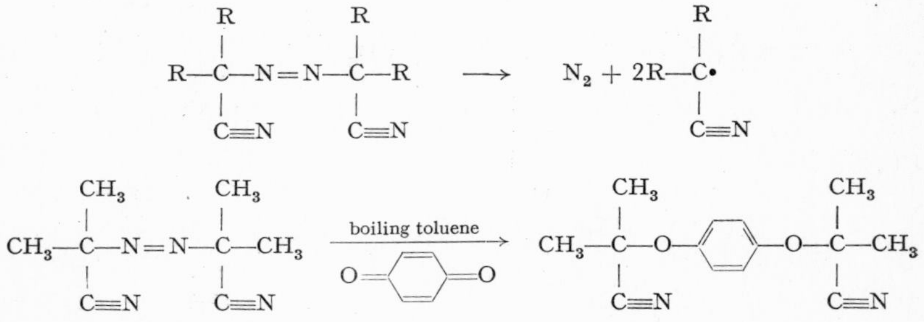

The corresponding azodicarboxylic ester does the same thing.

[58] H. Loebl, G. Stein, and J. Weiss, *J. Chem. Soc.*, **1949**, 2074.

The autoxidation of 2-nitropropane in basic solution is believed to go by way of an intermediate free radical.[59] It is catalyzed by ferric ion and inhibited by arsenic trioxide.

$$\text{H}-\overset{\text{CH}_3}{\underset{\text{CH}_3}{\text{C}}}-\text{NO}_2 \underset{\xleftarrow{\hspace{1cm}}}{\xrightarrow{\text{base}}} {}^{(-)}\overset{\text{CH}_3}{\underset{\text{CH}_3}{\text{C}}}-\text{NO}_2 \xrightarrow{[\text{O}]} \cdot\overset{\text{CH}_3}{\underset{\text{CH}_3}{\text{C}}}-\text{NO}_2 \xrightarrow{\text{O}_2} \cdot\text{O}-\text{O}-\overset{\text{CH}_3}{\underset{\text{CH}_3}{\text{C}}}-\text{NO}_2$$

$$\text{O}_2\text{N}-\overset{\text{CH}_3}{\underset{\text{CH}_3}{\text{C}}}-\text{O}-\text{O}\cdot + \text{O}_2\text{N}-\overset{\text{CH}_3}{\underset{\text{CH}_3}{\text{C}}}{}^{(-)} \longrightarrow \text{O}_2\text{N}-\overset{\text{CH}_3}{\underset{\text{CH}_3}{\text{C}}}-\text{O}-\text{O}^{(-)} + \text{O}_2\text{N}-\overset{\text{CH}_3}{\underset{\text{CH}_3}{\text{C}}}\cdot \quad \text{etc.}$$

$$\text{O}_2\text{N}-\overset{\text{CH}_3}{\underset{\text{CH}_3}{\text{C}}}-\text{OOH} + {}^{(-)}\overset{\text{CH}_3}{\underset{\text{CH}_3}{\text{C}}}-\text{NO}_2 \longrightarrow \text{HO}-\overset{\text{CH}_3}{\underset{\text{CH}_3}{\text{C}}}-\text{NO}_2 + \text{O}_2\text{N}-\overset{\text{CH}_3}{\underset{\text{CH}_3}{\text{C}}}-\text{O}^{(-)}$$

$$\downarrow$$

$$\overset{\text{CH}_3}{\underset{\text{CH}_3}{\text{C}}}=\text{O} + \text{HNO}_2$$

Radicals are also formed in solution by the decomposition of other radicals, which are not always carbon free radicals, and by removal of hydrogen atoms from solvent molecules. Because radicals are usually uncharged, the rates and equilibria of radical reactions are usually less affected by changes in solvent than are those of polar reactions. If new radicals are being made from the solvent by hydrogen abstraction, and if the new radicals participate in chain reactions, this may not be true of course. But even in cases of non-chain radical reactions in which no radicals actually derived from the solvent take part in a rate-determining step, the indifference of the solvent has perhaps been overemphasized. This will be discussed more fully when radical and polar reactions are compared in Chapter XII.

[59] G. A. Russell, *J. Am. Chem. Soc.*, **76**, 1595 (1954).

Rearrangement of Carbon Radicals

The rearrangement that we have already noted of carbon free radicals in the gas phase also occurs with the more complicated radicals that can be generated in the liquid phase.

When an alkyl halide is treated with phenylmagnesium bromide in the presence of cobaltous chloride, the products obtained are partly those to be expected from unrearranged alkyl radicals and partly from rearranged ones.[60]

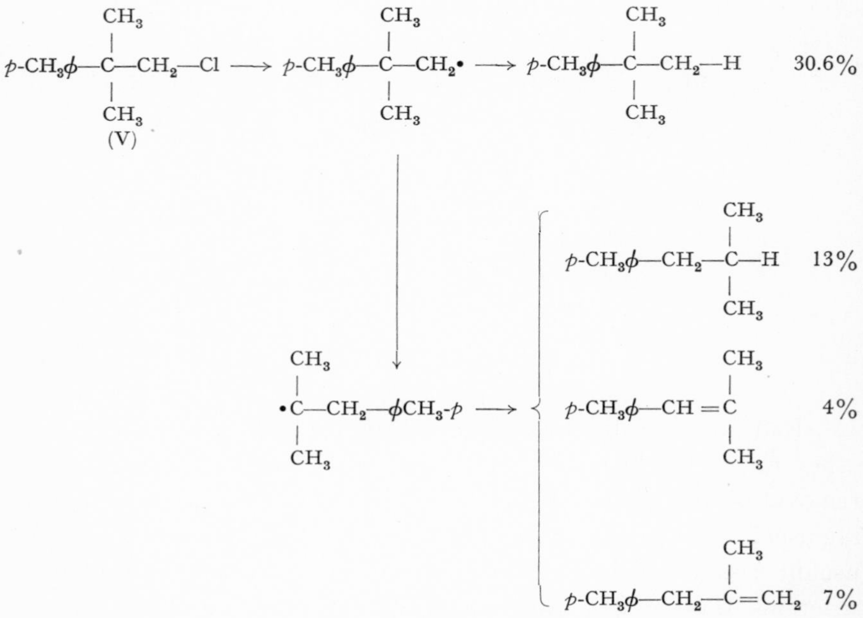

$$
\underset{(V)}{p\text{-}CH_3\phi \overset{\overset{\displaystyle CH_3}{|}}{\underset{\underset{\displaystyle CH_3}{|}}{C}} CH_2 Cl} \longrightarrow p\text{-}CH_3\phi \overset{\overset{\displaystyle CH_3}{|}}{\underset{\underset{\displaystyle CH_3}{|}}{C}} CH_2 \cdot \longrightarrow p\text{-}CH_3\phi \overset{\overset{\displaystyle CH_3}{|}}{\underset{\underset{\displaystyle CH_3}{|}}{C}} CH_2 H \qquad 30.6\%
$$

$$
\cdot \overset{\overset{\displaystyle CH_3}{|}}{\underset{\underset{\displaystyle CH_3}{|}}{C}} CH_2 \text{---} \phi CH_3\text{-}p \longrightarrow
\begin{cases}
p\text{-}CH_3\phi\text{---}CH_2\text{---}\overset{\overset{\displaystyle CH_3}{|}}{\underset{\underset{\displaystyle CH_3}{|}}{C}}\text{---}H & 13\% \\[2em]
p\text{-}CH_3\phi\text{---}CH = \overset{}{\underset{\underset{\displaystyle CH_3}{|}}{C}}{\overset{\overset{\displaystyle CH_3}{|}}{}} & 4\% \\[2em]
p\text{-}CH_3\phi\text{---}CH_2\text{---}\overset{\overset{\displaystyle CH_3}{|}}{C}=CH_2 & 7\%
\end{cases}
$$

In similar experiments in which an ethyl group was used in place of the para-tolyl group of compound V there was no rearrangement. Apparently aromatic but not aliphatic groups will migrate under these mild conditions. The same results have been obtained in experiments in which the radical is formed by a different method:

[60] W. H. Urry and N. Nicolaides, *J. Am. Chem. Soc.*, **74**, 5163 (1952).

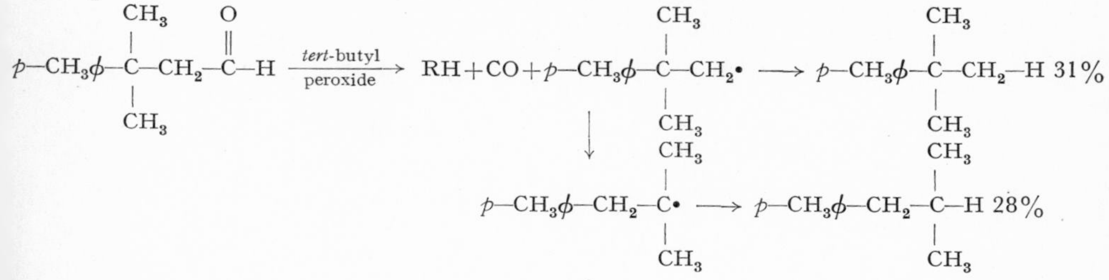

$$p-CH_3\phi-\overset{\overset{\displaystyle CH_3}{|}}{\underset{\underset{\displaystyle CH_3}{|}}{C}}-CH_2-\overset{\overset{\displaystyle O}{\|}}{C}-H \xrightarrow[\text{peroxide}]{\textit{tert}\text{-butyl}} RH+CO+p-CH_3\phi-\overset{\overset{\displaystyle CH_3}{|}}{\underset{\underset{\displaystyle CH_3}{|}}{C}}-CH_2\bullet \longrightarrow p-CH_3\phi-\overset{\overset{\displaystyle CH_3}{|}}{\underset{\underset{\displaystyle CH_3}{|}}{C}}-CH_2-H\ 31\%$$

$$\downarrow$$

$$p-CH_3\phi-CH_2-\overset{\overset{\displaystyle CH_3}{|}}{\underset{\underset{\displaystyle CH_3}{|}}{C}}\bullet \longrightarrow p-CH_3\phi-CH_2-\overset{\overset{\displaystyle CH_3}{|}}{\underset{\underset{\displaystyle CH_3}{|}}{C}}-H\ 28\%$$

In radical rearrangements, phenyl and tolyl groups have about the same migration aptitudes, in contrast to the corresponding carbonium ion rearrangements. This result is in accord with our previous observations that hyperconjugation is less effective in stabilizing radicals and that radicals are less selective in their reactions anyway. Both the radical and polar rearrangements can be classed as internal substitution reactions, and in the case of the radical there is a higher probability that any group that swings into the proper position will react.

In carbonium ion rearrangements, the rearrangement is often concerted with the formation of the ion. When an unrearranged intermediate ion is written for such a reaction it is often for the sake of simplicity and does not necessarily mean that the difficult question of concerted versus consecutive formation and rearrangement has been settled. In still other cases the reaction sticks half way and a relatively stable bridged *intermediate*, rather than a bridged transition state, is produced. The mechanisms of the corresponding radical rearrangements are for the most part not known in this much detail, but in at least one case it has been demonstrated that rearrangement and formation of the radical are not concerted. Seubold has found that the proportion of rearranged to unrearranged product in the following reaction is not constant but increases as the concentration of aldehyde is decreased.[61]

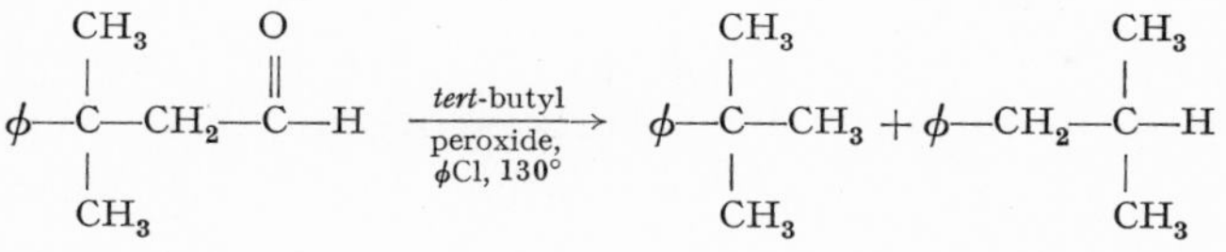

$$\phi-\overset{\overset{\displaystyle CH_3}{|}}{\underset{\underset{\displaystyle CH_3}{|}}{C}}-CH_2-\overset{\overset{\displaystyle O}{\|}}{C}-H \xrightarrow[\substack{\text{peroxide,}\\ \phi Cl,\ 130°}]{\textit{tert}\text{-butyl}} \phi-\overset{\overset{\displaystyle CH_3}{|}}{\underset{\underset{\displaystyle CH_3}{|}}{C}}-CH_3 + \phi-CH_2-\overset{\overset{\displaystyle CH_3}{|}}{\underset{\underset{\displaystyle CH_3}{|}}{C}}-H$$

[61] F. H. Seubold, Jr., *J. Am. Chem. Soc.*, **75**, 2532 (1953).

The steps in the reaction are as follows:

(1)   Peroxide $\longrightarrow$ radicals for chain initiation

$$
(2)\quad R\bullet + \phi\!-\!\underset{\underset{CH_3}{|}}{\overset{\overset{CH_3}{|}}{C}}\!-\!CH_2\!-\!\overset{\overset{O}{\|}}{C}\!-\!H \quad\longrightarrow\quad RH + CO + \phi\!-\!\underset{\underset{CH_3}{|}}{\overset{\overset{CH_3}{|}}{C}}\!-\!CH_2\bullet \;\text{(neophyll radical)}
$$

$$
(3)\quad \phi\!-\!\underset{\underset{CH_3}{|}}{\overset{\overset{CH_3}{|}}{C}}\!-\!CH_2\bullet + \phi\!-\!\underset{\underset{CH_3}{|}}{\overset{\overset{CH_3}{|}}{C}}\!-\!CH_2\!-\!\overset{\overset{O}{\|}}{C}\!-\!H \quad\longrightarrow\quad \phi\!-\!\underset{\underset{CH_3}{|}}{\overset{\overset{CH_3}{|}}{C}}\!-\!CH_3 + \phi\!-\!\underset{\underset{CH_3}{|}}{\overset{\overset{CH_3}{|}}{C}}\!-\!CH_2\bullet + CO
$$

Thus the average lifetime of the neophyll radical depends on the probability of encountering an aldehyde molecule and hence on the aldehyde concentration. At high aldehyde concentrations the radical is removed by reaction (3) before it has an opportunity to rearrange. This would not be the case if rearrangement were simultaneous with formation of the radical.

Factors Affecting the Lifetime of Radicals

When a free radical is described as unstable in this chapter it is not meant that such a radical tends to fly apart into its constituent atoms, but merely that it has a higher free energy than various reaction products and tends to disappear rapidly for that reason. If a radical can be isolated from other reactive molecules, and especially from other radicals, it should persist indefinitely. There is some evidence that just such a stabilization by isolation has been achieved.[62] The radical chain polymerization of chloroprene to a solid polymer gives a product that reacts as though it contains stuck free radicals whose activity is confined to an occasional exchange of hydrogen atoms with neighboring polymer molecules. The exchange process is evidently so slow that it is not an adequate substitute for the process of diffusion by which radicals are able to approach each other in a liquid. The solid will react with iodine, presumably forming alkyl iodides from the stuck radicals, but

[62] S. S. Medvedev, *Acta Physicochim. U.R.S.S.*, **19**, 457 (1944).

if dissolved and re-precipitated it loses this property. Dissolving the polymer releases the stuck high molecular weight free radicals and allows them to come together and dimerize. It is regrettable that the existence of the stuck free radicals has not yet been confirmed by a magnetic resonance experiment in this case. This has been done for sodium-initiated styrene polymer,[63] but the fact that a mixture of styrene and methyl methacrylate reacts with sodium to give a polymer that is at least 99% polymethacrylate indicates that the latter reaction at least is the growth of a carbanion rather than the growth of a radical.[64] Either the mechanism in styrene is different from what it is in the mixture, or the radicals are not simply left over from the polymerization reaction but arise in some other way.

A less ambiguous result has been obtained with ethyleneglycol dimethacrylate. The radical polymerization of ethyleneglycol dimethacrylate by any of several well-known radical chain initiators gives a crosslinked polymer containing, on the basis of magnetic resonance measurements, up to 10^{-3} M stuck free radicals. The radicals are still observable in the polymer after as long as three months.[65] A highly crosslinked polymer such as that formed from ethyleneglycol dimethacrylate is likely to be seriously strained. Even polystyrene usually has enough strain to show up in polarized light. The strain in the crosslinked, less flexible polymer is likely to take the form of broken carbon-carbon bonds, and the radicals resulting from this process may be responsible for part of the paramagnetic resonance absorption. In other words, the 10^{-3} M concentration of radicals in the polymer may not represent the steady state concentration of radicals during the fluid stages of the polymerization.

An unusually highly crosslinked, and therefore insoluble, form of polystyrene called popcorn polymer may also contain stuck free radicals. It has the lifelike property of growing when put into fresh

[63] D. Lipkin, D. E. Paul, J. Townsend, and S. I. Weissman, *Science*, **117**, 534 (1953).

[64] C. Walling, E. R. Briggs, W. Cummings, and F. R. Mayo, *J. Am. Chem. Soc.*, **72**, 48 (1950).

[65] G. K. Fraenkel, J. M. Hirshon, and C. Walling, *J. Am. Chem. Soc.*, **76**, 3606 (1954).

styrene monomer. The monomer is able to diffuse to the radical in the interior of the popcorn and react with it to give a longer but still stuck radical. The resulting swelling causes fissures to appear in the polymer, giving its characteristic tortured appearence, and perhaps forming still more radicals mechanically. The formation of popcorn polymer in fractionating columns after long use in the distillation of styrene is a highly unwelcome phenomenon that will eventually result in the total plugging of the column unless the last trace of popcorn seed is removed. In this respect it is comparable to water hyacinth in a river.

Research is currently in progress on free radicals immobilized in supercooled solvents and as clathrate complexes.[66] A clathrate complex is a crystal which contains isolated small molecules in regularly spaced cavities of the crystal lattice. These molecules are liberated when the crystal is crushed.

Phenomena somewhat related to the stuck radical problem are the ion radicals produced photochemically from Wurster's blue in an organic glass, and the formation of color in inorganic glasses by x-ray and other high energy radiation. When the colored glass from an old x-ray tube is heated it loses its color; it also loses its color and emits a flash of light when it is broken. All of these phenomena depend on the mechanical properties of the medium. The Wurster's blue ion is discussed more fully in Chapter IV.

The process of radical chain polymerization involves steps of three different types: production of radicals by decomposition of an initiator, growth of the radicals by successive stages of reaction with olefinic monomer, and termination of the chain by the dimerization of two radicals. As the reaction proceeds and the concentration of polymer increases, the viscosity of the reaction mixture also increases. The theory of the effect of viscosity increases on reaction rates has been worked out by Rabinowitch and Wood.[67] By analogy with a mechanical model, they predict that collisions will occur in sets, the reagents being prevented from diffusing away from one another by the surrounding cage of solvent molecules. Now for ordinary reactions the viscosity of the medium will make very little difference, because if an increase in

[66] *Chem. Eng. News*, **30**, 4640 (1952).
[67] E. Rabinowitch and W. C. Wood, *Trans. Faraday Soc.*, **32**, 1381 (1936).

viscosity makes encounters (sets of collisions) between reagent molecules less frequent it also makes it more difficult for them to diffuse apart, thus prolonging the set of collisions that occurs when they do meet. The total number of collisions is therefore unchanged. But in case the reaction is one that is probable at the first collision, the other collisions in the the set will usually be wasted and the reaction rate is proportional to the number of sets of collisions rather than to the number of collisions. This is the limiting result if no molecule ever survives the set of collisions without reacting.

We therefore recognize that although ordinary reactions will be independent of viscosity unless the viscosity approaches that of a glass, reactions of very low free energy of activation will be slowed down by an increase in viscosity. This is just what happens to the radical recombination reaction which serves to stop the chains in radical chain polymerization. The radical recombination is slowed down, and since the chain breaking reaction is a sort of damper of the overall reaction, and since the other steps are not affected by the increased viscosity, the net result is an almost explosive increase in rate when the viscosity exceeds a critical value. This phenomenon has been studied for methyl methacrylate polymerization by Schulz and Harborth.[68] While the free radical in Medvedev's solid polymer might be called stuck, the growing radicals in the explosive stage of methyl methacrylate polymerization at least have a very greatly reduced mobility and enhanced lifetime.

Possible Production of Radicals by
Mechanical Means

A Maxwell demon of the type possessing personal magnetism, but nevertheless unable to electrify his friends, would probably pull large molecules apart into radicals rather than ions. It is too much to expect that a demon would be content for long with the unglamorous occupation of a mere gatekeeper as proposed in the older literature. Mechanical motion, whether of demoniacal or human origin, can be regarded as a sort of anisotropic heat, and mechanical stress applied to a molecule should not differ in principle from the stress that it undergoes when

[68] G. V. Schulz and G. Harborth, *Makromol. Chem.*, 1, 106 (1947).

excessive thermal energy concentrates in some one bond. Polymeric substances, especially crosslinked ones, contain relatively fewer molecules and these are very likely somewhat entwined. Milling such substances, or subjecting them to shear by passage through a small orifice or by treatment with ultrasonic vibrations reduces their molecular weight, but it is not certain that the mechanism is a radical one.[69] Methyl methacrylate polymer apparently is degraded by a "zipper" process: that is, the polymer either goes all the way back to monomer or not at all, and by a reaction progressing along the chain. The ultrasonic degradation of very high molecular weight polymer does give polymer molecules of lower molecular weight but without initiating the polymerization of monomer used as the solvent.

[69] H. W. Melville, *Science Progr.*, **38**, 1 (1950).

CHAPTER III

Diradicals

A diradical is an atom or molecule containing two unpaired electrons. The properties of diradicals are for the most part like those of monoradicals. They are paramagnetic and show paramagnetic resonance absorption. Although they are very reactive chemically, this is not a reliable criterion for the diradical state. Spectroscopically the diradical will probably be a triplet state if a double bond structure coupling the two electrons is geometrically possible. But when the two electrons are fairly well isolated from each other the state is probably a double doublet, like two independent radicals.

Any unsaturated molecule has diradical as well as singlet (non-radical) states. Usually one of the non-radical states will have a decisively lower free energy than the most stable of the diradical states, in which case the substance is not paramagnetic. Special circumstances can make the diradical state the ground state; then the singlet state is an excited one. Some substances have detectable amounts of both forms in equilibrium. It is unknown whether the radical-like reactions of some compounds are characteristic of their singlet states directly or due to an undetectable amount of a more reactive triplet state in equilibrium.

Stable Diradicals

The most familiar diradical is the oxygen molecule. Due to the fact that its uppermost occupied orbital is degenerate and consists of two orbitals of equal energy, the last two electrons each occupy one of these and the ground state is a diradical. A recently developed analytical method for oxygen depends on its paramagnetism. The oxygen diradical couples with most organic radicals to form peroxy radicals:

$$R\bullet + \bullet O-O\bullet \longrightarrow R-O-O\bullet$$

But the comparable reaction of organic radicals with olefins does not necessarily mean that the reacting olefins are first excited to a diradical state. In fact, as will be discussed later, there is some reason to believe that diradicals are not involved in the purely thermal polymerization of olefins either.

The most stable diradicals are related to triphenylmethyl. The compound with the para connection between the phenyl groups of two triphenylmethyl radicals exists largely in the singlet, non-radical state. However, the paramagnetic resonance method reveals that the triplet or diradical state of this molecule is relatively low lying and is thermally populated to the extent of about 4% at room temperature.[70] Earlier measurements of the paramagnetism rather than the paramagnetic resonance absorption had indicated that it was entirely in the singlet state, probably because of uncertainty in the diamagnetic correction. The reactions of this compound are characteristic of radicals, but will require further investigation to determine whether the diradical form is always the sole reagent.

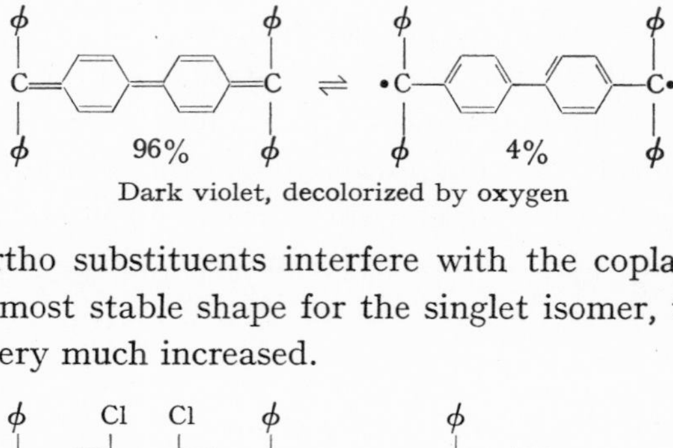

Dark violet, decolorized by oxygen

When ortho substituents interfere with the coplanar structure, which is the most stable shape for the singlet isomer, the amount of diradical is very much increased.

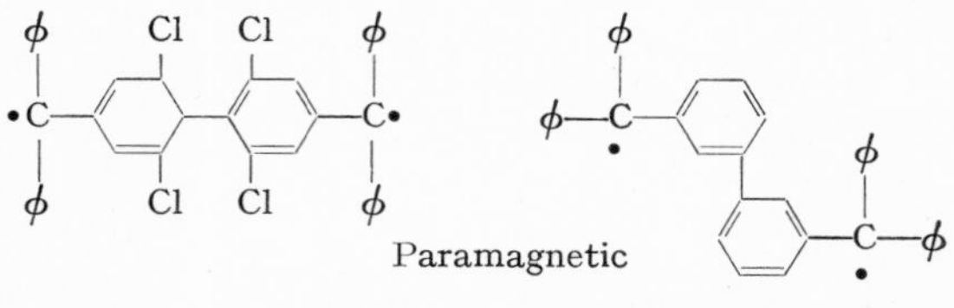

Paramagnetic

[70] C. A. Hutchison, Jr., A. Kowalsky, R. C. Pastor, and G. W. Wheland, *J. Chem. Phys.*, **20**, 1485 (1952).

When the junction between the component triphenylmethyl radicals is meta, non-polar structures coupling the unpaired electrons are no longer possible. On the other hand, polar structures that would allow the two unpaired electrons to couple through a meta double bond system (see page 13) are of high energy owing to charge separation.

When the junction between the rings is ortho, the question of diradical versus singlet states is eliminated by the irreversible formation of a third ring.[71]

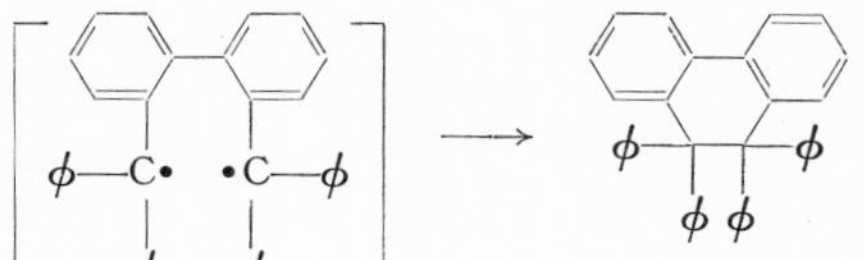

When the central pair of benzene rings in the para-connected diradical is replaced by three or more benzene rings, the substance is markedly paramagnetic in spite of the fact that a coplanar structure is sterically possible.

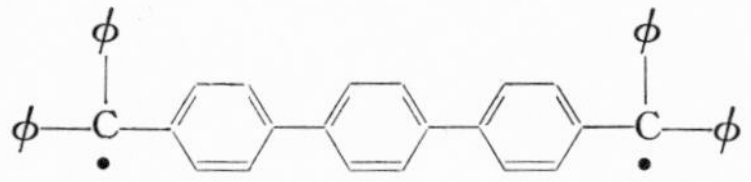

The rigid coplanar structure would of course involve considerable loss of entropy.

Porphyrindine has been shown to be a diradical both by its paramagnetism and by paramagnetic resonance absorption.[72,75]

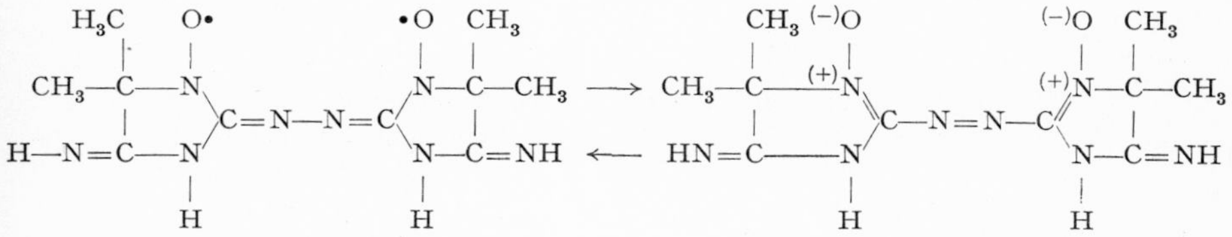

low temperatures   high temperatures

Porphyrindine

[71] F. Seel, *Z. Electrochem.*, **52**, 182 (1948).
[72] T. L. Chu, G. E. Pake, D. E. Paul, J. Townsend, and S. I. Weissman, *J. Phys. Chem.*, **57**, 504 (1953).

Unstable Diradicals Produced Photochemically

When a molecule in its singlet ground state is excited to the fluorescent state by absorption of radiation, it may re-emit the radiation immediately (fluoresce) or decay to the diradical, triplet state. The triplet state slowly returns to the ground state with delayed emission of radiation. The delayed radiation is called phosphorescence. Some molecules are capable of direct excitation to the triplet state, although the corresponding absorption bands are usually weak due to the change in multiplicity involved in the transition. The triplet nature of the phosphorescent state has been proved by Lewis and Calvin, who succeeded in measuring its paramagnetism.[73, 74] They stabilized the phosphorescent state of fluorescein by creating it in a rigid boric acid glass, thus preventing the collisions which ordinarily lead to rapid deactivation.

While it is in the triplet state a molecule may undergo typical diradical reactions. This provides a plausible mechanism for radical-like reactions of substances that are largely diamagnetic. They are partly converted to the triplet state by light, or in the case of low lying triplet states, by heat. Probable examples of this mechanism are the photooxidation of rubrene and the photooxidation and dimerization of anthracene and higher members of the acene series.[76]

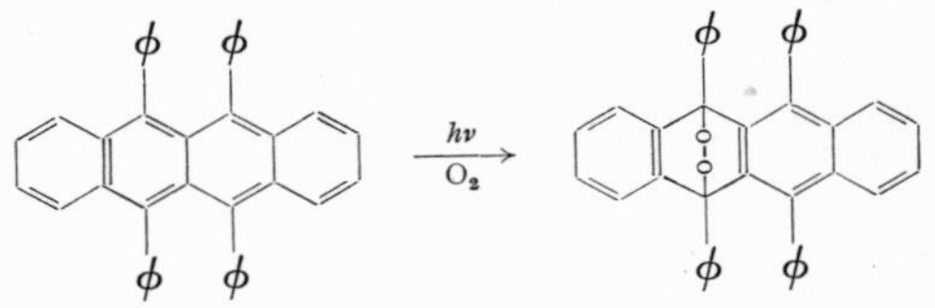

Rubrene　　　　　　　　　　Rubrene peroxide
(red)　　　　　　　　　　　　(colorless)

[73] G. N. Lewis and M. Calvin, *J. Am. Chem. Soc.*, **67**, 1232 (1945).

[74] M. Kasha, *Chem. Revs.*, **41**, 401 (1947).

[75] In the case of most organic diradicals, it is possible to convert a classical diradical formula into a classical non-radical formula by a process of opening and closing double bonds. This is true of porphyrindine only if the unpaired electrons are on nitrogen.

[76] A. Etienne, *Traité de Chimie Organique*, Volume XVII, Masson et Cie, Paris, 1949, p. 1299.

On heating, rubrene peroxide gives up most of its oxygen to regenerate rubrene.

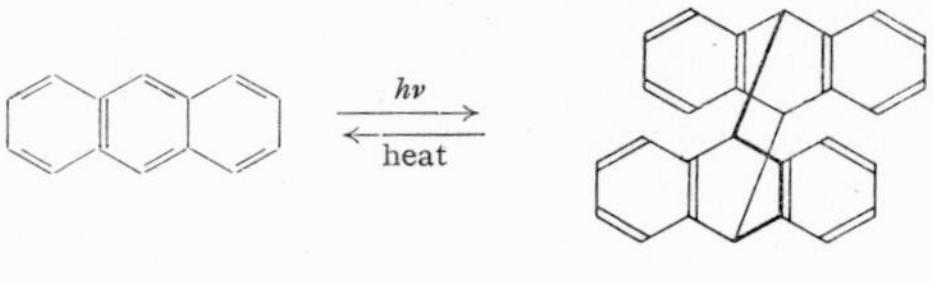

The explanation for these diradical reactions can not be quite so simple as the one hinted at above however, since the quantum yield of rubrene peroxide does not appear to depend only on the concentration of photoactivated rubrene triplet molecules but also on the concentrations of rubrene itself and of oxygen.[77]

The Base Strength of Diradicals

A diradical is likely to be more polarizable and a stronger base than the corresponding singlet state. If so, reaction with an acid should shift the equilibrium enough for the diradical to be detectable in otherwise diamagnetic substances. This seems to be the case for the substances shown below, in which paramagnetic resonance absorption indicates the presence of the diradical conjugate acid to the extent of 10%.[78]

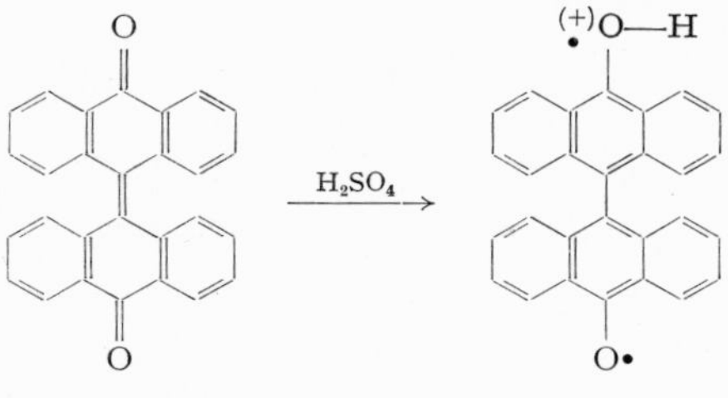

Bianthrone

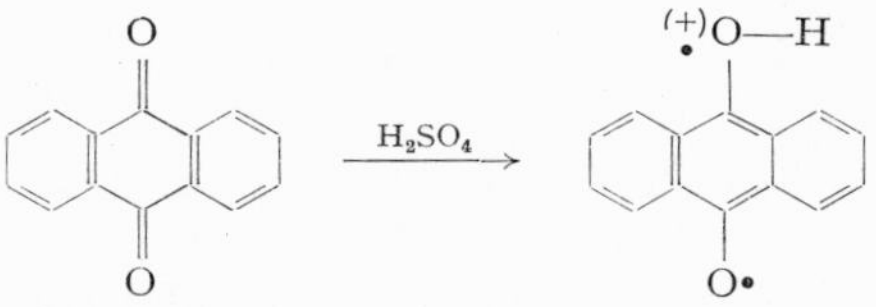

Anthraquinone

[77] W. Koblitz and H. J. Schumacher, *Z. physik. Chem.*, **35B**, 11 (1937).
[78] J. M. Hirshon, D. M. Gardner, and G. K. Fraenkel, *J. Am. Chem. Soc.*, **75**, 4115 (1953).

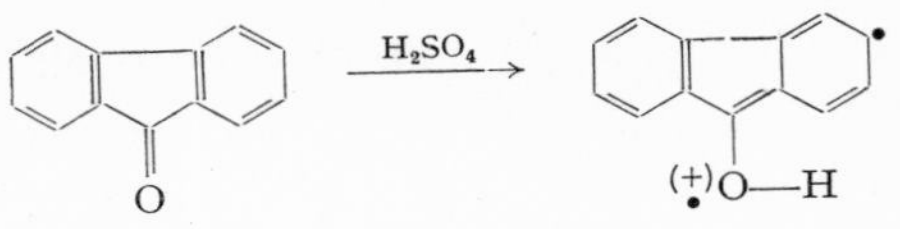

Fluorenone

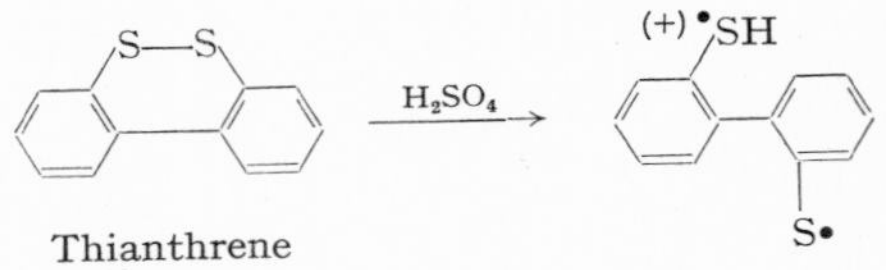

Thianthrene

Bianthrone and thianthrene also dissolve in aluminium chloride and ether to give red solutions exhibiting paramagnetic resonance.

Bianthrone and variously substituted bianthrones are yellow but melt to give blue substances. Pressure makes the crystals bluish. Solutions in inert solvents are yellow-green at low temperatures but become blue-green reversibly when heated. The color is not due to the shift or broadening of an existing absorption band but to the appearance of an entirely new one. Since the hot solutions are paramagnetic it is likely that the color is due to a triplet state low lying enough to be populated thermally.[79] When the paramagnetic solution in sulfuric acid, which is red, is poured into water, a dark green solid is formed which slowly reverts to the usual yellow color. It is likely that the dianthrone diradical conjugate acid forms dianthrone diradical which, in the solid, reverts to dianthrone only slowly.

The marked shift in the singlet-triplet equilibrium produced by sulfuric acid and aluminium chloride is important because it undermines one of the commonly applied criteria for polar mechanisms: we can no longer be quite certain that an acid-catalyzed reaction is a polar one on the basis of the catalysis alone. Fortunately, the radical mechanism can often be ruled out on other grounds.

Some Diradical Intermediates

The decomposition of diphenylenediazomethane produces the diphenylenemethylene diradical as an intermediate. This intermediate will only be a diradical in case the two electrons follow the usual rule

[79] W. T. Grubb and G. B. Kistiakowsky, *J. Am. Chem. Soc.*, **72**, 419 (1950).

about occupying separate orbitals of equal energy. Otherwise it will be the conjugate base of a carbonium ion.

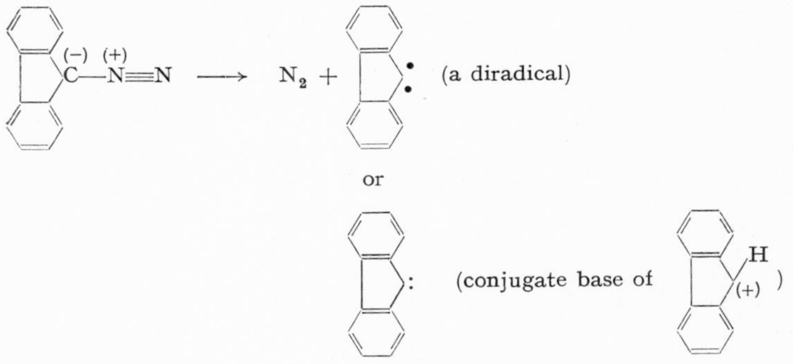

or

Whether or not the intermediate is a diradical, its reactions with organic bases are those appropriate for an electron deficient or electrophilic substance.[80]

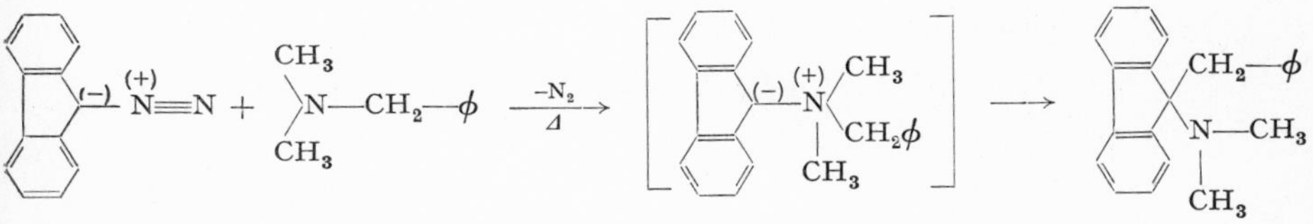

Diazomethane when heated with copper powder gives nitrogen and an insoluble polymethylene, indicating that one of its reactions is the decomposition into methylene radicals. The methylene radical can also be formed in the gas phase and detected by a mirror experiment.[81] The pyrolysis of ketene in the gas phase gives carbon monoxide and methylene radical. The methylene radical both reacts with itself to give ethylene and removes tellurium mirrors, forming tellurformaldehyde.[82] Thus the methylene diradical(?) behaves as expected.

Although the Wolf rearrangement of diazoketones in the presence of silver benzoate and triethylamine in methanol could involve rearrangement of an intermediate diradical or carbonium ion conjugate

[80] W. R. Bamford and T. S. Stevens, *J. Chem. Soc.*, **1952**, 4675.

[81] F. O. Rice and A. L. Glasebrook, *J. Am. Chem. Soc.*, **56**, 2381 (1934).

[82] R. G. W. Norrish and G. Porter, *Discussions Faraday Soc.*, No. **2**, 97. (1947).

base, the evidence indicates a chain reaction instead.[83] The reaction requires an atom of hydrogen on the diazo carbon and is inhibited by hydroquinone.

Chain initiating steps:

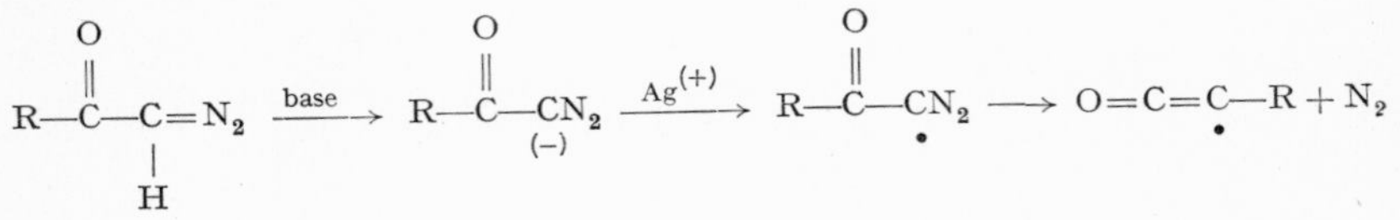

$$
\underset{\substack{|\\ H}}{R-\overset{\overset{\displaystyle O}{\|}}{C}-C}=N_2 \xrightarrow{\text{base}} \underset{(-)}{R-\overset{\overset{\displaystyle O}{\|}}{C}-CN_2} \xrightarrow{Ag^{(+)}} R-\overset{\overset{\displaystyle O}{\|}}{C}-\overset{\bullet}{C}N_2 \longrightarrow O=C=\overset{\bullet}{C}-R+N_2
$$

Chain carrying steps:

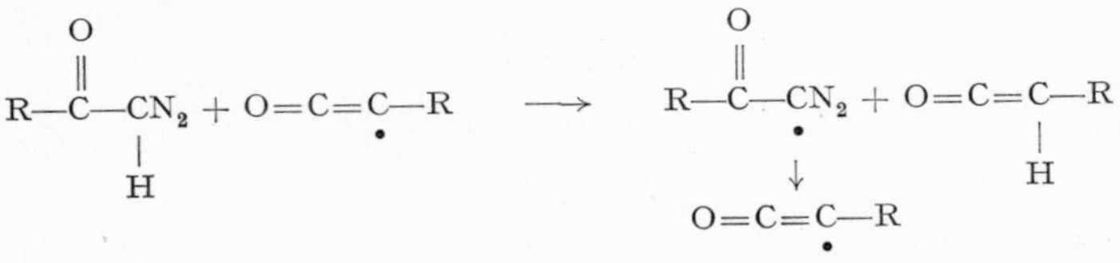

$$
\underset{\substack{|\\ H}}{R-\overset{\overset{\displaystyle O}{\|}}{C}-CN_2} + O=C=\overset{\bullet}{C}-R \longrightarrow R-\overset{\overset{\displaystyle O}{\|}}{\underset{\bullet}{C}}-CN_2 + O=C=\underset{\substack{|\\ H}}{C}-R
$$

$$
\downarrow
$$

$$
O=C=\overset{\bullet}{C}-R
$$

Product formation:

$$
O=C=\underset{\substack{|\\ H}}{C}-R + CH_3OH \longrightarrow CH_3O-\overset{\overset{\displaystyle O}{\|}}{C}-CH_2-R
$$

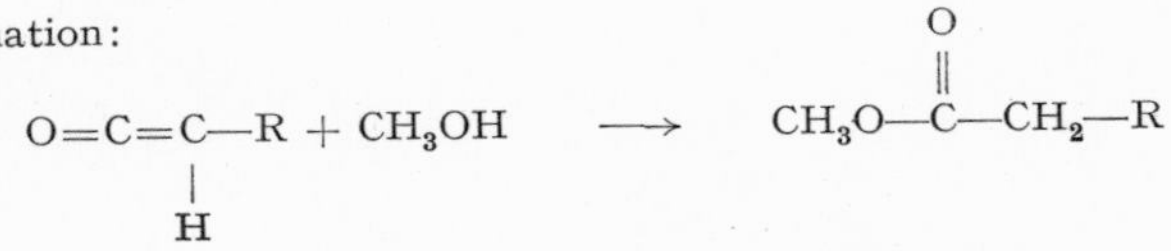

Hine has explained the solvolysis of chloroform by means of a diradical (or carbonium ion conjugate base) intermediate:[84]

$$
CHCl_3 + HO^{(-)} \rightleftharpoons {}^{(-)}CCl_3 + H_2O
$$

$$
{}^{(-)}CCl_3 \longrightarrow Cl^{(-)} + \overset{\bullet}{\underset{\bullet}{C}}Cl_2
$$

$$
\overset{\bullet}{\underset{\bullet}{C}}Cl_2 \xrightarrow[H_2O]{HO^{(-)}} CO + HCO_2{}^-
$$

In the presence of thiophenate ion the intermediate is trapped as phenyl orthothioformate, even though the reaction of sodium thiophenate with chloroform itself is slower than that of sodium hydroxide, and hence sodium thiophenate can not be competing with hydroxide ion

[83] M. S. Newman and P. F. Beal, III, *J. Am. Chem. Soc.*, **72**, 5163 (1950).
[84] J. Hine, *J. Am. Chem. Soc.*, **72**, 2438 (1950).

in the rate-determining step. The intermediate has also been trapped as a cyclopropane derivative: [85]

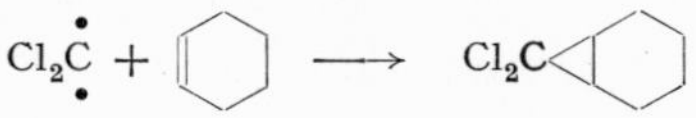

$$Cl_2\overset{\bullet}{\underset{\bullet}{C}} + \bigcirc \longrightarrow Cl_2C \triangleleft \bigcirc$$

The well known pyrolysis of azides and the reaction of N-chloramines with soda lime are regarded as rearrangements of a nitrogen diradical:

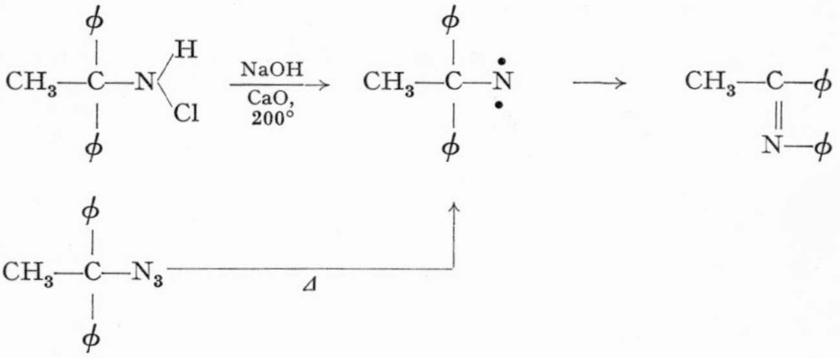

$$CH_3-\overset{\phi}{\underset{\phi}{C}}-N\overset{H}{\underset{Cl}{\diagdown}} \xrightarrow[\substack{CaO, \\ 200°}]{NaOH} CH_3-\overset{\phi}{\underset{\phi}{C}}-\overset{\bullet}{\underset{\bullet}{N}} \longrightarrow CH_3-\overset{\phi}{\underset{\parallel}{C}}$$
$$N-\phi$$

$$CH_3-\overset{\phi}{\underset{\phi}{C}}-N_3 \xrightarrow{\quad \Delta \quad}$$

For the reaction shown below the migration aptitudes appear to decrease in the order $H>\phi>CH_3$.[86] But there may be a special chain mechanism for H.

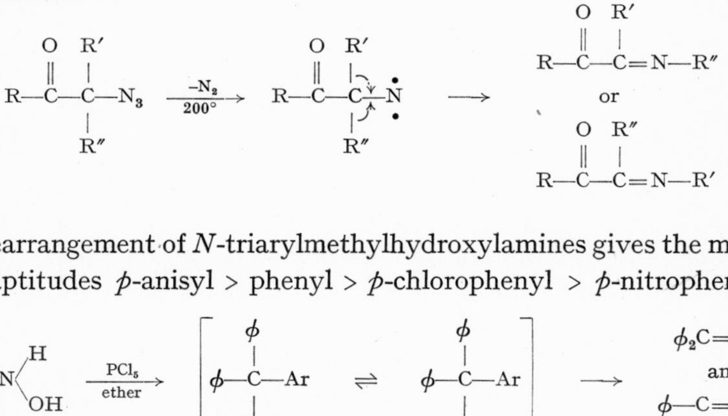

$$R-\overset{O}{\overset{\parallel}{C}}-\overset{R'}{\underset{\underset{R''}{|}}{C}}-N_3 \xrightarrow[200°]{-N_2} R-\overset{O}{\overset{\parallel}{C}}-\overset{R'}{\underset{\underset{R''}{|}}{\overset{\bullet}{C}}}N \longrightarrow$$

$$R-\overset{O}{\overset{\parallel}{C}}-\overset{R'}{C}=N-R''$$
or
$$R-\overset{O}{\overset{\parallel}{C}}-\overset{R''}{C}=N-R'$$

The rearrangement of N-triarylmethylhydroxylamines gives the migration aptitudes p-anisyl > phenyl > p-chlorophenyl > p-nitrophenyl.[87]

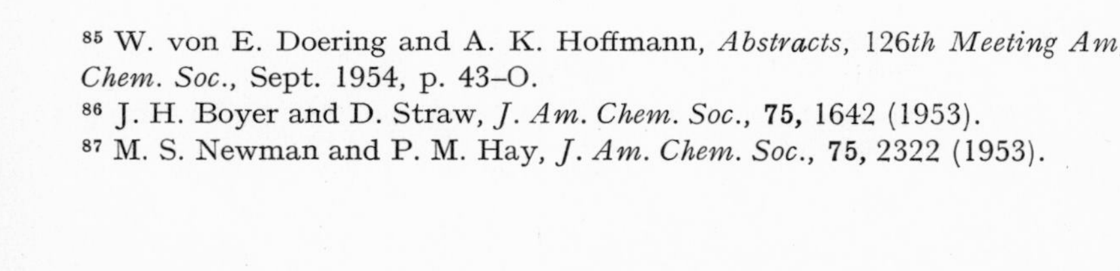

$$\phi-\overset{\phi}{\underset{Ar}{C}}-N\overset{H}{\underset{OH}{\diagdown}} \xrightarrow[ether]{PCl_5} \left[\phi-\overset{\phi}{\underset{(+)N-H}{C}}-Ar \rightleftharpoons \phi-\overset{\phi}{\underset{\bullet N \bullet}{C}}-Ar \right] \longrightarrow \begin{array}{c} \phi_2C=NAr \\ and \\ \phi-\overset{\phi}{\underset{Ar}{C}}=N-\phi \end{array}$$

[85] W. von E. Doering and A. K. Hoffmann, *Abstracts, 126th Meeting Am, Chem. Soc.,* Sept. 1954, p. 43–O.

[86] J. H. Boyer and D. Straw, *J. Am. Chem. Soc.,* **75**, 1642 (1953).

[87] M. S. Newman and P. M. Hay, *J. Am. Chem. Soc.,* **75**, 2322 (1953).

In addition to mono and diradicals, the conjugate base of a nitrogen positive ion is a possible intermediate in the above reactions.

The decomposition of hydrazoic acid in a low pressure electrical discharge seems to give a similar intermediate.[88]

$$HN_3 \longrightarrow H\overset{\bullet}{\underset{\bullet}{N}} + N_2 \xrightarrow[\text{condenser}]{\text{liquid } N_2} (NH)_x \xrightarrow{-125°} NH_4^{(+)}N_3^{(-)}$$

A blue solid

The acid catalyzed rearrangements of peroxides, in which the migrating groups show the same migration aptitudes as in carbonium ion rearrangements, may be represented as rearrangements of oxygen cations.[89-91]

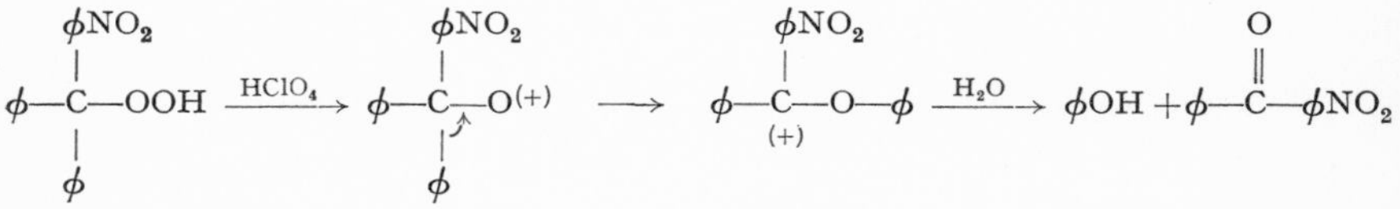

$$\underset{\phi}{\overset{\phi NO_2}{\phi-C-OOH}} \xrightarrow{HClO_4} \underset{\phi}{\overset{\phi NO_2}{\phi-C-O^{(+)}}} \longrightarrow \overset{\phi NO_2}{\underset{(+)}{\phi-C-O-\phi}} \xrightarrow{H_2O} \phi OH + \overset{O}{\overset{\|}{\phi-C}}-\phi NO_2$$

In the presence of ferrous salts the hydroperoxide decomposition goes by way of an oxygen monoradical intermediate, with different migration aptitudes. Para nitrophenyl rather than phenyl migrates under the radical conditions. Although the oxygen cation resembles the carbonium ion both chemically and in charge type, it may also be a diradical:

$$R-\overset{\cdot\cdot}{\underset{\cdot\cdot}{O}}\ (+) \quad \text{or} \quad R-\overset{\cdot\cdot}{O}\bullet\ (+)$$

Oxygen and nitrogen electron-deficient intermediates will be discussed as analogs of carbonium ions in Chapter VIII.

Diradicals have been postulated as the growing entity in the thermally or photochemically initiated polymerization of olefins.

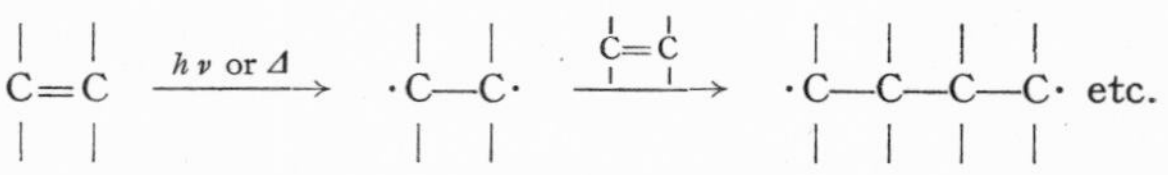

$$\underset{|\ \ |}{\overset{|\ \ |}{C=C}} \xrightarrow{h\nu\ or\ \Delta} \underset{|\ \ |}{\overset{|\ \ |}{\cdot C-C\cdot}} \xrightarrow{\overset{\overset{|}{C}=\overset{|}{C}}{|\ \ |}} \underset{|\ \ |\ \ |\ \ |}{\overset{|\ \ |\ \ |\ \ |}{\cdot C-C-C-C\cdot}} \text{ etc.}$$

[88] F. O. Rice and M. Freamo, *J. Am. Chem. Soc.*, **75**, 548 (1953).
[89] P. D. Bartlett and J. D. Cotman, Jr., *J. Am. Chem. Soc.*, **72**, 3095 (1950).
[90] J. E. Leffler, *Chem. Revs.*, **45**, 385 (1949).
[91] M. S. Kharasch, A. C. Poshkus, A. Fono, and W. Nudenberg, *J. Org. Chem.*, **16**, 1458 (1951).

However, the diradicals formed by the photolysis of 1,4,5-oxadithi-acycloheptane in methyl methacrylate add at most a few monomer units before the chain is stopped by ring closure.[92]

One of the possible mechanisms of cis-trans isomerization of olefins is excitation to the triplet or diradical state.[93-95] The two paths, one by way of singlet and triplet states and the other solely by way of singlet states, are diagrammed in Fig. 1. The two lines with minima at 0° and

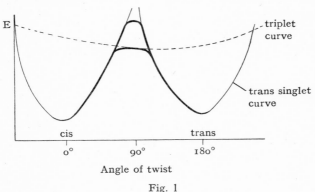

Fig. 1

180° represent potential energy curves for the torsion of the cis and trans singlet states, respectively, while the dotted line represents the potential energy curve for the torsion of the triplet state and has its shallow minimum at 90°. The heavy lines represent the two reaction paths. Note that the path of lower activation energy is the one that requires a singlet-triplet transition and back again. Because such transitions involve changes in electronic angular momentum or multi-plicity they are quantum mechanically forbidden, which should show up as an unusually negative entropy of activation. Since isomerization reactions include examples with high activation energies and relatively positive entropies of activation as well as others with low activation energies and relatively negative entropies of activation, it is likely that both paths are traversed. This is supported by the fact that para-

[92] K. E. Russell and A. V. Tobolsky, *J. Am. Chem. Soc.*, **76**, 395 (1954).

[93] V. Gold, *Trans. Faraday Soc.*, **45**, 196 (1949).

[94] R. A. Harman and H. Eyring, *J. Chem. Phys.*, **10**, 557 (1942).

[95] J. L. Magee, W. S. Shand, Jr., and H. Eyring, *J. Am. Chem. Soc.*, **63**, 677 (1941).

magnetic substances catalyze the reaction. The theory of the catalysis by paramagnetic substances, other than those that add to the double bond, is that an inhomogeneous magnetic field lifts the quantum mechanical interdiction of the singlet-triplet transition. On the other hand, the cis-trans isomerization of a series of substituted stilbenes exhibits a continuous range of activation energies linearly related to the activation entropies. It is therefore unlikely that there is any abrupt change in mechanism in that particular series, whichever the mechanism may be. The low entropies of activation of some members of the series are understandable even without a forbidden transition if the transition state is stabilized by solvent-orienting dipolar structures. It should also be remembered that the lowest triplet level, represented by the dotted line in Fig. 1, may not be low enough to intersect the usual singlet path, in which case the triplet path can be excluded on grounds of energy alone.

An elimination-addition mechanism has been suggested for the substitution of amino for chloro in chlorobenzene.[95a] The neutral and symmetrical intermediate is called benzyne although it can not contain an ordinary linear bond system like that of acetylene. It is not known whether it is a distorted acetylene, a triplet (diradical), or a zwitterion.

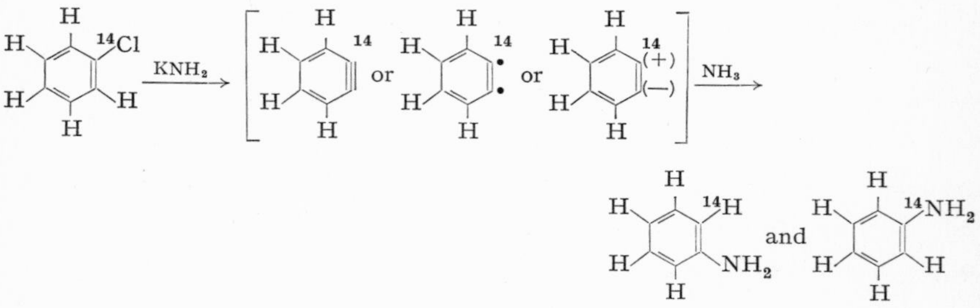

[95a] J. D. Roberts, H. E. Simmons, Jr., L. A. Carlsmith, and C. W. Vaughan, J. Am. Chem. Soc., 75, 3290 (1953).

CHAPTER IV

Heteroradicals

Heteroradical is a convenient term for radicals in which the odd electron is either exclusively or largely associated with an atom other than carbon.

Stable Oxygen Radicals

Besides the diradical oxygen molecule, there are known some relatively stable oxygen radicals discovered by Goldschmidt.[96] Because they are dissociated by light,[97] their spontaneous dissociation as measured by the color has probably been overestimated.

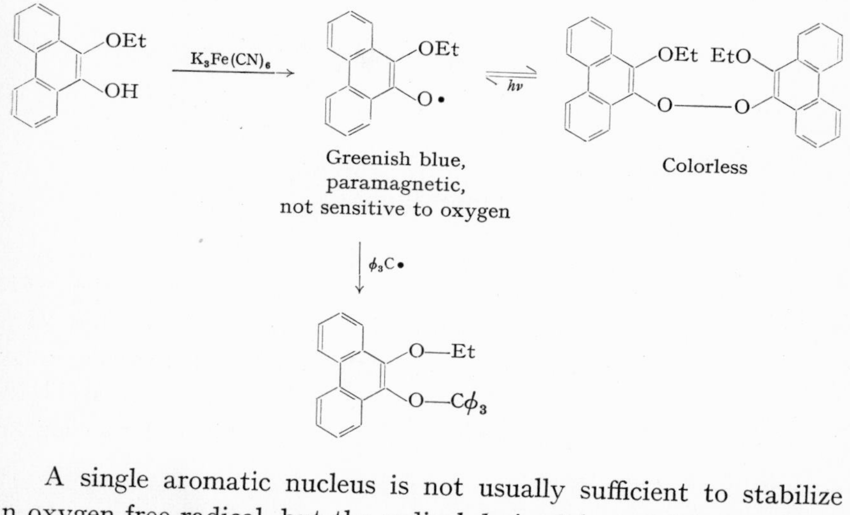

OEt
OH
K₃Fe(CN)₆
OEt
O•
hν
OEt EtO
O
O
Greenish blue,
paramagnetic,
not sensitive to oxygen
Colorless
φ₃C•
O—Et
O—Cφ₃

A single aromatic nucleus is not usually sufficient to stabilize an oxygen free radical, but the radical derived from 2,4,6-tritertiary-butylphenol is protected from dimerization or attack on the nucleus

[96] S. Goldschmidt and W. Schmidt, *Ber.*, **55**, 3197 (1922).
[97] H. G. Cutforth and P. W. Selwood, *J. Am. Chem. Soc.*, **70**, 278 (1948).

by its steric hindrance.[98] The reaction of the radical with acidified sodium iodide may be used to titrate it.[98] The radical also gives many of the other typical radical reactions. The peroxide formed by reaction with oxygen gives one mole of isobutylene on decomposition, probably by a β-cleavage reaction.[98,99]

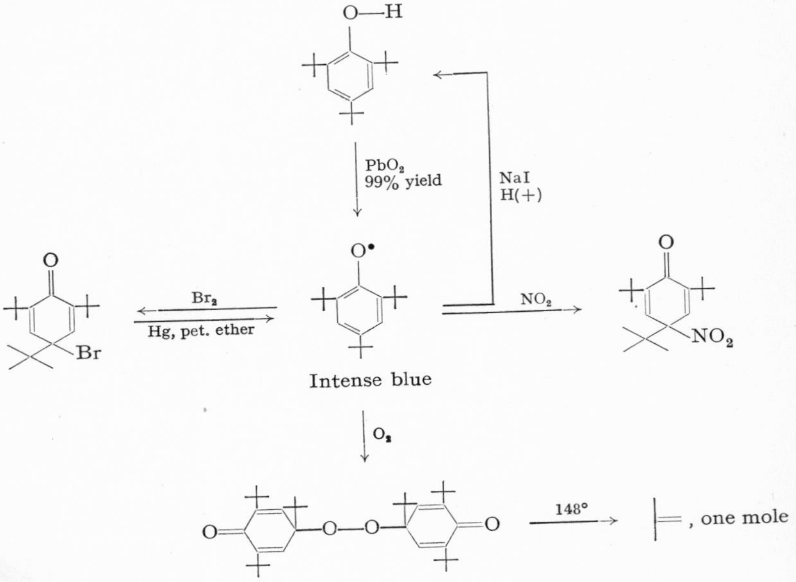

Intense blue

Semiquinones

Most quinone reductions go through an intermediate radical or semiquinone stage, usually revealed by a one-electron step in the redox potential.[100] The radical formed by the reduction of compound VI is especially stable, probably because of the additional involvement of the benzoyl group.[101] The ordinary semiquinones are more stable in basic solution since some of the resonance structures of the neutral radical involve separation of charges.

[98] C. D. Cook and R. C. Woodworth, *J. Am. Chem. Soc.*, **75**, 6242 (1953).
[99] J. E. Leffler, *Chem. Revs.*, **45**, 385 (1949).
[100] L. Michaelis, *Chem. Revs.*, **16**, 243 (1935); L. Michaelis and M. P. Schubert, *ibid.*, **22**, 437 (1938).
[101] R. Scholl and H. Hähle, *Ber.*, **54**, 2376 (1921).

The oxygen radical and ion-radical are not the only species of intermediate degree of oxidation between quinones and hydroquinones, for there is often formed a very dark colored molecular

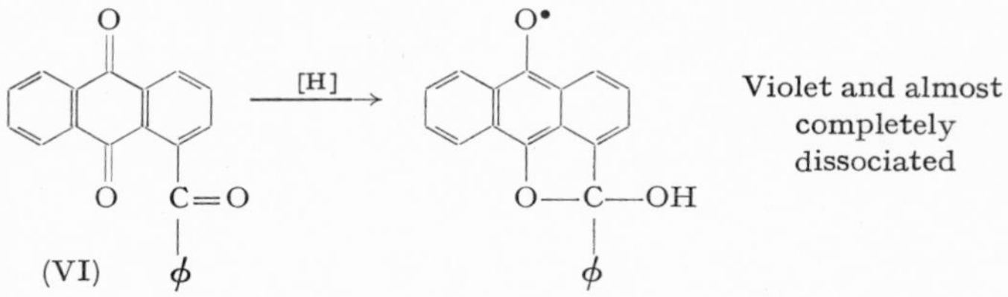

Violet and almost completely dissociated

(VI)

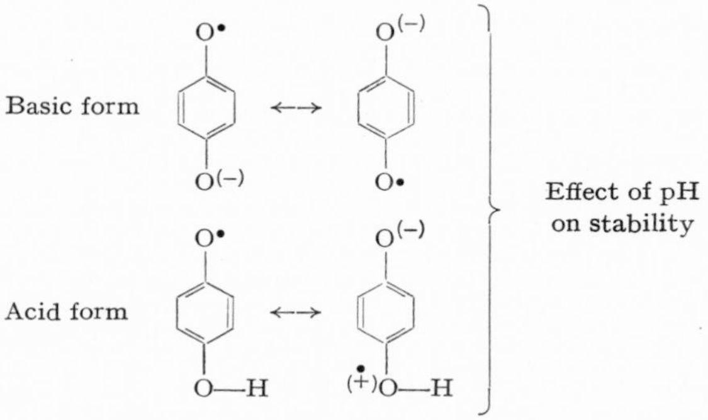

Basic form

Acid form

Effect of pH on stability

complex or quinhydrone. The quinhydrone is composed of quinone and hydroquinone in a one to one ratio.[102] The dark color suggests a structure like VII in which the rings overlap and interact as in molecular complexes of the π-bonded type. The same geometry would allow the molecule to be held together in some degree by hydrogen bonds as well.

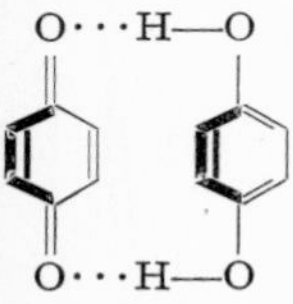

(VII) 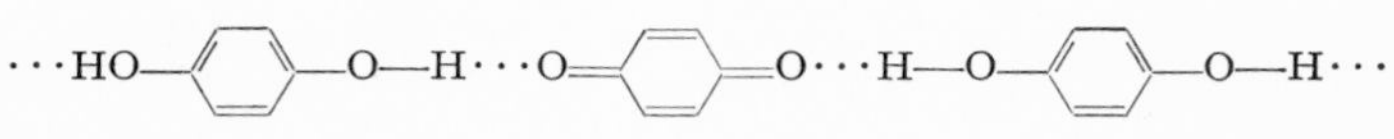   (VIII)

A linear hydrogen-bonded structure VIII has also been proposed, but accounts less satisfactorily for the color. The surprising thing about these complexes is the lack of any measurable exchange of the hydroxyl hydrogen atoms from the hydroquinone moiety to the quinone moiety

[102] L. Michaelis and S. Granick, *J. Am. Chem. Soc.*, **66**, 1023 (1944).

in the solid complex.[103] Exchange does take place in solution however, and apparently by the mechanism given below (the asterisk indicates carbon-14):[104]

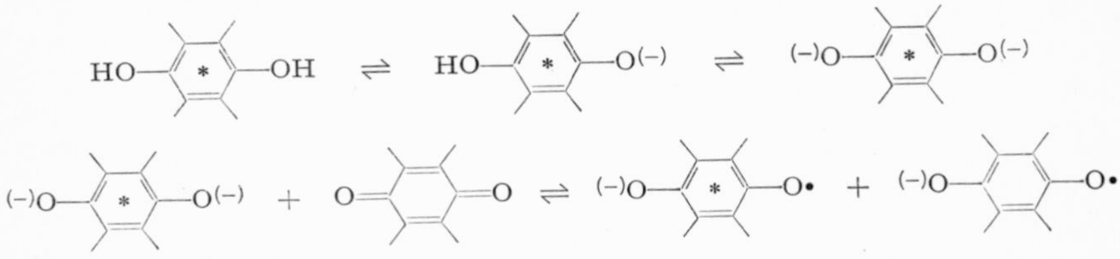

The oxidation of dihydroxy aromatic compounds under the conditions used by Goldschmidt ususually leads to the formation of quinones rather than diradicals. For example, p,p'-dihydroxydiphenyl gives p-diphenoquinone. Several attempts have been made to oxidize o,o'-dihydroxydiphenyl, but without success. The product would be of special interest because of the possible equilibrium among diradical, quinone, and peroxide isomers:

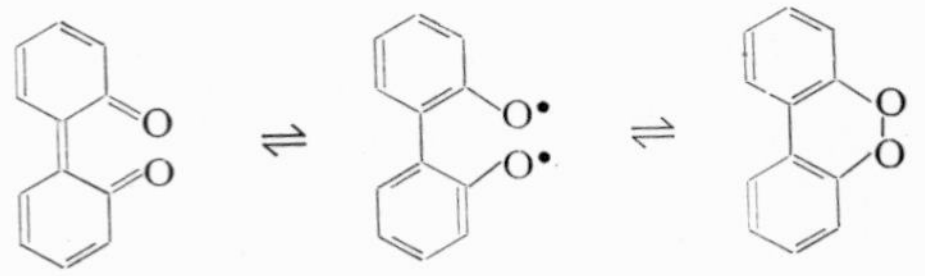

However, a corresponding naphthalene derivative can be made, perhaps because of the stabilization by a methoxy substituent:[105]

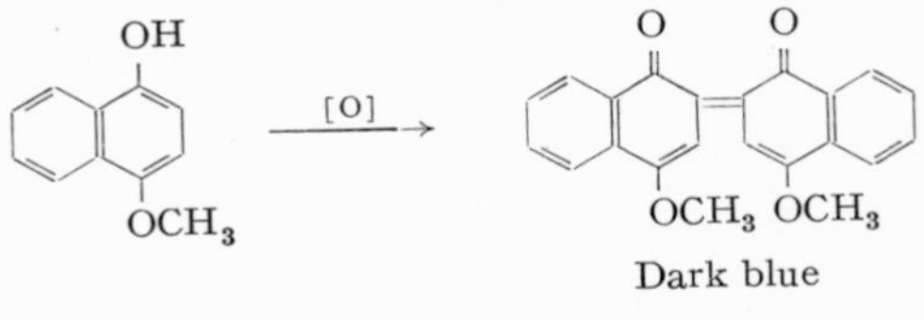

Dark blue

Since the product is dark blue it is probably the quinone or the diradical rather than the cyclic peroxide originally proposed.

Data are lacking on hetero diradicals analogous to the Chichibabin type of carbon diradical favored by strain in the singlet state.

[103] A. A. Bothner-By, *J. Am. Chem. Soc.*, **73**, 4228 (1951); I. P. Gragerov and G. P. Miklukhin, *Doklady Akad. Nauk. S.S.S.R.*, **62**, 79 (1948).

[104] A. A. Bothner-By, *J. Am. Chem. Soc.* **75**, 728 (1953).

[105] S. Goldschmidt and H. Wessbecher, *Ber.*, **61**, 372 (1928).

Although a patent claims the synthesis of the quinone shown below, the method is ambiguous and it is doubtful that a substance of this precise structure has been prepared.[106] It should exist as a polymeric peroxide or as a diradical.

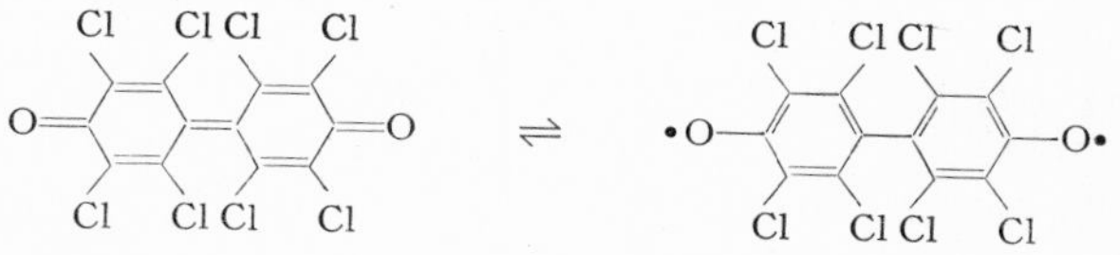

Quinones, and hence semiquinones, are of considerable importance to biochemistry because of the many vitamins and other biologically functioning substances of quinone or quinonoid structure. Since the reader can no doubt recall many examples, only two of the more exotic ones will be mentioned here. One such substance is pyocyanine, a blue antibiotic produced by the pus-forming *bacillus pyocyaneus*. In the first volume of *Annales de Chimie* there appeared an article entitled[107] "Observation sur une singulière altération du Sang par l'effet d'une maladie." It dealt with the case of a patient who died in one of the Paris hospitals and who, in the medical terminology of that day, was suffering from languor and inertia due to the decomposition of the fluids. The most striking symptom was the exudation of a blue pus, very likely colored by pyocyanine. The color was tentatively identified, in a reasonable use of the information then available, as Prussian blue, since blood was already known to contain both iron and nitrogen and the formation of new substances by breakdown of precursors in the blood fitted the diagnosis of "decomposition of the

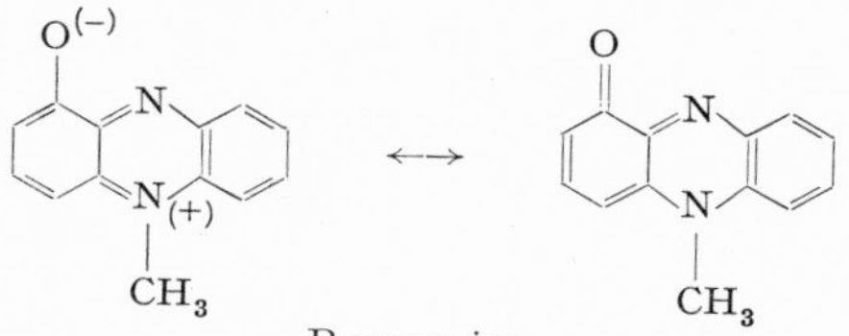

Pyocyanine

[106] F. D. Smith, U.S. Patent 2,449,088 (1948).
[107] de Fourcroy, *Ann. chim.*, **1**, 65 (1789). Readers interested in such modern problems as photosynthesis and protein structure will find this volume rewarding. It also contains a curious mixture of phlogiston and oxygen terminology.

fluids." Later a similar, if not identical, substance was identified as the phenazine derivative shown on p. 55.[108]

The leuco form is readily oxidized to a paramagnetic green ion-radical and thence to pyocyanine itself.

Another naturally occurring quinone is echinochrome, a substance found in sea-urchin eggs.[109]

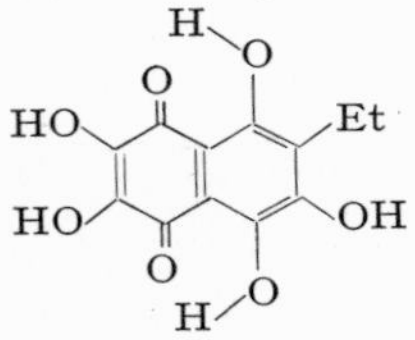

Echinochrome

Less Stable Oxygen Radicals

The decomposition of aliphatic peroxides produces oxygen radicals too unstable for paramagnetic measurement. These radicals initiate the polymerization of olefins and give the complex mixtures of decomposition products associated with radical mechanisms. On the other hand, aliphatic peroxides are also capable of polar decomposition reactions, a subject to be taken up in Chapter VIII. The characteristic reactions of the less stable oxygen free radicals are β-cleavage to form

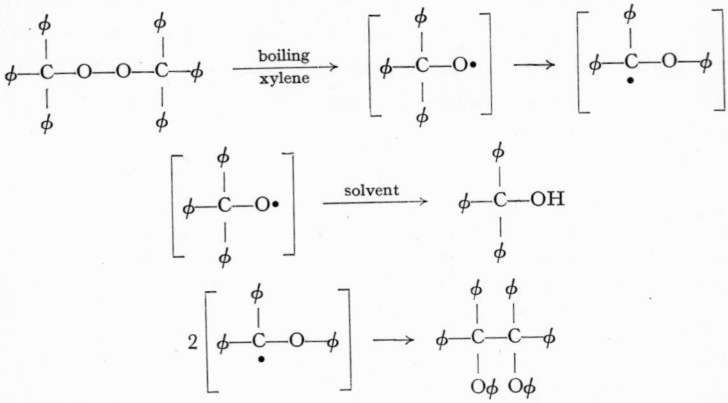

[108] F. Wrede and E. Strack, *Ber.*, **62**, 2051 (1929); R. Kuhn and K. Schön, *ibid.*, **68**, 1537 (1935).
[109] R. Kuhn, *Angew. Chem.*, **53**, 1 (1940).

carbonyl groups, rearrangement, hydrogen abstraction, and addition to other radicals or unsaturated systems.

An example of the rearrangement reaction is afforded by the decomposition of triphenylmethyl peroxide.[110],[99]

Hydroperoxides behave similarly if the radical rather than the polar mode of decomposition is ensured by the presence of ferrous salts.[111]

Kharasch has pointed out that there are two very similar and not easily distinguished reactions of oxygen radicals, β-cleavage and rearrangement.[111] The difficulty is that they can often lead to the same final product.

$$
\begin{array}{c}
R \\
| \\
R\!-\!C\!-\!O\bullet \\
| \\
R
\end{array}
\longrightarrow
\begin{array}{c}
R \\
| \\
R\!-\!C\!=\!O + R\bullet
\end{array}
\qquad \beta\text{-Cleavage}
$$

$$
\begin{array}{c}
R \\
| \\
R\!-\!C\!-\!O\bullet \\
| \\
R
\end{array}
\longrightarrow
\begin{array}{c}
R \\
| \\
R\!-\!C\!-\!O\!-\!R \\
\bullet
\end{array}
\qquad \text{Rearrangement}
$$

For example, in the ferrous ion-initiated radical decomposition of some hydroperoxides, Kharasch suggests that the reaction is β-cleavage rather than rearrangement since ketones but no rearranged radical dimers are formed.

$$
\begin{array}{c}
\phi \\
| \\
CH_3\!-\!CH_2\!-\!C\!-\!OOH + Fe^{(++)} \\
| \\
(IX) \quad CH_3
\end{array}
\longrightarrow
HO^{(-)} + Fe^{(+++)} +
\left[
\begin{array}{c}
\phi \\
| \\
CH_3CH_2\!-\!C\!-\!O\bullet \\
| \\
CH_3
\end{array}
\right]
$$

$$
\left[
\begin{array}{c}
\phi \\
| \\
CH_3CH_2\!-\!C\!-\!O\bullet \\
| \\
CH_3
\end{array}
\right]
\longrightarrow
\begin{array}{c}
O \\
\| \\
CH_3\!-\!C\!-\!\phi
\end{array}
\text{ but no }
\begin{array}{c}
\phi \quad \phi \\
| \quad | \\
EtO\!-\!C\!-\!\!-\!C\!-\!OEt \\
| \quad | \\
CH_3 \ CH_3
\end{array}
$$

$$
\text{but }
\begin{array}{c}
\phi \\
| \\
\phi\!-\!C\!-\!OOH \\
| \\
\phi
\end{array}
\xrightarrow{Fe^{(++)}}
\begin{array}{c}
O\!-\!\phi \ O\!-\!\phi \\
| \quad | \\
\phi\!-\!C\!-\!\!-\!C\!-\!\phi \\
| \quad | \\
\phi \quad \phi
\end{array}
$$

[110] H. Wieland, *Ber.*, **44**, 2550 (1911).

[111] M. S. Kharasch, A. C. Poshkus, A. Fono, and W. Nudenberg, *J. Org. Chem.*, **16**, 1458 (1951).

The decomposition of the peroxide IX, which gives acetophenone when the conditions are such as to favor the radical mechanism, gives methyl ethyl ketone if the reaction is run in acid. This is because of the superior migration aptitude of phenyl groups in real or incipient oxygen cations.[112]

The decomposition of *tert*-butyl triarylmethyl peroxides is particularly well suited to the measurement of migration aptitudes in oxygen radicals because the nature of the product leaves no doubt that the reaction is in fact a rearrangement rather than a β-cleavage.

$$
\begin{array}{c}
\underset{\displaystyle CH_3}{\overset{\displaystyle CH_3}{\underset{|}{\overset{|}{CH_3-C}}}}-O-O-\underset{\displaystyle \phi}{\overset{\displaystyle Ar}{\underset{|}{\overset{|}{C}}}}-\phi \xrightarrow[\text{cumene}]{120\text{--}140°} \underset{\displaystyle CH_3}{\overset{\displaystyle CH_3}{\underset{|}{\overset{|}{CH_3-C}}}}-O\bullet + \bullet O-\underset{\displaystyle Ar}{\overset{\displaystyle \phi}{\underset{|}{\overset{|}{C}}}}-\phi
\end{array}
$$

$$
R\bullet + H-\underset{\displaystyle CH_3}{\overset{\displaystyle CH_3}{\underset{|}{\overset{|}{C}}}}-\phi \longrightarrow RH + \bullet\underset{\displaystyle CH_3}{\overset{\displaystyle CH_3}{\underset{|}{\overset{|}{C}}}}-\phi
$$

Cumene

$$
\phi-\underset{\displaystyle Ar}{\overset{\displaystyle \phi}{\underset{|}{\overset{|}{C}}}}-O\bullet \longrightarrow \phi-\underset{\displaystyle \bullet}{\overset{\displaystyle \phi}{\underset{|}{\overset{|}{C}}}}-OAr
$$

$$
\phi-\underset{\displaystyle CH_3}{\overset{\displaystyle CH_3}{\underset{|}{\overset{|}{C}}}}\bullet + \bullet\underset{\displaystyle \phi}{\overset{\displaystyle \phi}{\underset{|}{\overset{|}{C}}}}-OAr \longrightarrow \phi-\underset{\displaystyle CH_3}{\overset{\displaystyle CH_3}{\underset{|}{\overset{|}{C}}}}-\underset{\displaystyle \phi}{\overset{\displaystyle \phi}{\underset{|}{\overset{|}{C}}}}-OAr
$$

In this reaction para-xenyl and α-naphthyl groups migrate six times as readily as competing phenyl or para-tolyl groups.[111]

The decomposition of ditertiarybutyl peroxide in a mixture of an alcohol and an olefin initiates the radical chain addition of the alcohol to the olefin. The alcohol derived intermediate is a carbon free radical rather than an oxygen free radical.[113]

[112] E. G. E. Hawkins, *J. Chem. Soc.*, **1949**, 2076.
[113] W. H. Urry, F. W. Stacey, O. O. Juveland, and C. H. McDonnell, *J. Am. Chem. Soc.*, **75**, 250 (1953).

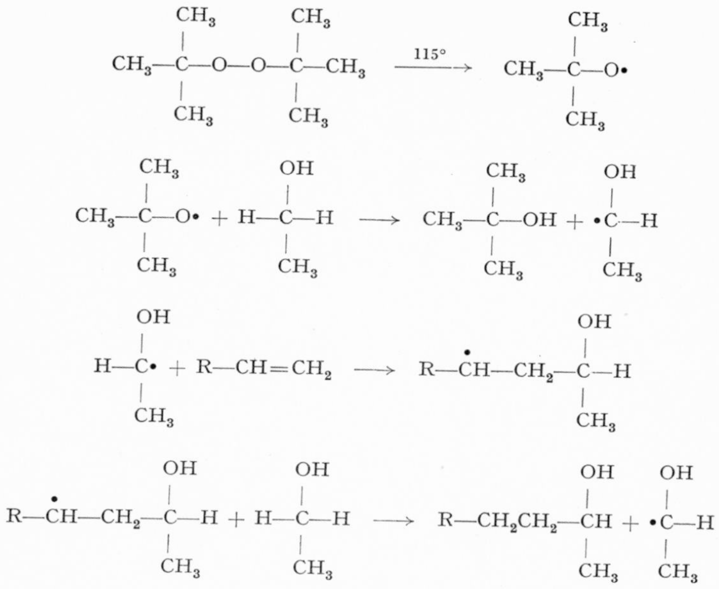

$$\underset{\overset{|}{CH_3}}{\overset{\overset{CH_3}{|}}{CH_3-C-O}}-O-\underset{\overset{|}{CH_3}}{\overset{\overset{CH_3}{|}}{C-CH_3}} \xrightarrow{115°} \underset{\overset{|}{CH_3}}{\overset{\overset{CH_3}{|}}{CH_3-C-O\bullet}}$$

$$\underset{\overset{|}{CH_3}}{\overset{\overset{CH_3}{|}}{CH_3-C-O\bullet}} + \underset{\overset{|}{CH_3}}{\overset{\overset{OH}{|}}{H-C-H}} \longrightarrow \underset{\overset{|}{CH_3}}{\overset{\overset{CH_3}{|}}{CH_3-C-OH}} + \underset{\overset{|}{CH_3}}{\overset{\overset{OH}{|}}{\bullet C-H}}$$

$$\underset{\overset{|}{CH_3}}{\overset{\overset{OH}{|}}{H-C\bullet}} + R-CH=CH_2 \longrightarrow R-\overset{\bullet}{CH}-CH_2-\underset{\overset{|}{CH_3}}{\overset{\overset{OH}{|}}{C-H}}$$

$$R-\overset{\bullet}{CH}-CH_2-\underset{\overset{|}{CH_3}}{\overset{\overset{OH}{|}}{C-H}} + \underset{\overset{|}{CH_3}}{\overset{\overset{OH}{|}}{H-C-H}} \longrightarrow R-CH_2CH_2-\underset{\overset{|}{CH_3}}{\overset{\overset{OH}{|}}{CH}} + \underset{\overset{|}{CH_3}}{\overset{\overset{OH}{|}}{\bullet C-H}}$$

Even though the radical attacking ethyl alcohol in the above reaction generated α-hydroxyethyl rather then ethoxy free radical, there seems to be little or no tendency for alkoxy free radicals to rearrange to α-hydroxyalkyl radicals. Thus in the reaction

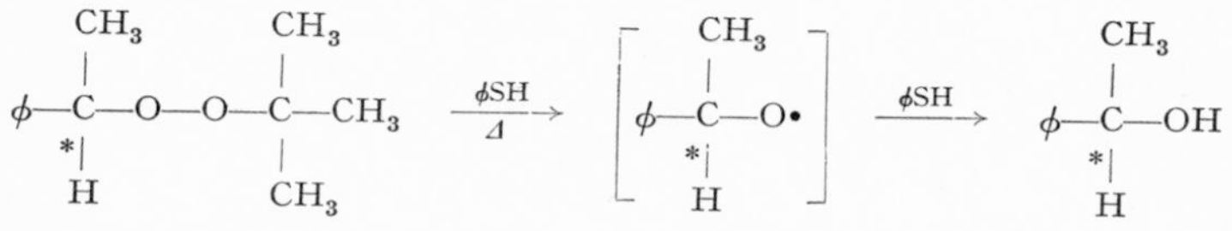

$$\underset{\overset{*|}{H}}{\overset{\overset{CH_3}{|}}{\phi-C-O}}-O-\underset{\overset{|}{CH_3}}{\overset{\overset{CH_3}{|}}{C-CH_3}} \xrightarrow[\Delta]{\phi SH} \left[\underset{\overset{*|}{H}}{\overset{\overset{CH_3}{|}}{\phi-C-O\bullet}} \right] \xrightarrow{\phi SH} \underset{\overset{*|}{H}}{\overset{\overset{CH_3}{|}}{\phi-C-OH}}$$

optical activity is retained, which would not be the case if a hydrogen atom migration led to a carbon free radical intermediate before formation of the alcohol.[114]

Diacyl peroxides exhibit behavior somewhat like that of the di-alkyl peroxides. Benzoyl peroxide decomposes into radicals partly by a unimolecular and partly by a chain mechanism. In at least the case of benzoyl peroxide itself, if not for similar compounds, the first step is the production of benzoyloxy radicals rather than phenyl radicals and

[114] N. Kornblum and H. E. De La Mare, *J. Am. Chem. Soc.*, **74**, 3079 (1952).

carbon dioxide. Carbon dioxide is usually formed, but not in the presence of a really efficient trap for the benzoyloxy radicals.

$$\phi-\overset{\overset{\displaystyle O}{\|}}{C}-O-O-\overset{\overset{\displaystyle O}{\|}}{C}-\phi \longrightarrow 2\,\phi-\overset{\overset{\displaystyle O}{\|}}{C}-O\cdot$$

$$\text{not}\quad \phi-\overset{\overset{\displaystyle O}{\|}}{C}-O\cdot + \phi\cdot + CO_2$$

For example, when benzoyl peroxide is allowed to decompose in the presence of an olefin and iodine a high yield of the olefin dibenzoate is formed and very little carbon dioxide. Since Hammond has shown that the rate of the decomposition is independent of the iodine concentration, the iodine must not participate in the rate-determining initial step. It probably reacts with the benzoyloxy radicals to form benzoyl hypoiodite.[115, 116]

$$\phi-\overset{\overset{\displaystyle O}{\|}}{C}-O-O-\overset{\overset{\displaystyle O}{\|}}{C}-\phi \longrightarrow 2\,\phi-\overset{\overset{\displaystyle O}{\|}}{C}-O\cdot$$

$$\phi-\overset{\overset{\displaystyle O}{\|}}{C}-O\cdot + I_2 \longrightarrow \phi-\overset{\overset{\displaystyle O}{\|}}{C}-O-I$$

$$2\,\phi-\overset{\overset{\displaystyle O}{\|}}{C}-O-I + \overset{|}{C}=\overset{|}{\underset{|}{C}} \longrightarrow \begin{array}{c}\phi-\overset{\overset{\displaystyle O}{\|}}{C}-O-\overset{|}{\underset{}{C}}-\\ \phi-\underset{\underset{\displaystyle O}{\|}}{C}-O-\overset{}{\underset{|}{C}}-\end{array} + I_2$$

When either diacetyl or dibenzoyl peroxide is decomposed in benzene in the presence of metallic mercury an organomercuric salt is obtained.[117] The reaction is similar to the mirror removing reaction observed in gas phase experiments.

$$CH_3-\overset{\overset{\displaystyle O}{\|}}{C}-O-O-\overset{\overset{\displaystyle O}{\|}}{C}-CH_3 \xrightarrow[\text{Hg}]{\phi H} Hg-O-\overset{\overset{\displaystyle CH_3}{|}}{\underset{\underset{\displaystyle O}{\|}}{C}}-CH_3 \ 64.7\%$$

[115] G. S. Hammond, *J. Am. Chem. Soc.*, **72**, 3737 (1950).
[116] A. Perret and R. Perrot, *Helv. Chim. Acta*, **28**, 558 (1945).
[117] G. A. Razuvaev, Yu. A. Ol'dekop, and L. N. Grobov, *Zhur. Obshchei Khim.*, **23**, 589 (1953).

$$\phi-\overset{\overset{O}{\|}}{C}-O-O-\overset{\overset{O}{\|}}{C}-\phi \quad \xrightarrow[\text{Hg}]{\phi\text{H}} \quad Hg-O-\overset{\overset{\phi}{|}}{\underset{\underset{O}{\|}}{C}}-\phi \qquad 31.5\%$$

The question of rearrangement in acyloxy radicals is still unsettled. In the case of the decomposition of *p*-methoxy-*p*'-nitrobenzoyl peroxide rearrangement is observed, but the other circumstances indicate a polar mechanism for the reaction.[118]

$$p-O_2N\phi-\overset{\overset{O}{\|}}{C}-O-O-\overset{\overset{O}{\|}}{C}-\phi OCH_3-p \quad \xrightarrow{SOCl_2} \quad p-O_2N\phi-\overset{\overset{O}{\|}}{C}-\underset{(-)}{O} \ \underset{(+)}{O}-\overset{\overset{O}{\|}}{C}-\phi OCH_3-p$$

Ion pair

↓

$$p-O_2N\phi-\overset{\overset{O}{\|}}{C}-O-\overset{\overset{O}{\|}}{C}-O-\phi OCH_3-p \quad \longleftarrow \quad p-O_2N\phi-\overset{\overset{O}{\|}}{C}-\underset{(+)}{\overset{(-)}{O}} \ \overset{\overset{O}{\|}}{C}-O-\phi OCH_3-p$$

Another carboxy inversion reaction has been noted in the case of ditriptoyl peroxide decomposing in benzene.[119]

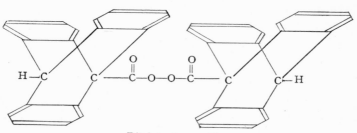

Ditriptoyl peroxide

Since ditriptoyl peroxide is electrically symmetrical, and since benzene is not outstanding in its ability to solvate polar transition states, it seems probable that the inversion reaction in this case is due to the rearrangement of an acyloxy radical rather than cation. It may be that failure to isolate comparable products from other peroxides under free radical conditions is due to competition from very fast substitution

[118] J. E. Leffler, *J. Am. Chem. Soc.*, **72**, 67 (1950).
[119] P. D. Bartlett and F. D. Greene, *J. Am. Chem. Soc.*, **76**, 1088 (1954).

reactions displacing the carbon dioxide. The hindered triptycene derivative would be less accessible to that sort of attack and since the triptycyl radical is not stabilized by resonance there is no reason to expect a unimolecular β-cleavage reaction.

The decomposition of tertiary butyl perbenzoates in diphenyl ether is one of several radical reactions following the Hammett rho-sigma relationship, although the entropy of activation is far from constant.[120,121] The activation energy, which is highest with electron-withdrawing groups, is linearly related to the activation entropy. It is very likely the precision of the latter relationship that is responsible for the fit to the Hammett plot in this case. The Hammett equation is derived for reactions of constant entropy of activation but is also obeyed if the energies and entropies are linearly related.

The inhibited unimolecular decomposition of symmetrically di-substituted benzoyl peroxides into radicals also obeys the Hammett rho-sigma relationship. Unfortunately, no extensive activation para-meter data are available. The effect of the substituent changes on the rates at the single temperature has been explained in terms of dipole-dipole repulsion in the peroxide.[122]

Boozer and Hammond have shown, by the absence of an isotope effect, that autoxidation inhibitors like phenols and aromatic amines can not, as previously supposed, function by donating an hydrogen atom to the chain-carrying radical.[123] They suggest instead that the inhibitor forms a molecular complex with the chain-carrying peroxy radical and that the complex is less reactive in chain carrying than the original radical. Such an effect by a complexing agent in stabilizing a radical suggests that solvents should interact considerably with some free radicals even though somewhat less than with a comparable charged particle. In several of the cases where the pertinent data are available it is, in fact, found that much of the apparent indifference of

[120] L. P. Hammett, *Physical Organic Chemistry*, McGraw-Hill, New York, 1940.

[121] A. T. Blomquist and I. A. Berstein, *J. Am. Chem. Soc.*, **73**, 5546 (1951).

[122] C. G. Swain, W. H. Stockmayer, and J. T. Clarke, *J. Am. Chem. Soc.*, **72**, 5426 (1950).

[123] C. E. Boozer and G. S. Hammond, *J. Am. Chem. Soc.*, **76**, 3861 (1954).

radical reactions to the solvent is actually due to compensating changes in the activation energy and entropy, the one tending to decrease the rate while the other tends to increase it. The reaction rates are less affected by solvent changes than the activation parameters.

Metal Ketyls

Metal ketyls are ion-radicals analogous to semiquinone ion radicals and may be considered either oxygen or carbon free radicals. They are readily prepared by treating aromatic ketones with alkali metals in dry ether, benzene, or liquid ammonia under an inert atmosphere.[124],[125] Benzophenone potassium has been shown to be paramagnetic in the solid state.[126]

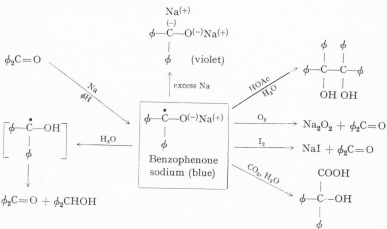

The ketyl radical is in equilibrium with the pinacolate doubly negative ion. The color and degree of dissociation as measured by the paramagnetism depend not only on the solvent but also on the metal.[127]

[124] W. Schlenk and A. Thal, *Ber.*, 46, 2840 (1913).
[125] W. E. Bachmann, *J. Am. Chem. Soc.*, 55, 1179 (1933).
[126] F. L. Allen and S. Sugden, *J. Chem. Soc.*, 1936, 440.
[127] R. N. Doescher and G. W. Wheland, *J. Am. Chem. Soc.*, 56, 2011 (1934).

The bimolecular reduction of ketones to pinacols by magnesium may involve ketyls as intermediates, the bivalence of magnesium favoring the bimolecular reduction product. Ketyl formation with sodium in liquid ammonia eventually leads to the reduction of the ketone to the alcohol. The corresponding pinacol is also cleaved to the alcohol under the same conditions.[128]

A reaction analogous to the formation of metal ketyls is the formation of negative ion-radicals not only from aromatic nitro compounds but also from aromatic hydrocarbons like naphthalene. These substances are highly colored and exhibit paramagnetic resonance absorption.[129]

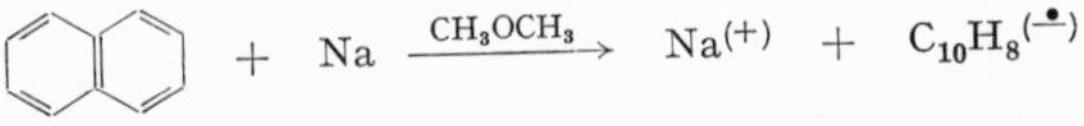

The ion radical might be represented by resonance structures such as:

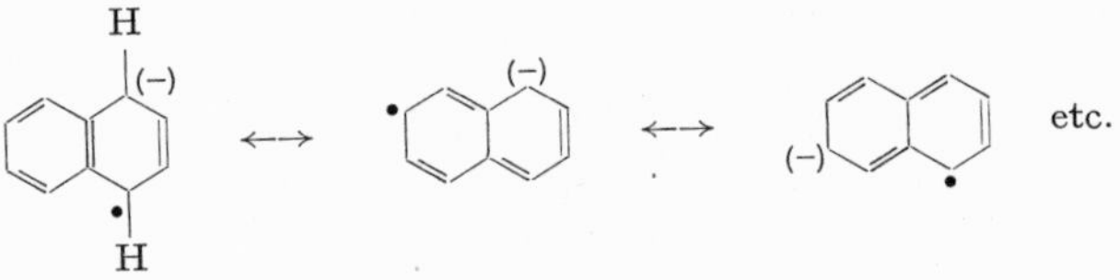

Sulfur Radicals

One sulfur compounds, X, is known which becomes reversibly colored and paramagnetic (even in the dark) in toluene at 80°.[130] It is used in rubber processing.

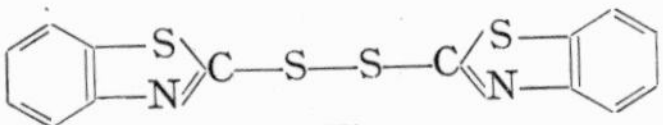

(X)

2,2′-Benzothiazyl disulfide

Sulfur itself is of course the best known rubber additive, and it also is a possible source of free radicals. At elevated temperatures it is an equilibrium mixture of S_8 rings and chain polymer. In the tempera-

[128] G. W. Watt, *Chem. Revs.*, **46**, 317 (1950).
[129] D. Lipkin, D. E. Paul, J. Townsend, and S. I. Weissman, *Science*, **117**, 534 (1953); T. L. Chu and S. C. Yu, *J. Am. Chem. Soc.*, **76**, 3367 (1954).
[130] H. G. Cutforth and P. W. Selwood, *J. Am. Chem. Soc.*, **70**, 278 (1948).

ture range 190–375° the amount of free radical, as measured by paramagnetic resonance absorption, increases reversibly by a factor of 100 to 200.[131] The radicals are very likely intermediates in the interconversion of cylic to polymeric sulfur.

Thianthrene and diphenyl disulfide show no detectable paramagnetic resonance absorption in inert solvents, but appear to dissociate somewhat in sulfuric acid solution.[78]

The addition of mercaptans to methyl acrylate is catalyzed both by base and by sources of free radicals. The direction of addition is the same in either case, but the radical initiated reaction produces a good deal of polymeric byproduct.

$$R{-}SH + CH_2{=}CH{-}\overset{\overset{O}{\|}}{C}{-}O{-}CH_2 \longrightarrow R{-}S{-}CH_2{-}CH_2{-}\overset{\overset{O}{\|}}{C}{-}O{-}CH_3$$

The ion RS^- is a probable intermediate in the cleaner base catalyzed reaction, the radical $RS\cdot$ in the other.

Nitrogen Radicals

The dissociation of the nitrogen to nitrogen bond is complete or nearly complete even in the solid state in the case of the diphenylpicrylhydrazyl free radical.[132] The complete dissociation is supported both by ortho-para hydrogen conversion experiments and by measurements of the paramagnetism.[133,126] Diphenylpicrylhydrazyl crystals resemble potassium permanganate and can be stored in the crystalline form for years without any special precaution. This radical is not affected by oxygen. It is made by oxidizing the corresponding hydrazine.

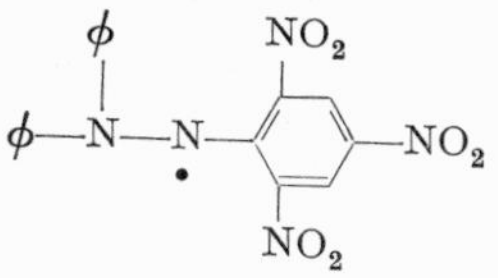

Diphenylpicrylhydrazyl

[131] D. M. Gardner and G. K. Fraenkel, *J. Am. Chem. Soc.*, **76**, 5891 (1954).
[132] S. Goldschmidt and K. Renn, *Ber.*, **55**, 628 (1922).
[133] L. G. Harrison and C. A. McDowell, *Proc. Roy. Soc. (London)*, **A220**, 77 (1953).

The dipole moment of the radical is higher than that of the parent hydrazine, indicating a greater polarizability on the part of free radicals.

Bawn and Mellish have shown that diphenylpicrylhydrazyl provides a convenient analytical method for following radical producing reactions.[134] The rate is measured by the decrease in color of the diphenylpicrylhydrazyl as it is removed by reaction with the radicals produced in the reaction. It is particularly useful for very slow reactions. The number of radicals produced during a run need not be very large since even a 10^{-4} to 10^{-5} M solution of diphenylpicrylhydrazyl is highly colored. In the case of rather stable radicals like triphenylmethyl, oxygen must be excluded since it competes successfully with the diphenylpicrylhydrazyl. The product of the reaction of triphenylmethyl with diphenylpicrylhydrazyl is not the result of a simple coupling at the classical location of the odd electron on one of the central nitrogen atoms, but seems to include some reduction and addition of triphenylmethyl to one of the phenyl groups of the diphenylpicrylhydrazyl.

By extrapolation from the behavior of diphenylpicrylhydrazyl, the dissociation of tetraaryl hydrazines into colored, reactive substances in solution at high temperatures is probably a radical reaction. It is only partly reversible, owing to disproportionation.

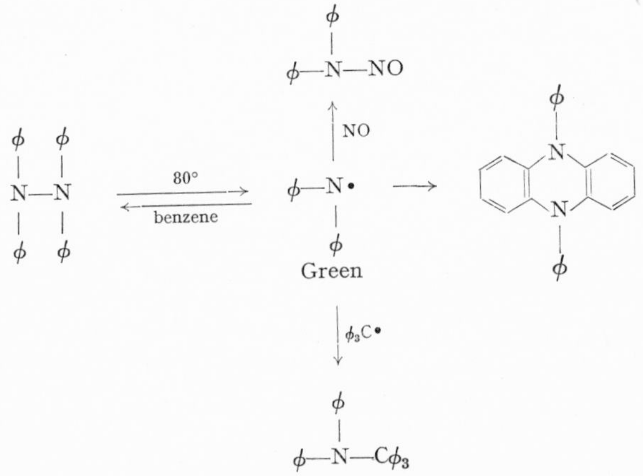

[134] C. E. H. Bawn and S. F. Mellish, *Trans. Faraday Soc.*, **47**, 1216 (1951).

Tetra-*p*-anisylhydrazine is green in benzene at room temperature.[135] On the other hand, 1,2-diphenyl-1,2-di-*p*-nitrophenylhydrazine appears not to be dissociated at all. If this difference in degree of dissociation is real, and not a specious one due merely to a difference in color or reactivity of the radicals, it presents a puzzling contrast to the case of diphenylpicrylhydrazyl and to the triphenylmethyl series in which both kinds of substituent stabilize the radical.

Hexaphenyltetrazane is intensely blue in solution but decomposes rapidly at room temperature.

$$\phi_2N\text{—}N\text{—}N\text{—}N\phi_2 \;\rightleftharpoons\; \phi_2N\text{—}N\cdot \xrightarrow{\;\phi_3C\cdot\;} \phi_2N\text{—}N\text{—}C\phi_3$$

with ϕ substituents below, labeled "Blue" under the middle species, and an NO arrow leading down to:

$$\phi_2N\text{—}N\text{—}NO$$
$$|$$
$$\phi$$

The influence of various substituents on the dissociation of 1,1,4,4-tetra-phenyl-2,3-dibenzoyltetrazane has been correlated by the Hammett rho-sigma treatment.[136] The substituents were in the para positions of the four phenyl groups, the solvent was toluene, and the value of rho was negative. This signifies that under these conditions electron-releasing groups favor the dissociation while electron-attracting groups suppress it. The increase in the dissociation constant parallels the decrease in the heat of dissociation.[137]

The reduction of hydroxylamine by titanous salts in water produces the free amino radical, a reaction analogous to the formation of tri-phenylmethyl from the carbinol and a reducing agent.[138] The amino radical will attack benzene to give diaminocyclohexadiene and di-(aminocyclohexadienyl); it converts cyclohexene into cyclohexyl-amine.[139]

[135] H. Wieland, and H. Lecher *Ber.*, **45**, 2600 (1912).

[136] N. Schwartz and W. K. Wilmarth, *J. Chem. Phys.*, **20**, 748 (1952).

[137] S. Goldschmidt and J. Bader, *Ann.*, **473**, 137 (1929).

[138] P. Davis, M. G. Evans, and W. C. E. Higginson, *J. Chem. Soc.*, **1951**, 2563.

[139] H. Seaman, P. J. Taylor, and W. A. Waters, *J. Chem. Soc.*, **1954**, 4690.

Charged Nitrogen Radicals

The oxidation of N,N-diphenylhydroxylamine with silver oxide produces a red substance shown to be a completely dissociated radical by its color (unchanged at $-50°$), by cryoscopy in benzene, and by its paramagnetism.[140] Its reactions are typical of free radicals.[141]

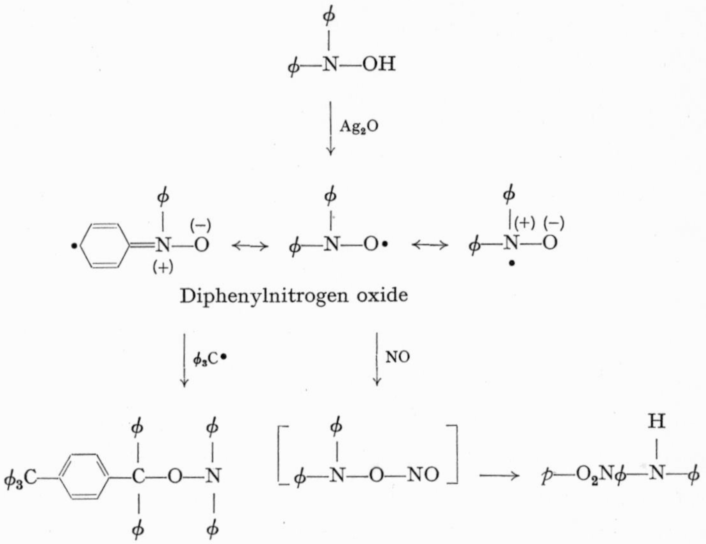

$$\phi$$
$$|$$
$$\phi\text{—N—OH}$$

$$\downarrow \text{Ag}_2\text{O}$$

Diphenylnitrogen oxide

Although diphenylnitrogen oxide is unstable, dianisylnitrogen oxide may be kept for a long time.

A somewhat similar type of ion radical is made by oxidizing amines:

$$\phi_3\text{N}: \xrightarrow{\text{Br}_2} \overset{(+)\cdot (-)}{\phi_3\text{N}} \text{Br}_3 \quad \text{Triphenylaminium tribromide (blue)}$$

$$(p\text{—CH}_3\phi)_3\text{N}: \xrightarrow{\text{ClO}_4} (p\text{—CH}_3\phi)_3\text{N}\overset{\cdot}{(+)}\text{ClO}_4{}^{(-)}$$

Measurements of the paramagnetism of tris-(p-tolyl)aminium perchlorate indicate complete dissociation.

In rigid media the photooxidation of tetraphenylhydrazine pro-

[140] H. Wieland and M. Offenbächer, *Ber.*, **47**, 2111 (1914).
[141] H. Wieland and K. Roth, *Ber.*, **53**, 210 (1920).

duces an ion-radical that is destroyed not only by return of the electron but by decomposition into an ion and a radical.[142]

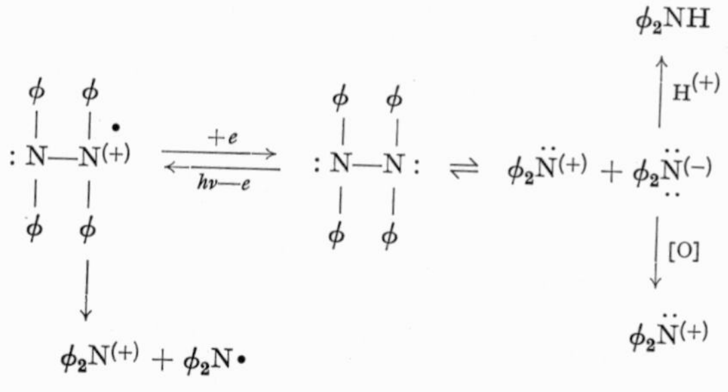

Lewis and Bigeleisen suggested that tetraphenylhydrazine is in rapid equilibrium with ionic dissociation products as well as with the neutral radicals previously mentioned. The green color produced by the action of either acids or oxidizing agents is due mostly to the diphenylnitrogen positive ion, whose concentration is increased by any reagent which removes the diphenylnitrogen negative ion from the equilibrium.[142] The violet color reported by Weitz and Müller is unexplained, but it is not obtained in the absence of air.[143]

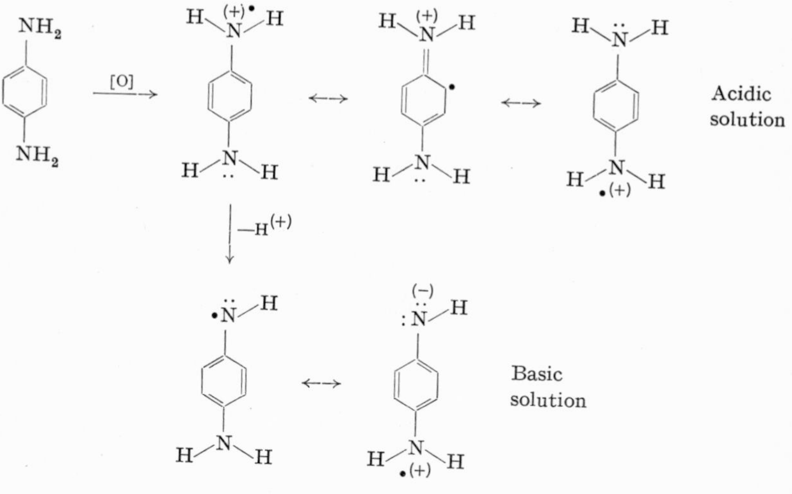

---

[142] G. N. Lewis and D. Lipkin, *J. Am. Chem. Soc.*, **64**, 2801 (1942); G. N. Lewis and J. Bigeleisen, *ibid.*, **64**, 2808 (1942).
[143] E. Weitz and L. Müller, *Ber.*, **68**, 2306 (1935).

Radicals in which the odd electron is on a nitrogen next to an aromatic ring are stabilized by resonance analogous to that of triphenylmethyl. In the case of Wurster's salts, the nitrogen analogs of semiquinones, there are two equivalent resonance structures in the acid form, but in the less stable basic form one of the structures requires separation of charge. Evidence for the unpaired electron has been obtained by measurement of the paramagnetism.[144]

Related ion-radicals have been prepared photochemically in rigid media by Lewis.[145] When tetramethylbenzidine is exposed to ultraviolet light in a rigid medium, an electron is ejected as in the production of color centers in glass.

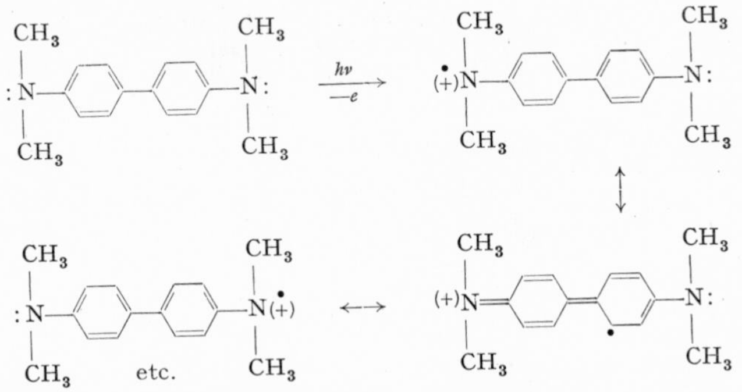

If plane polarized light is used to eject the electron, only those molecules that are properly oriented with respect to the electric vector are ionized. This produces a colored glass (a supercooled liquid is used) that is dichroic. In the case of tetramethylbenzidine the ion-radicals absorb most strongly when the beam with which the color is measured is polarized in the same plane as the beam that produced the ions. However, in the case of Wurster's blue the optical axis of the amine is perpendicular to that of the resulting ion so that the maximum absorption is obtained with the measuring beam polarized at right angles to the polarization of the exciting beam.

As the ether-isopentane-ethanol glass containing oriented Wurster's blue ions is allowed to warm up from liquid air temperatures, the

144 H. Katz, Z. Physik., 87, 238 (1934); P. Rumpf and F. Trombe, Compt. rend., 206, 671 (1938), J. chim. phys., 35, 110 (1938).
145 G. N. Lewis and J. Bigeleisen, J. Am. Chem. Soc., 65, 520 (1943).

molecules become free to rotate and the dichroism, which is an effect due to their orientation, disappears. It is interesting that rotation of the molecules occurs before the blue color is discharged. Apparently the

leuco form ion-radical

Optical axes of Wurster's blue

leuco form ion-radical

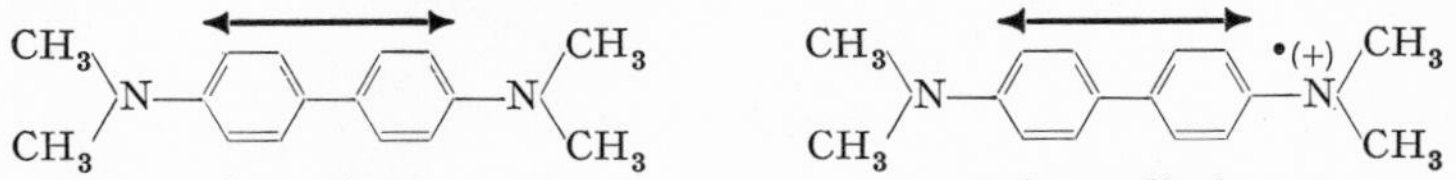

Optical axes of tetramethylbenzidine

process by which the electron returns to the ion-radical is more inhibited by a high viscosity than is the rotation. The returning electron must therefore be solvated. The spectrum characteristic of alkali metals in liquid ammonia has been explained in terms of an electron in a potential well, formed by surrounding solvent dipoles pointing at the electron. It would seem that the potential well migrates rather than release the electron.

The electrolysis of quaternary ammonium salts in liquid ammonia gives blue solutions like those of the alkali metals in liquid ammonia.[146]

$$Et_4N^{(+)} \xrightarrow[NH_3]{e^{(-)}} \underset{\text{Blue}}{Et_4N^{(+)} + e^{(-)}\text{ (solvated)}}$$

The blue color is attributed to the solvated electron. The blue solutions react with ketones to form highly colored substances resembling the metal ketyls formed by reaction with the alkali metals. The blue solutions decompose into trialkylamine and hydrocarbon on standing at the boiling point of liquid ammonia.

$$2\ Et_4N^{(+)}e^{(-)} \longrightarrow 2\ Et_3N + \underset{\text{(not isolated)}}{CH_3CH_2CH_2CH_3}$$

[146] H. H. Schlubach, *Ber.*, **53**, 1689 (1920); H. H. Schlubach and F. Ballauf, *ibid.*, **54**, 2811 (1921).

The fading that occurs at still lower temperatures is due to some other reaction, since the colorless solutions still show the characteristic reactions of the blue solution and do not give triethylamine.

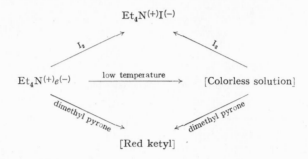

[Red ketyl]

The nature of the colorless substance is unknown, but Schlubach and Ballauf were of the opinion that it was not tetraethylammonium amide since they observed no hydrogen evolution during the fading. The colorless substance can also be made from tetraethylammonium chloride with potassium in liquid ammonia. Due to the interfering color of the potassium it is not known whether the blue substance is again an intermediate in the formation of the colorless substance. A neutral quaternary nitrogen radical would, of course, use one of the higher orbitals for the odd electron and if such a substance is formed at all it should be reversibly, returning the electron to the solvent.

Electrolysis of tetramethylammonium salts in alcohol at —34° with a mercury cathode gives tetramethylammonium amalgam.[147] The amalgam is not blue since the electron whose solvation is responsible for the blue color of ammonia solutions of the free radical now occupies one of the conductivity bands of the alloy. Ammonium amalgam itself can be readily prepared by adding sodium amalgam to an aqueous solution of ammonium chloride. The results are quite spectacular, since the ammonium amalgam is in the form of an extraordinarily voluminous gray sponge which is extruded from the mouth of the reaction vessel. On standing it slowly collapses into a small pool of mercury.

[147] H. N. McCoy and F. L. West, *J. Phys. Chem.*, 16, 261 (1911).

Porter has recently shown that decomposing tetramethylammonium amalgam is a source of trimethylamine and methyl free radicals.[148] When a current of nitrogen is passed over the amalgam, tellurium mirrors downstream are removed.[148]

[148] G. B. Porter, *J. Chem. Soc.*, **1954**, 760.

CHAPTER V

Carbonium Ions by Reversible Dissociation

Status of Ionic Reaction Mechanisms

Strictly speaking, an ion should be defined in terms of its net charge, or operationally in terms of its migration and transport of charge in an electrical field. The operational definition excludes not only neutral molecules and molecules with somewhat polar bonds, as is obviously proper, but it also excludes intimate and even solvent-separated ion pairs, and this may impair its usefulness for chemical purposes. In the chemistry of ions and polar molecules there is lacking a sharp dichotomy like that which distinguishes any radical from any non-radical in terms of paramagnetism. Ions, ion pairs, and covalent molecules merge almost indistinguishably, and it is quite permissible to speak of a molecule as a resonance hybrid between an ion-pair and a covalent structure.

The chemical behavior of ions, ion pairs, and polarizable molecules partakes of the same indistinctness as the definitions of these species. Any attempt to make a complete catalog of the reactions of ions will almost certainly include borderline reactions whose intermediates are in fact ion-pairs or even covalent molecules. For many purposes the identification of a reaction as "carbonium ion-like," or what the Germans would call "Krypto-ionenreaktion," is as useful as the certain knowledge that the intermediate is actually a carbonium ion. Many of the ionic reaction mechanisms in the literature do not represent actual free ions and were not so intended by their authors. The ionic representation is often merely a convenient simplification; if it is an over-simplification it is one that is easily rectified when the pertinent data become available. The value of such approximate mechanisms is that they help to reveal broad and useful generalizations for which certain details may be irrelevant. Much can be said for a preliminary skirmish with something less than the whole truth:

> *"...clear sight, bemused*
> *by this landscape's diversity*
> *began to be advised*
> *by snowfall of a poised,*
> *underlying simplicity..."*[149]

The role of approximate mechanisms in organic chemistry is somewhat like that of the perfect gas laws in physical chemistry. The fact that an approximate mechanism has some value does not of course mean that precise mechanisms are not still better.

Most of the discussion of ions in this book will be concerned with large complicated ions in the liquid phase rather than with small simple ions in the vacuum of the mass spectrometer. Organic chemistry is the chemistry of complicated molecules and for this reason the organic chemist will be most interested in the large radicals and ions whose usual habitat is the liquid phase. Perhaps this is why the boundary between physical and organic chemistry has somewhere been defined as the liquid-vapor interface. Certainly it is only in the amicable sense of a preoccupation with his natural habitat that the organic chemist should regard physical chemistry with a fishy eye.

Experimental Methods

Conductivity Measurements

It is appropriate to open a discussion of carbonium ions with the evidence from conductivity work since it is this property that is most closely related to the definition of an ion. Other methods for detecting or measuring the concentration of ions are valuable largely to the extent that their results can be related to the results of conductivity experiments.

---

[149] James Kirkup, *The Sunglasses*, Manchester Guardian Literary Supplement, 1951.

The fact that triarylmethyl halides and related compounds ionize in liquid sulfur dioxide was established by the pioneering work of Walden[150] and Gomberg[151], who showed that such solutions were comparable to those of familiar ionic substances like methylammonium chloride or potassium iodide which are good electrolytes in water as well as in sulfur dioxide. The failure of the triarylmethyl halides to ionize reversibly in water is due simply to the fact that water is very reactive towards the resulting ion. Later workers used conductivity in sulfur dioxide to establish the effect of changes in structure on the ionization.[152-154] It was soon found that some substances such as methyl-substituted or methoxy-substituted triphenylmethyl perchlorates were all completely ionized and that therefore the relative stabilization of the ion by the substituents could not be established in that system.[152] On the other hand, the conductivity curves of substituted triphenylmethyl chlorides in sulfur dioxide were found to depend very much on the nature of the substituent, the chlorides not being uniformly strong electrolytes.[152] Table IV presents the quantitative results of Lichtin and Bartlett[155] and Lichtin and Glazer[156] for such a series of triarylmethyl chlorides in liquid sulfur dioxide. In that solvent higher ionic aggregates may be ignored, but ion pairs are important. Since conductance measures free ions, the experimental dissociation constants K_{exp} are really composites of an ionization constant and a dissociation constant of the ion pair.

$$RCl \quad \overset{K_1}{\rightleftharpoons} \quad R^{(+)}Cl^{(-)} \quad \overset{K_2}{\rightleftharpoons} \quad R^{(+)} + Cl^{(-)}$$

$$K_{exp} = \frac{K_1 K_2}{1 + K_1} \quad \text{or} \quad K_1 = \frac{K_{exp}}{K_2 - K_{exp}}$$

It seems reasonable to assume that K_2, the dissociation constant of the ion pairs, is very nearly the same for all the various triarylmethyl

[150] P. Walden, *Ber.*, **35**, 2018 (1902).
[151] M. Gomberg, *Ber.*, **35**, 2403 (1902).
[152] K. Ziegler and H. Wollschitt, *Ann.*, **479**, 90 (1930).
[153] K. Ziegler and W. Mathes, *Ann.*, **479**, 111 (1930).
[154] S. T. Bowden and T. L. Thomas, *J. Chem. Soc.*, **1940**, 1242.
[155] N. N. Lichtin and P. D. Bartlett, *J. Am. Chem. Soc.*, **73**, 5530 (1951).
[156] N. N. Lichtin and H. Glazer, *J. Am. Chem. Soc.*, **73**, 5537 (1951).

chlorides. This assumption has stood the experimental test at least for the series of triarylcarbonium perchlorates. The latter substances are completely ionized and their conductivities measure K_2 alone. Ziegler and Wollschitt[152] found identical dissociation constants for the whole series within experimental error. Assuming, then, a constant value of K_2 for the triarylmethyl chloride series, it must be at least as large as K_{exp}, even for the most highly dissociated member of the series since

$$K_2 = \left(1 + \frac{1}{K_1}\right) K_{exp} .$$

This allows a convenient approximation to be applied to the less dissociated members of the series:

$$K_1 = \frac{K_{exp}}{K_2 - K_{exp}} \approx \frac{K_{exp}}{K_2}$$

Hence the experimental equilibrium constants of Table IV are proportional to the constants for ionization into ion pairs, and the ratios of the K_{exp} reflect differences in the tendency of different molecules to form ion pairs. Since standard free energies are proportional to the logarithms of equilibrium constants, differences in the tabulated free energies represent differences in the standard free energy change for ionization, even though the individual values represent the standard free energy for the overall process of ionization plus dissociation.

Trityl chloride and tris-p-tertiarybutylphenylmethyl chloride have been studied at $-17°$ as well as $0°$, thus affording overall enthalpies and entropies of ionization in sulfur dioxide.[155] The thermodynamic quantities will be found in Table IV. It will be noted that both ΔH and ΔS are changed by the introduction of the tertiary butyl substituents. The net effect (at the temperatures used) is to increase the degree of ionization. But this net effect is the result of a less negative entropy of ionization, the reaction actually being less exothermic than before. Any final theoretical interpretation of the effect of substituents on the ionization should await the accumulation of similar enthalpy and entropy data for the other substituents. Neither the enthalpy nor the free energy is known with certainty to parallel potential energy quantities in cases like the present one. Yet most of our ideas of substituent effects such as resonance, the inductive effect, electron release, etc. concern changes in potential energy and so far do not deal adequately with reactions in which kinetic energy and entropy changes are important. It is to be anticipated that empirical or semi-empirical relationships between structure and enthalpy and between structure and entropy will be worked out when the data become available. Such relationships are preferable to those dealing with free energy alone, because the free energy changes too rapidly with temperature. The analogous situation existing in the field of kinetics has led Hammett to write: "A major weakness in present thinking about the problem of structure and reactivity in organic compounds arises from uncertainty about the extent to which the relative reactivity of two substances is

TABLE IV

Conductimetric Dissociation Constants of Some Substituted Triphenylmethyl Chlorides in Sulfur Dioxide at 0°

Ref.	Substituents or structure	$10^5 K_{exp}$ at 0°	Λ_0 mhos cm.²/mole	$\Delta F°$ kcal./mole	ΔH kcal./mole	$\Delta S°$ cal./mole°
[a]	none	4.03	208	+5.49	—8.9	—53
	m-methyl	9.2	201	5.04		
	m-tert-butyl	16.0	201	4.74		
	p-methyl	71	196	3.93		
	p-tert-butyl	76	190	3.90		
	bis-(p-tert-butyl)	340	191	3.08		
	tris-(p-tert-butyl)	800	182	2.62	—1.8	—17
	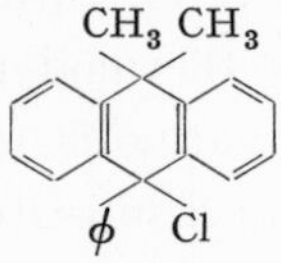 [structure: CH$_3$ CH$_3$ / φ Cl]	179	204	3.43		
[b]	m-phenyl	3.41	173	5.58		
	p-phenyl	23.2	190	4.54		
[c]	bis-p-phenyl	99	169	3.75		
	tris-(p-phenyl)	290	164	3.17		

[a] N. N. Lichtin and P. D. Bartlett, *J. Am. Chem. Soc.* **73**, 5530 (1951).
[b] N. N. Lichtin and H. Glazer, *J. Am. Chem. Soc.* **73**, 5537 (1951).
[c] K. Ziegler and H. Wollschitt, *Ann.* **479**, 108 (1930), calculations by Lichtin and Glazer.

determined by factors other than the energy of activation. This is equivalent to uncertainty about the extent to which observed relative reactivities are determined by the accident of the temperature at which measurements are made."[157]

An example of the empirical correlation of structure and entropy is the work of Cobble on aqueous solutions.[158] Similar work for other solvents is badly needed since there is no reason to believe that the entropies will be independent of solvent.

Other conductivity data are available that can not be interpreted in terms of ionization constants but which do serve to arrange the compounds in the order of increasing tendency to ionize. Such sequences should have a common temperature, solvent, and departing negative ion if they are to be interpreted in terms of structural effects on the stability of the carbonium ion. The conductivity work of Ziegler and Wollschitt[152] and of Ziegler and Mathes[153] indicates that in sulfur dioxide at 0° there is no difference between the perchlorates of triphenylmethyl with one, two, or three para methyl or para methoxy groups, all of these compounds being completely ionized strong electrolytes. But triarylmethyl chlorides in sulfur dioxide at 0° can be arranged in the following order of increasing tendency towards ionization:

phenyl-bis-(p-nitrophenyl)methyl chloride
9-phenylfluorenyl chloride
diphenyl-p-nitrophenylmethyl chloride
p-anisyl-bis-(p-nitrophenyl)-methyl chloride
triphenylmethyl chloride
diphenyl-β-naphthylmethyl chloride
diphenyl-p-xenylmethyl chloride
phenylanisyl-p-nitrophenylmethyl chloride
diphenyl-α-naphthylmethyl chloride
phenyl-bis-(p-xenyl)-methyl chloride ⎫
diphenyl-p-tolylmethyl chloride ⎭ equally dissociated

[157] J. B. Levy, R. W. Taft, Jr., D. Aaron, and L. P. Hammett, *J. Am. Chem. Soc.*, **73**, 3792 (1951).
[158] J. W. Cobble, *J. Chem. Phys.*, **21**, 1451, (1953).

diphenyl-*o*-methoxyphenylmethyl chloride
p-nitrophenyl-bis-(*p*-anisyl)methyl chloride
tris-(*p*-xenyl)-methyl chloride
tris-(*o*-anisyl)-methyl chloride
α-naphthyl-bis-(*p*-xenyl)-methyl chloride
phenyl-bis-(*p*-tolyl)-methyl chloride
tris-*p*-tolylmethyl chloride
diphenyl-*p*-methoxyphenylmethyl chloride (a strong electrolyte)

There are several interesting features in the above sequence. With minor exceptions ions that would be expected to be more stable *in vacuo* on quantum mechanical grounds are also more stable in liquid sulfur dioxide. Thus the nitro group, with unfavorable resonance and dipole effects, reduces the degree of ionization while the methoxy group, with its possibility of resonance stabilization of the positive charge, increases the degree of ionization. The position of 9-phenyl-fluorenyl in the list should be especially interesting to quantum mechanicians. It is predicted that cyclic resonance systems with three pairs of unsaturation electrons will be more stabilized by resonance than will systems with two or four pairs of unsaturation electrons. Thus benzene, cyclopentadienyl anion, and cycloheptatrienylium cation are all conspicuously stable.[159]

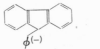

9-Phenylfluorenyl anion   Cyclopentadienyl anion

Apparently 9-phenylfluorenyl is not only a good anion but also a bad cation. The chloride probably shares in some of the resonance stabilization of the anion while the cation does not. Another example of a connection between the resonance of an anion and the properties of a related covalent compound is provided by the hydrocarbon triphenyl-methylcyclopentadiene, which has an unusually high dipole moment although it does not conduct in liquid sulfur dioxide.[160]

[159] W. von E. Doering and L. H. Knox, *J. Am. Chem. Soc.*, **76**, 3203 (1954).
[160] H. Hartmann and K. H. Flenner, *Z. physik. Chem.*, **194**, 278 (1950).

Although the general tendency of the variation of ionization with structure seems clear enough, a detailed explanation of, for example, the relationships among the mono and tris o-methoxy compounds and

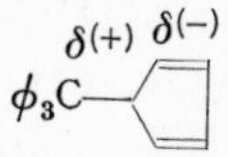

$$\delta^{(+)} \quad \delta^{(-)}$$

$$\phi_3C\!\!-\!\!\langle\;\;\rangle$$

Triphenylmethylcyclopentadiene

the p-methoxy compound requires an elaborate theoretical apparatus of resonance, steric, inductive, and probably solvation effects. It would appear to be worth while to defer such an effort until it is at least known to what extent the effects are due to enthalpy and entropy changes.

Bowden and Thomas report that the effect of methyl groups on the conductivity of trityl chloride in sulfur dioxide is in the order $p > o > m >$ none.[161] The trityl chloride-stannic chloride complex and a whole series of trityl bromides are strong electrolytes in sulfur dioxide.[150, 152] Benzhydryl chloride, m-chlorobenzhydryl chloride, and p,p'-dimethylbenzhydryl chloride do not conduct in sulfur dioxide. Earlier reports to the contrary may have been due to the use of impure compounds.[162] Dimesitylmethyl chloride has also been reported to conduct in sulfur dioxide.[163]

Dielectric Polarization

If ion pairs but not free ions are formed, the extent of ion pair formation may be estimated from the dielectric properties of the solution. This method has been used in studying the effect of Lewis acids on alkyl halides.[164]

Spectrophotometry

When a certain spectrum always appears in conducting solutions but not in non-conducting solutions of a given substance, and when the

[161] S. T. Bowden and T. L. Thomas, *J. Chem. Soc.*, **1940**, 1242.
[162] L. C. Bateman, E. D. Hughes, and C. K. Ingold, *J. Chem. Soc.*, **1940**, 1012.
[163] W. T. Nauta and P. J. Wuis, *Rec. trav. chim.*, **56**, 535 (1937).
[164] F. Fairbrother, *J. Chem. Soc.*, **1945**, 503.

intensity of the absorption tends to parallel the conductivity, it is reasonable to assign the spectrum to an ion formed by the dissociation of the dissolved substance. Comparision with related substances tells which ion is responsible for the spectrum. Since fairly drastic changes in solvent make only minor changes in the shape and position of absorption bands rather than render them unrecognizable, it is likely that the spectrum of an ion pair is very much like that of the constituent ions. Thus spectrophotometry measures free ions plus ion aggregates rather than free ions alone. From the dependence of the absorption on the concentration it is possible to deduce whether the ions are kinetically independent or largely in the form of ion pairs. For example, in a solvent in which there are very few ion pairs, but only molecules and ions, the ratio of the concentration of the colored (ions) form to the colorless (molecular) form depends on the stoichiometric concentration. On the other hand, in a solvent in which there are molecules and ion pairs but very few free ions, the ratio of colored (ion pairs) to colorless material (molecules) is relatively independent of the stoichiometric concentration.

$$AB \; \underset{\longleftarrow}{\overset{K}{\rightleftharpoons}} \; A^{(+)} + B^{(-)} \qquad \frac{[A^{(+)}]}{[AB]} = \frac{K}{[B^{(-)}]}$$

$$AB \; \underset{\longleftarrow}{\overset{K'}{\rightleftharpoons}} \; A^{(+)}B^{(-)} \qquad \frac{[A^{(+)}B^{(-)}]}{[AB]} = K'$$

Sometimes the evaluation of the extinction coefficient presents a problem. If the molecule being studied never approaches complete ionization in the solvent being used, the extinction coefficient of the ion must be estimated from experiments in a better ionizing solvent.[165] The main effect of a solvent change on the visible or ultraviolet spectrum is that some detail is smoothed out in highly polar solvents and the absorption bands may be shifted several millimicrons, the direction of the shift depending on whether it is due to the change in dielectric constant or to a more specific effect such as hydrogen bonding. The extinction coefficient at a wave length corresponding to a steep part of the absorption curve may be changed drastically by a change in solvent even though the absorption curve itself is merely shifted

[165] A. Bentley, A. G. Evans, and J. Halpern, *Trans. Faraday Soc.*, **47**, 711 (1951).

slightly. The best procedure in the rare cases where it is possible is to use the oscil ator strength rather than the absorption at a given wave length as a measure of the concentration of ions. The oscillator strength is the integrated absorption or area under the absorption curve. Its advantage is that an absorption curve might gain width at the expense of height without changing the oscillator strength. The next best procedure is to use the extinction coefficient at the wavelength of maximum extinction and to conduct the measurements in the new solvent at the new wave length of maximum extinction.

When a shift toward longer wave lengths occurs in the case of a band in the near ultraviolet, visible color may appear in the new solvent. It is important not to attribute this color to an entirely new absorption band characteristic of a new species being formed in the new solvent. Thus reports of relative degrees of ionization in a series of solvents based on color alone may be misleading. Especially in the case of a nitro compound an apparent onset of ionization may be due to a slight invasion of the visible region by a band due to the un-ionized molecule. In other cases a more intense color may represent no greater amount of an ion, but may be due merely to the fact that a greater proportion of the absorption due to the ion is taking place in the visible region.

It is frequently necessary to subtract from the total absorption a part owing to the un-ionized molecule in measuring the amount of ion present. If a given solute exists in two forms, such as a molecule and an ion, it is quite likely that the absorption curves of the two forms will intersect at some point. The intersection is known as an *isobestic* point, and at the wave length of the isobestic point the extinction depends only on the total amount of solute and not on the proportion of the two forms.[166] One investigator who had the bad luck to pick the isobestic wave length for all his experiments came to the mistaken conclusion that it was not possible to determine the position of his particular equilibrium by optical means. A medium effect will cause a family of absorption curves to intersect in a small region rather than in a point, but failure to show an isobestic point even approximately means that the solute exists in more than two forms.

[166] L. A. Flexser, L. P. Hammett, and A. Dingwall, *J. Am. Chem. Soc.*, **57**, 2103 (1935).

It should be mentioned that medium effects do not usually change the characteristic shape of an absorption spectrum to such an extent that it can not be recognized. Thus the characteristic Bactrian camel shape of the absorption band of solutions of trityl chloride in sulfuric acid and in nitromethane leaves no doubt that essentially the same ion is present in both solvents.

In the older literature there are reports of colorless but conducting solutions of triarylmethyl derivatives. It seems well-established that triarylmethyl cations are colored, but an oxonium ion formed by the covalent attachment of a carbonium ion to an ether oxygen atom, for example, would be colorless.

The ionization of certain substances, notably triarylmethyl cyanides, is promoted by light, so that spectrophotometric analysis for carbonium ions is no exception to the rule that the analyst should be alert for any parallelism between the duration of exposure to light during the analysis and the result.[167-169]

Cryoscopy

The freezing point depression of a solvent is proportional to the concentration of solute particles and may be used to measure the extent of ionization once the new particles have been identified qualitatively as ions. The method has the obvious disadvantage of not allowing measurements over a range of temperatures in a single solvent. It is almost certainly not worth while to compute an enthalpy of ionization from ionization constants at two different temperatures in two different solvents. Usable solvents are limited not only by the requirement that the melting point be at a convenient temperature but also by the requirement that the solvent be capable of producing ions yet not be sufficiently nucleophilic to react irreversibly with them once they are formed. For this reason most cryoscopic work has been done in sulfuric acid or methanesulfonic acid.[170]

[167] I. Lifschitz and G. Girbes, *Ber.*, **61**, 1463 (1928).
[168] L. Harris, J. Kaminsky, and R. G. Simard, *J. Am. Chem. Soc.*, **57**, 1151 (1935).
[169] G. N. Lewis, T. T. Magel, and D. Lipkin. *J. Am. Chem. Soc.*, **64**, 1774 (1942).
[170] R. A. Craig, A. B. Garrett, and M. S. Newman, *J. Am. Chem. Soc.*, **72**, 163 (1950).

Triphenylcarbinol in sulfuric acid solution has a spectrum indicating the presence of the same carbonium ion responsible for the conductivity of triphenylmethyl chloride in liquid sulfur dioxide.[171] In confirmation of this the freezing point depression is four times that of substances dissolving to give only one mole of particles per mole of dissolved substance.[171-173]

$$\phi-\overset{\displaystyle\phi}{\underset{\displaystyle\phi}{C}}-OH + 2H_2SO_4 \;\underset{\leftarrow}{\longrightarrow}\; \phi-\overset{\displaystyle\phi}{\underset{\displaystyle\phi}{C}}{}^{(+)} + H_3O^{(+)} + 2HSO_4{}^{(-)}$$

One solute particle   Four solute particles

Similar results have been obtained with substituted triphenylcarbinols in sulfuric acid.[174] Some unsaturated hydrocarbons form carbonium ions by simple addition of a proton, as do some carboxylic acids.[175-177] But other carboxylic acids behave like the triarylcarbinols, the most prominent example being mesitoic acid.

$$CH_3-\underset{CH_3}{\overset{CH_3}{\bigcirc}}-\overset{O}{\overset{\|}{C}}-OH + 2H_2SO_4 \;\underset{\leftarrow}{\longrightarrow}\; CH_3-\underset{CH_3}{\overset{CH_3}{\bigcirc}}-\overset{O}{\overset{\|}{C}}{}^{(+)} + H_3O^{(+)} + 2HSO_4{}^{(-)}$$

One particle   Four particles

$$\phi_2C{=}CH_2 + H_2SO_4 \;\underset{\leftarrow}{\longrightarrow}\; \phi_2\overset{(+)}{C}-CH_3 + HSO_4{}^{(-)}$$

One particle   Two particles

The cryoscopic constant of sulfuric acid can be estimated from actual measurements with solutes assumed to be entirely in some particular state of ionization, or it can be calculated from the heat of

[171] A. Hantzsch, Z. physik. Chem., 61, 257 (1908).
[172] A. Hantzsch, Ber., 55, 953 (1922).
[173] L. P. Hammett, and A. J. Deyrup, J. Am. Chem. Soc., 55, 1900 (1933).
[174] M. S. Newman and N. C. Deno, J. Am. Chem. Soc., 73, 3644 (1951).
[175] V. Gold, B. W. V. Hawes, and F. L. Tye, J. Chem. Soc., 1952, 2167.
[176] L. P. Hammett and H. P. Treffers, J. Am. Chem. Soc., 59, 1708 (1937).
[177] M. S. Newman, J. Am. Chem. Soc., 63, 2431 (1941).

fusion of sulfuric acid.[178] The value obtained in the latter way is 6.12° per unit molality.

Chemical Detection of Ions

Solutions containing ions give chemical reactions expected of the ions. For example, mesitoic acid, which resists esterification by other methods, is readily esterified when its sulfuric acid solution is poured into an alcohol.[177]

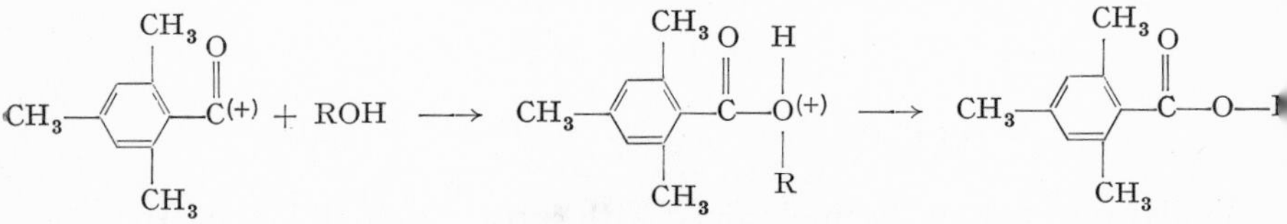

Nevertheless, chemical methods have not been used for determining ionization equilibrium constants. The analytical reaction would have to be almost instantaneous and the formation of the ions relatively slow. Also the analytical reagent must not react directly with the unionized molecule. In contrast to their disuse in studies of ionic equilibrium, fast chemical reactions of the ion have been used extensively in measuring the rate of ionization, especially in circumstances where unavoidable irreversible reactions make it impossible to study the equilibrium. The only requirement for the use of chemical methods in ionization kinetics is that the overall rate be independent of the concentration of the added reagent, i.e., that simple ionization be the slow and rate-determining step.

Interpretation

Effects of Carbonium Ion Structural Changes on Ionization Equilibrium

The extent of dissociation into ions is a function of the structure of that part of the molecule that becomes the carbonium ion as well as the often quite different structure of the ion itself. There are always geometrical differences between the "carbonium ion" part of the

[178] R. J. Gillespie, *J. Chem. Soc.*, **1954**, 1851.

molecule and the carbonium ion itself and sometimes topological differences as well, the carbonium ion being produced directly as a rearranged or bridged structure. Such topological difference in structure between the molecule and the ion will be discussed in Chapter VI.

In addition to the dependence on the structure of the carbonium ion, the extent of dissociation is also a function of the departing negative group, the solvent, the ionizing catalyst, and the temperature. Although it is almost certainly true that the dependence of the degree of ionization on the structure of the carbonium ion will itself be a function of the other variables, the available data are as yet too scant and qualitative to do justice to such cross terms. For the most part it will be assumed that a given structural effect will be qualitatively the same with a different departing anion, in a different solvent, or at a different temperature. But it should be emphasized that this assumption will break down if the change in the other variable is too drastic. Thus an amino group can hardly be expected to have the same effect in a neutral solvent as in a solvent in which it is largely protonated. And a structural change that happens to increase both the activation energy and the activation entropy to a comparable extent can either increase or decrease the extent of ionization, depending on the temperature. In spite of these difficulties, certain structural changes produce such large and consistent effects on the ionization that their interpretation seems quite clear. The major structural effects are steric and electronic, the latter including both resonance and inductive effects.

For a given departing negative ion and solvent there will be a rather small range of structures for which an experimental comparision of the stability of the ions can be made. A large group of structures will be off scale, the concentration of either the ion or the molecule being immeasurably small. As a result the available data on the effect of structural changes in the carbonium ion consists of brief series of structures arranged in order of decreasing tendency to ionize. Since the series overlap somewhat an overall order of ionization tendency can be established, though subject to the reservations expressed in the preceding paragraph. A long series based on the conductivity of the chlorides in sulfur dioxide is to be found in Table IV and on pages 79–80.[155,156,152]

The effects of substituents in the meta and para positions of the triphenylmethyl group agree qualitatively with the electronic resonance and inductive effects usually assigned. Thus para methoxy or amino groups have a powerful stabilizing effect on the ion, as is illustrated by the various ionic triphenylmethane dyes bearing these substituents. On the other hand, electron-withdrawing substituents like the nitro group have a powerful destabilizing effect on the carbonium ion. Almost any resonating substituent will stabilize a free radical but a positive charge is more selective, being accomodated only on certain groups. Thus a para methoxy group can interact with a positive charge as indicated by structure XI while the nitro group not only fails to stabilize a positive charge by structures like XII, but actually destabilizes it. The adjacent positive charges in structure XIII raise the energy of that structure as compared to the corresponding one in compounds lacking the nitro group.

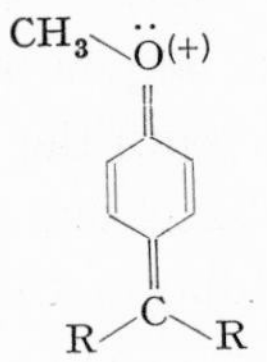

(XI) 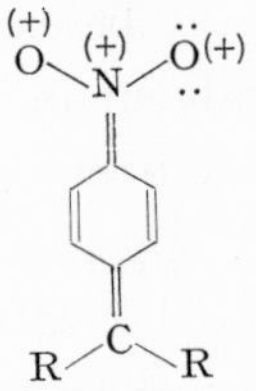 (XII) (XIII)
(open sextet on O)

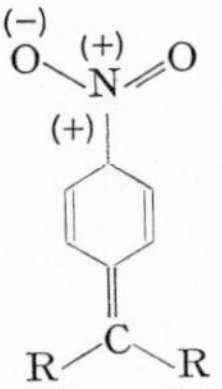

Whichever the direction of the effect, two of a given kind of group do more than one, and three groups do still more. One para-methoxy group is sufficient in overcoming the opposite effect of one para-nitro group, but is in turn overcome by two para-nitro groups. Para and meta-phenyl substituents have opposite effects on the ionization, and an electron-withdrawing inductive effect superimposed on the resonance effect has been suggested for the phenyl group in the para position. The increased ionization produced by the phenyl substituent in the para position is a resonance effect diminished by an unfavorable inductive effect, while the decreased ionization produced by the phenyl group in the meta position is due to the inductive effect acting alone. Although meta tertiary butyl stabilizes the ion more than meta methyl, the two groups have about the same effect in the para position. This suggests that tertiary butyl has a stronger electron-releasing inductive effect, while methyl has a stronger electron-releasing resonance effect due to overlap of the hydrogen orbitals of the methyl group with the π-orbitals of the benzene ring, hyperconjugation in resonance terminology.

The geometrical requirements for the maximum stabilization of the ion by resonance are similar to those for the stabilization of the radical, which have already been discussed. The compromise between perfect coplanarity and the relief of steric interaction between the ortho-hydrogen atoms of adjacent benzene rings results in a slightly feathered propeller geometry for the triphenyl carbonium ion. Because resonance stabilization is lost when one of the rings passes through the extreme non-coplanar intermediate position on its way to another approximately coplanar "reverse feathered" position, there is a slight energy barrier to such a rotation and two isomeric propeller forms of the ion have independent existence.[179]

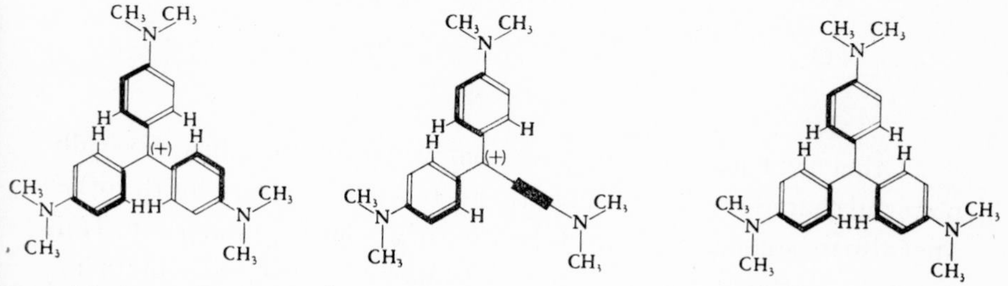

symmetrical propeller, most transition state unsymmetrical propeller, less
nearly planar, lower energy   nearly planar, higher energy

Geometrical isomers of crystal violet

The crystal violet ion has a main absorption band at about 5900 Å, and another so close to it as to appear to be a shoulder on the main band. As the temperature is raised the main band shrinks while the shoulder becomes more prominent. This is interpreted as due to the increased conversion of the low energy form, responsible for the main absorption band, into the high energy form, responsible for the shoulder. The energy difference can be calculated by plotting the logarithm of the

[179] G. N. Lewis, T. T. Magel, and D. Lipkin, *J. Am. Chem. Soc.*, **64**, 1774 (1942).

ratio of the two isomers against the reciprocal of the absolute temperature. The unsymmetrical propeller form has about 0.5 kcal. more energy
than the symmetrical propeller, probably because the latter has more
resonance stabilization or sacrifices less of it in steric strain. Dyes like
malachite green, with one unsubstituted phenyl ring, do not have any
shoulder in their absorption spectra and hence exist in only one form.
Resonance with the unsubstituted ring is relatively so unimportant
compared to the resonance involving the substituted rings that the
unsubstituted ring can be in a non-coplanar, non-resonating position
with very little loss in energy.

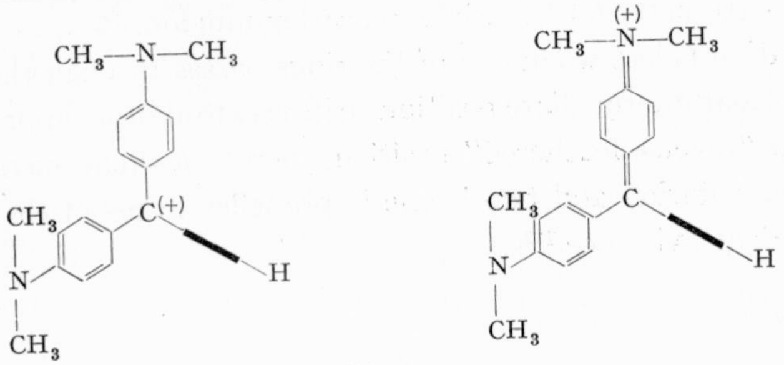

Malachite green

Other evidence also indicates that when one ring has especially
powerful charge-stabilizing substituents it is not necessary for the other
rings also to be coplanar for the formation of a relatively stable ion. Thus
tri-o-tolyl carbinol and tri-p-tolyl carbinol *both* give carbonium ion
spectra in sulfuric acid solutions so dilute that triphenyl carbinol is
colorless.[180] The para-methyl groups are presumably stabilizing the
carbonium ion by hyperconjugation in all three rings, but this is out
of the question for the ortho-substituted carbinol. At best only one ring
at a time can approach coplanarity with the bonds about the central
carbon atom. The effect of the ortho-methyl groups is probably a
destabilization of the carbinol by crowding the hydroxyl group, plus
stabilization of the ion by resonance acting only in one ring at
a time.

The degrees of ionization of triphenylmethyl chloride, p,p'-di-
methoxybenzhydryl chloride, and dimesitylmethyl chloride in liquid

[180] M. S. Newman and N. C. Deno, *J. Am. Chem. Soc.*, **73**, 3644 (1951).

sulfur dioxide are about the same.[181,182] Apparently one ring of the triphenylcarbonium ion may be dispensed with entirely if the other two rings are suitably substituted. The ionization of dimesitylmethyl chloride is probably the combined result of steric hindrance in the chloride and some resonance and inductive effects in the ion. Although the chloride can not be assembled at all with the usual scale models because of the spacial demands of the four methyl groups, a model of the ion can be made and it even appears that a modest approach to coplanarity is possible for one of the rings at a time.

The triptycyl ion, whose corresponding radical has already been discussed, is a model compound in which the bridged structure ensures that all three rings will always deviate from coplanarity with the bonds about the central carbon atom to the maximum possible extent. Triptycyl bromide exhibits none of the tendency to ionize that is shown by the closely analogous triphenylmethyl bromide.[183] Possibly some part of the instability or low rate of formation of the ion may be due to the inability of solvent molecules to solvate both sides of the ion, one side being protected by the cage structure. However, the rate of ionization of highly hindered though acyclic alkyl halides is in fact enhanced by alkyl substituents that must shield the carbon from solvent; the loss of solvation is not sufficient to counteract the favorable effect of the substituents in that case and is probably only a minor factor contributing to the instability of the triptycyl cation. It is therefore likely that the major reason for the instability of this cation is steric inhibition of resonance with the rings and steric inhibition of the usual sp^2 planar bond hybridization at the central carbon atom.

Effect of Solvent Changes on Ionization Equilibrium

On the basis of classical electrostatic theory, a large part of the free energy of a pair of ions depends on the dielectric constant of the medium. In a solvent of high dielectric constant, a charged object creates oriented solvent dipoles by polarization or orients existing

[181] W. T. Nauta and P. J. Wuis, *Rec. trav. chim.*, **56**, 535 (1937).
[182] F. Straus and A. Dützmann, *J. prakt. Chem.*, **103**, 1 (1921).
[183] P. D. Bartlett and E. S. Lewis, *J. Am. Chem. Soc.*, **72**, 1005 (1950).

solvent dipoles in such a way as to lower the free energy; the dielectric constant of the solvent is a measure of this effect. If specific chemical effects could be ignored, it would be possible to make the following predictions from classical electrostatic theory:

(a) Solvents of equal dielectric constant would facilitate ionization equally.

(b) A large ion would be less stabilized by solvent than a small one of the same charge.

(c) Solvents of higher dielectric constant would reduce the free energy of ionization. The direction of the effect on the enthalpy and on the entropy of ionization would be calculable from the experimentally observed variation of the dielectric constant with temperature.[184]

Unfortunately, the available data are neither reliable nor extensive enough to test all of these predictions for carbonium ionization equilibrium. The reason for the inadequacy of the data is the relative scarcity of ionizing solvents that do not react irreversibly with the ions, and the fact that much of the data consists merely of observations of the color of solutions in various solvents. As we have seen, the color may or may not parallel the ionization.

Although much work remains to be done with ionization equilibria, it is possible to forecast some of the results (but we should not rely on this indefinitely) from the data already available on the analogous problem of ionization rates. Judging from the effect of solvent changes on ionization rates, "ionizing power" is a rather specific chemical property of the solvent and one that is at best only partially coincident with the dielectric constant. Thus chemically different solvent mixtures of equal dielectric constant usually produce different ionization rates. Although the free energy of activation for ionization reactions is usually lower in a solvent of higher dielectric constant, the prediction of the direction of the change in enthalpy and entropy of activation frequently fails.[185] In favor of basing theories of solvent effect on the dielectric constant it may be said that the simplest approach can often be modified to fit the facts. For example, in the case of the misbehaving mixed solvents it can be assumed that the

[184] R. W. Gurney, *Ionic Processes in Solution*, McGraw-Hill, New York, 1953.
[185] R. G. Pearson, *Abstracts, 126th Meeting Am. Chem. Soc.*, Sept. 1954, p. 24R.

local dielectric constant in the immediate neighborhood of the ion has some reasonable value different from that of the bulk of the solution. Against too ready acceptance of the dielectric constant approach it can be pointed out that a higher dielectric constant is usually a property of a more reactive molecule; specific chemical effects may parallel the dielectric constant to some extent.

Another feature of stable organic ions is their large size and the fact that for purposes of interacting with the solvent the charge can appear at more than one place. The appearance of charge at more than one place can occur either by resonance or by a resonance-like equilibrium. The equilibrium distribution of the charge, in contrast to the resonance distribution, does not require the *simultaneous* coplanarity of all parts of the system. It is by no means certain that this equilibrium distribution of charge at several points reduces the free energy of interaction with the solvent to the degree predicted by theory for the case of a charge distributed on the homogeneous surface of a conducting sphere rather than concentrated at a point.

Complexing and Effect of Solvent Changes

As has been suggested in the previous section, explanations of solvent effects on the basis of the macroscopic physical properties of the solvent are not very successful. The alternative approach is to make use of the microscopic or chemical properties of the solvent and to consider the detailed interaction of solvent molecules with their own kind and with solute molecules. If a configuration in which one or more solvent molecules interacts with a solute molecule has a particularly low free energy, it is feasible to describe at least that part of the solute-solvent interaction as the formation of a molecular complex and to speak of an equilibrium between solvated and non-solvated molecules. Such a stabilization of a particular solute by solvation will shift any equilibrium involving that solute. For example, in the case of formation of carbonium ions from triphenylcarbinol, the equilibrium is shifted in favor of the carbonium ion by an acidic solvent that reacts with hydroxide ion and with water. The carbonium ion concentration in sulfuric acid is greater than it is in methanol-sulfuric acid mixtures because of the higher acidity of the sulfuric acid.[180,186] Similarly, the promotion of the ionization of triphenyl-methyl bromide when stannic bromide or other Lewis acid is added to the solution in an inert solvent is explicable as a reduction of the activity of the ion pair by formation of a complex ion pair.[187] The language of the preceding sentence is thermodynamic: another way of putting it would be to say that the bromide ion is largely converted to a less nucleophilic species. In contrast to stannic bromide, the organometallic compound XIV in benzene is practically devoid of ionizing power for triphenylmethyl bromide.[187]

$$
\begin{array}{cc}
\begin{array}{c}
\text{Br} \\
| \\
\text{CH}_3\!-\!\text{Sn}\!-\!\text{Br} \\
| \\
\text{Br}
\end{array}
&
\left[\begin{array}{c}
\text{Br} \\
| \;\;\diagup\text{Br} \\
\text{CH}_3\!-\!\text{Sn} \\
| \;\;\diagdown\text{Br} \\
\text{Br}
\end{array}\right]^{(-)}
\\[1em]
\text{(XIV)} & \text{(XV)}
\end{array}
$$

It seems reasonable that the electron-releasing methyl group not only reduces the affinity of the Lewis acid XIV for bromide ion but also increases the reactivity of any complex XV towards carbonium ions.

With stannic bromide and less reactive alkyl halides there is evidently a rapid reaction producing carbonium ions (ion pairs) but with no detectable *equilibrium* concentration of the ions. Thus no increase in dielectric polarization is observed for the systems stannic bromide plus *tert.*-butyl bromide or stannic bromide plus benzyl bromide, although exchange of radioactive bromine between the alkyl halide and the Lewis acid takes place readily.[187] The stronger Lewis acid, aluminum tribromide, produces some ion pairs from ethyl bromide in cyclohexane, but slowly reacts to give a conducting solution, a reaction not likely to be simple ionization. Considerable work has been done on such systems with a view to elucidating the mechanism of the Friedel-Crafts reaction. It is unlikely that the simple carbonium ion or carbonium ion pair is the sole reagent in Friedel-Crafts reactions, since the conductivity of the alkyl halide-aluminum halide mixture

[186] V. Gold and B. W. V. Hawes, *J. Chem. Soc.*, **1951**, 2102.
[187] F. Fairbrother and B. Wright, *J. Chem. Soc.*, **1949**, 1058; F. Fairbrother, *ibid.*, **1945**, 503.

is very much enhanced by the addition of benzene.[188-190] This has been interpreted in terms of a ternary complex which provides, among other things, a highly polar medium for the Friedel-Crafts reaction.[190]

The extent of the ionization produced by a Lewis acid is dependent on the nature of the more inert solvent component as well as on the Lewis acid. A trityl bromide-stannic bromide complex of one to one stoichiometry exists in the form of orange-red crystals, obviously ionic. But as is always the case with crystalline substances, lattice energy is a very important factor in determining the stability and no quantitative predictions can be made about the behaviour of the same substance in solution. Thus the trityl bromide-stannic bromide system dilute in benzene solution seems to consist largely of free trityl bromide, free stannic bromide, and only a small amount of ion pairs.[187] There is not even any very considerable fraction of covalent trityl bromide-stannic bromide complex in solution. The extent of ion pair and ion formation roughly parallels the dielectric constant of the solvents used (Table V). The more polar solvent either provides a

TABLE V[187]

$$\phi_3C\!-\!Br + SnBr_4 \xrightarrow{\ K_1\ } [\phi_3C^{(+)}SnBr_5^{(-)}]$$

$$K_2 = K_3/K_1$$

$$\phi_3CBr + SnBr_4 \xrightarrow{\ K_3\ } \phi_3C^{(+)} + SnBr_5^{(-)}$$

Solvent	Dielectric constant	K_1	K_3	K_2	Fraction ionized to free ions in 5×10^{-3} M solution
Benzene	2.28	0.14	6.4×10^{-8}	4.6×10^{-7}	.0009
Ethylene dibromide	4.9	4.3	2.4×10^{-6}	5.6×10^{-7}	.023
Bromobenzene	5.4	3.8	2.3×10^{-6}	6.1×10^{-7}	.021
Chlorobenzene	5.9	3.0	5.0×10^{-6}	1.7×10^{-6}	.017
Ethyl bromide	9.5	8.6	1.4×10^{-3}	1.6×10^{-4}	.081

[188] H. Burton and P. F. G. Praill, *Quart. Rev. (London)*, 6, 302 (1952).
[189] E. Wertyporoch and T. Firla, *Z. physik. Chem.*, 162A 398 (1932); A. Wohl and E. Wertyporoch, *Ber.*, 64, 1357 (1931); E. Wertyporoch, *ibid.*, 64, 1372 (1931).
[190] H. C. Brown and H. W. Pearsall, *J. Am. Chem. Soc.*, 74, 191 (1952).

better dielectric for the separation of charges or participates more intimately in the formation of solvated complex ions: it is difficult to tell which is the better approximation. A similar ambiguity surrounds the role of solvents in uncatalyzed ionizations; the solvent both provides a medium with certain electrical properties and interacts intimately with, "solvates," or forms complexes with the resulting ions. The latter action of the solvent is like that of an added catalyst.

Just as interaction of the negative ion with solvent or with a catalyst can promote the ionization, the same is true of the interactions of the carbonium ion. The triaryl carbonium ions discussed so far should all be colored. Reports of colorless but conducting solutions of triarylmethyl derivatives are fairly common and may represent covalently solvated carbonium ions which are not expected to be colorless. For example, a colored solution of the ion XVI in acetic acid slowly fades when it is diluted with methanol containing enough acid to prevent the formation of any "color base." The fading is attributed to the formation of XVII.[191]

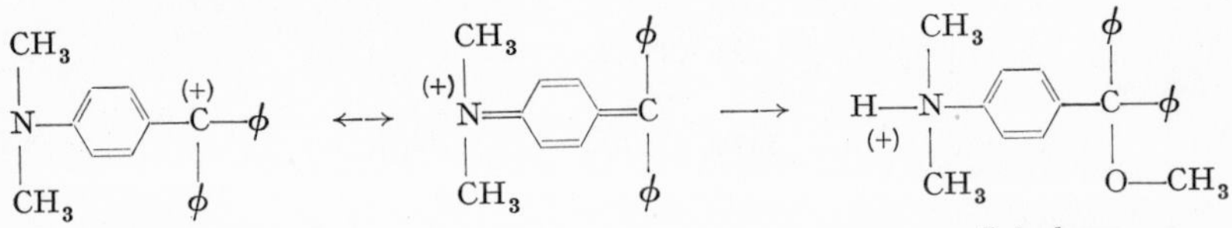

Colored
(XVI)

Colorless
(XVII)

No such fading in methanol is observed with the ion XVIII, in which the additional phenyl group extends the unsaturated system and stabilizes the ion XVIII, as compared with the ion XIX, in which the nitrogen atom insulates the two parts of the molecule.

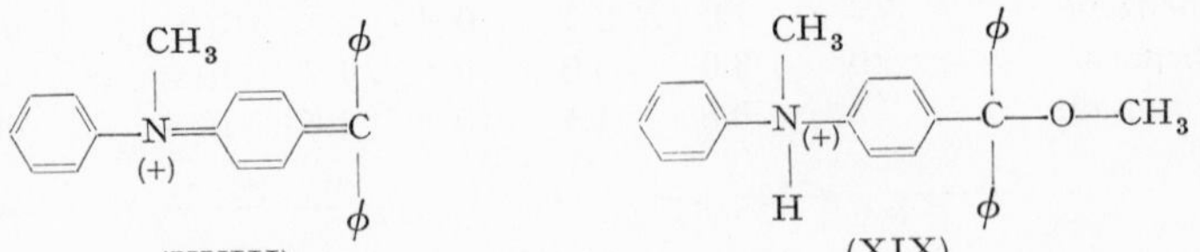

(XVIII)

(XIX)

Triphenylmethyl perchlorate is reported to be colored (red-brown) in

191 H. Walba and G. E. K. Branch, *J. Am. Chem. Soc.* **75**, 2149 (1953).

concentrated acetone solutions but colorless in dilute solutions, suggesting a reaction:[192]

$$\phi_3C^{(+)}ClO_4^{(-)} + CH_3\!-\!\overset{\overset{\displaystyle O}{\|}}{C}\!-\!CH_3 \longrightarrow \phi_3\!-\!\overset{(+)}{C}\!-\!O\!=\!\overset{\overset{\displaystyle CH_3}{|}}{\underset{\underset{\displaystyle CH_3}{|}}{C}} + ClO_4^{(-)}$$

Colored   Colorless

The frequently noted fading of carbonium ion colors when ether is added to the solution may also be due to the formation of similar colorless covalently solvated ions.[193]

A non-covalent carbonium ion-solvent complex is possible at least in principle and has been suggested as an intermediate in solvolysis reactions of the S_n1 or "limiting" type.[194, 195] The further progress of the reaction to give the stable covalently bonded solvolysis product makes it impossible to study the effect of the complexing on the ionization equilibrium directly. Perhaps a sterically hindered ether would favor the ionization by giving a non-covalent and therefore colored complex with the carbonium ion, the steric hindrance preventing the formation of a shorter and covalent bond. Hantzsch has reported that trityl perchlorate is deep violet in amyl ether solution.[193] This phenomenon deserves further investigation.

Less Specific Solvent Effects

In addition to the data already discussed on acids or Lewis acids as solvents, some data are available for solvents in which the interpretation in terms of molecular complexing is less obvious. For example, the ionization of trityl chloride has been compared spectroscopically in nitromethane, nitroethane, and 2-nitropropane.[196] Unfortunately the absorption band broadens as the solvent is changed, rendering a quantitative interpretation difficult. In the author's laboratory two

[192] I. Lifschitz and G. Girbes, *Ber.*, **61**, 1463 (1928).

[193] A. Hantzsch, *Ber.*, **54**, 2573 (1921).

[194] S. Winstein, E. Grunwald, and H. W. Jones, *J. Am. Chem. Soc.*, **73**, 2700 (1951).

[195] C. G. Swain, *J. Am. Chem. Soc.*, **70**, 1119 (1948).

[196] A. Bentley and A. G. Evans, *J. Chem. Soc.*, **1952**, 3468.

other difficulties have been noted.[197] Unless special care is taken, nitromethane contains formic acid as an impurity and formic acid promotes the ionization. The other difficulty is that dry nitromethane disproportionates quite rapidly in the presence of trityl chloride to give carbon dioxide and ammonia. It is reported that in the case of tris-*p*-tolylmethyl chloride there is no broadening of the absorption band, but it is possible that the other difficulties with nitromethane remain.[196] However, the ion pair formation in nitromethane is reported to be so much more extensive than in nitroethane that the difference is probably real. The dielectric constants of nitromethane and nitroethane are 39 and 30, respectively. The solvent effect might therefore be due to the changed physical properties of the medium or to a change in the solvating ability of the nitroalkane, which might also parallel the dielectric constant.

Triphenylmethyl bromide is said to be colorless (and therefore covalent) in carbon tetrachloride, trichloroethylene, tetrachloroethylene, and chloroform, but increasingly yellow in the series methylene chloride, dichloroethylene, benzonitrile, nitrobenzene, trichloronitromethane, 1,2,3-trichloropropane, tetrachloroethane, and nitromethane.[193] The position of some of the members of the series is certainly remarkable and perhaps warrants a detailed spectroscopic examination. Of course the series as it now stands is subject to the usual doubts as to the purity of the solvents and also to some possible confusion between shifts in wave length and an increased ionization. It is further reported that triphenylmethyl bromide solutions in tetrachloroethane, tetrabromoethane, trichloronitromethane, and tetranitromethane are atypical in that they become lighter as the temperature is raised, implying an exothermic ionization. The conductivity of malachite green chloride indicates an increasing dissociation in the solvent order nitrobenzene, acetonitrile, acetone, ethanol.[198] The color of malachite green azide solutions seems to depend on the solvent in wave length as well as in intensity. The colors are: alcohol, dark blue-green; chloroform, pale green; tetralin, pale green; benzene, ether, acetic acid, and petroleum ether all colorless. The lack of color in

---

[197] Bill B. Smith and J. E. Leffler, *J. Am. Chem. Soc.*, 77, 1700 (1955).
[198] I. Lifschitz and G. Girbes, *Ber.*, 61, 1463 (1928).

acetic acid may be due to the existence of the carbonium ion in a covalently solvated form. The color in tetralin may be due to autoxidation impurities in that solvent. Acetone, which ranked high in the malachite green conductivity series, gives only a pale colored solution with malachite green azide, a possible indication of covalent solvation.

Effect of Changes in Nature of the Negative Ion

The stabilization of the negative ion by extensive complexing might be considered as equivalent to a change in the nature of the negative ion. The change is in the direction of spreading the negative charge in the complexed as compared to the uncomplexed negative ion. The corresponding complex of the undissociated alkyl halide is more polarized than the alkyl halide itself. The latter phenomenon should be regarded as paralleling the ionization rather than causing it, since the complex is formed only to the extent that it has a lower free energy than the uncomplexed alkyl halide. A similar comparision can be made between triphenylmethyl chloride and triphenylmethyl bromide, the bromide being more ionized in most solvents than is the chloride. Chlorine, of course, is more electronegative than bromine but the additional ionic character of the triphenylmethyl-chlorine bond serves merely to strengthen it.

For a given carbonium ion the order of degree of ionization appears to be hydroxide, alkoxides, and carboxylates < cyanide < thiocyanate < ferrocyanide < azide < chloride < bromide < sulfate and perchlorate.

Acylium Ions

In some systems the acylium ion is formed reverisbly and to a detectable extent while in others, to be discussed in the next chapter, it is a hypothetical intermediate. The first evidence for a stable acylium ion was the fourfold depression of the freezing point of sulfuric acid by mesitoic acid.[176] The presence of the acylium ion in the sulfuric acid solutions of carboxylic acids with fourfold depressed freezing points is confirmed chemically by the high yield of ester obtained on pouring the

[199] H. A. Smith and R. J. Smith, *J. Am. Chem. Soc.*, **70**, 2400 (1948).

solution into an alcohol, a reaction that does not go with hindered acids under other circumstances.[177] Both mesitoic and 2,4,6-triisopropyl-benzoic acids can be esterified in this way. Benzoic acid, with an i-factor of only 2, also gives the ester but only if special care and speed is used to avoid hydrolyzing it. [199] Similarly, methyl mesitoate, but not methyl benzoate, is hydrolyzed completely when the sulfuric acid solution of the ester is poured into water.[176]

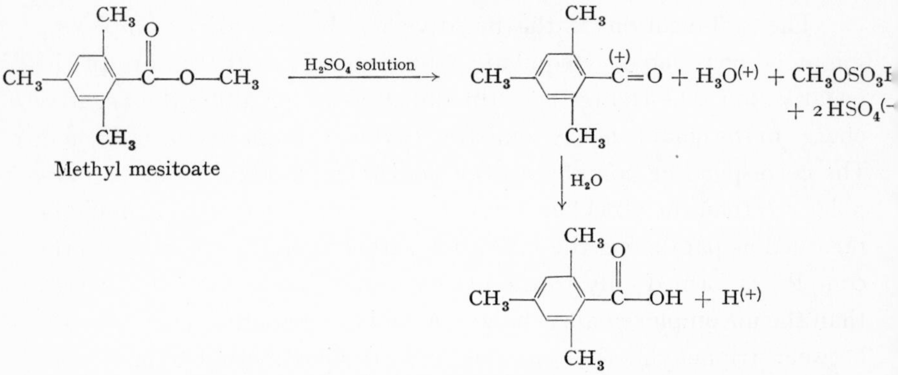

Methyl mesitoate

A combination of steric and electrostatic factors is presumably decisive with regard to the form of the acid most stable in sulfuric acid solution. The simple protonated form XX of benzoic acid is stabilized by resonance structures sterically prohibited in mesitoic acids. The ortho methyl groups of mesitoic acid would interfere with a coplanar dihydroxymethylene group. On the other hand, the inductive and resonance effects of the methyl groups help stabilize the acylium ion form of mesitoic acid as in the formulae XXI. In the case of 2,4,6-tribromobenzoic acid the steric effect and its abetting electronic effects are not sufficient, and this acid behaves like benzoic acid.[176,177]

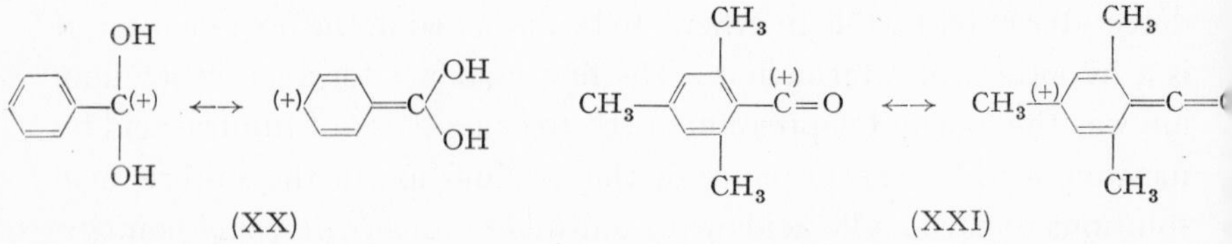

(XX)   (XXI)

The formation of the acylium ion from esters is favored by electron-withdrawing groups in the alcohol and electron-releasing groups in the acid.[200] Anisic acid has an i-factor of 3.38 but gives mostly anisic acid and only 15% methyl anisate when the sulfuric acid solution is poured into methanol.[200] It has been suggested that the intermediate i-factor is due to the formation of some acylium ions (i equals 4) but mostly acyl sulfate (i equals 3):

$$CH_3O\!-\!\!\langle\rangle\!\!-\!\overset{\overset{O}{\|}}{C}\!-\!OH \xrightarrow{H_2SO_4} CH_3O\!-\!\!\langle\rangle\!\!-\!\overset{\overset{O}{\|}}{C}\!-\!OSO_3H + H_3O^{(+)} + HSO_4^{(-)}$$

$$\updownarrow$$

$$CH_3O\!-\!\!\langle\rangle\!\!-\!\overset{(+)}{C}\!=\!O + HSO_4^{(-)}$$

The freezing point lowering of sulfuric acid by acetic anhydride and by benzoic anhydride also corresponds to i-factors of four.[201] Two explanations are possible in this case, but conductivity measurements favor the second one:[202]

$$(R\!-\!\overset{\overset{O}{\|}}{C})_2O \xrightarrow{H_2SO_4} R\!-\!\overset{(+)}{C}\!=\!O + R\!-\!\overset{\overset{O}{\|}}{C}\!-\!\overset{(+)}{O}H_2 + 2HSO_4^{(-)}$$

$$(R\!-\!\overset{\overset{O}{\|}}{C})_2O \xrightarrow{H_2SO_4} 2R\!-\!\overset{\overset{O}{\|}}{C}\!-\!O\!-\!SO_3H + H_3O^{(+)} + HSO_4^{(-)}$$

The behavior of acetic anhydride as a solvent system indicates an ionization:[201, 203]

$$CH_3\!-\!\overset{\overset{O}{\|}}{C}\!-\!O\!-\!\overset{\overset{O}{\|}}{C}\!-\!CH_3 \rightleftharpoons CH_3\!-\!\overset{\overset{O}{\|}}{C}^{(+)} + \overset{(-)}{O}\!-\!\overset{\overset{O}{\|}}{C}\!-\!CH_3$$

The evidence for this self-ionization is the conductivity of the anhydride which, though low, exceeds that of acetic acid.[204, 203] The ionization of acetic anhydride into acetylium and acetate ions is analogous to the ionization of water molecules into protons and

[200] L. P. Kuhn and A. H. Corwin, *J. Am. Chem. Soc.*, **70**, 3370 (1948).
[201] R. J. Gillespie, *J. Chem. Soc.*, **1950**, 2997.
[202] R. J. Gillespie and J. A. Leisten, *Quart. Revs. London*, **8**, 40 (1954).
[203] H. A. E. MacKenzie and E. R. S. Winter, *Trans. Faraday Soc.*, **44**, 159 (1948).
[204] N. F. Hall and H. H. Voge, *J. Am. Chem. Soc.*, **55**, 239 (1933).

hydroxide ions. Like the proton in water, the acetylium ion in acetic anhydride may be covalently solvated. A difference between the water and acetic anhydride solvent systems will be the greater importance of ion pairs in the latter. The chemical properties of acetic anhydride are consistent with the postulated ionization but of course do not suffice to prove it. Just as intact water molecules undoubtedly give many of the reactions of protons and hydroxide ions, the reactions of acetic anhydride will not be drastically different from those of the corresponding ions.

The acetylium ion is the strongest acid species in the acetic anhydride system, and acetyl fluoborate, which is a good conductor in liquid sulfur dioxide, is a strong acid in acetic anhydride. Acetyl fluoborate, chloride, thiocyanate, and benzene sulfonate may all be titrated as acids in acetic anhydride using sodium acetate, a strong base in that system.[203] The neutralization reaction is:

$$CH_3-\overset{\overset{O}{\|}}{C}{}^{(+)} + CH_3-\overset{\overset{O}{\|}}{C}-O^{(-)} \longrightarrow CH_3-\overset{\overset{O}{\|}}{C}-O-\overset{\overset{O}{\|}}{C}-CH_3$$

Acetyl perchlorate should be a strong acid in acetic anhydride, but it decomposes too rapidly for accurate measurement.[203]

Cycloheptatrienylium Ion

Quantum mechanical considerations predict that a π-electron system containing six electrons should be particularly stable.[205] Examples of conspicuously stable six electron systems are benzene and the cyclopentadienyl anion. The cycloheptatrienylium cation is also stable, presumably for the same reason.[206, 207]

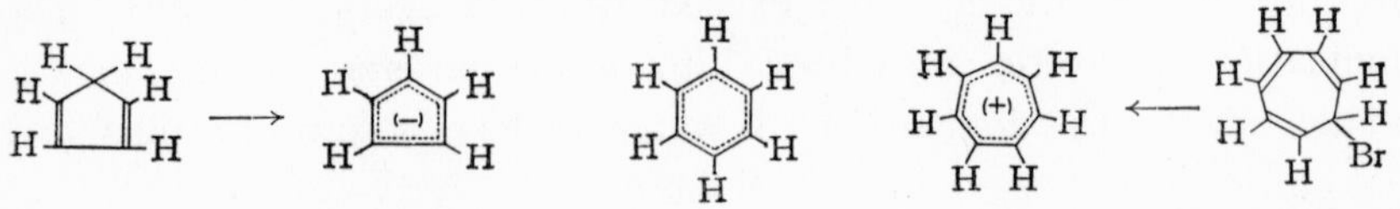

[205] E. Hückel, Z. Physik., 70, 204 (1931); G. W. Wheland, J. Chem. Phys., 2, 474 (1934); J. L. Franklin and F. H. Field, J. Am. Chem. Soc., 75, 2819 (1953).
[206] W. von E. Doering and L. H. Knox, J. Am. Chem. Soc., 76, 3203 (1954).
[207] H. Dauben, Abstracts 126th Meeting Am. Chem. Soc., Sept. 1954, p. 18-0.

Cycloheptatrienylium bromide, instead of having the properties of a typical covalent organic halide, melts at 203°, is strongly deliquescent, miscible with water, and insoluble in the less polar organic solvents. The infrared spectrum is a simple one consistent with the high degree of symmetry postulated for the ion.

CHAPTER VI

Carbonium Ions by Dissociation Under Irreversible Conditions

Just as some molecules imitate free radicals, other molecules act like carbonium ions. Thus the formation of an alcohol from an alkyl halide and hydroxide ion might be the result either of a direct reaction with the alkyl halide or of an indirect reaction with a previously formed carbonium ion. The latter possibility still remains open even when the equilibrium is too unfavorable or the subsequent reaction of the carbonium ion too rapid for its existence to be demonstrated physically. The hypothetical carbonium ion becomes more plausible if it can be shown that the structural and environmental conditions are in some degree analogous to those known to produce stable carbonium ions. Furthermore, if a series of reactions is being examined, use can be made of the expection that a reaction producing a carbonium ion should be accelerated by the kinds of solvent or structural changes that increase the stability of a carbonium ion. The reason for this expectation is that the transition state of a reaction that produces a carbonium ion should itself resemble a carbonium ion to some degree and respond similarly to structural and environmental changes. Unfortunately, it can be shown that this sort of response is sometimes also found for reactions in which the kinetic order indicates a direct attack on a molecule rather than a preliminary formation of a free carbonium ion as the rate determining step.[208] Presumably the transition states of such reactions can also resemble carbonium ions, for example, by virtue of the resonance structure XXII.[194]

$$R-X \longrightarrow [R^{(+)} \cdots X^{(-)} \longleftrightarrow RX] \longrightarrow R^{(+)} + X^{(-)}$$
Transition state

[208] R. M. Adams and C. A. VanderWerf, *J. Am. Chem. Soc.*, **72**, 4368 (1950).

$$Y^{(-)} + RX \longrightarrow [Y^{(-)} \cdots R-X \longleftrightarrow Y^{(-)} \cdots R^{(+)} \cdots X^{(-)} \longleftrightarrow Y-R \cdots X^{(-)}] \longrightarrow Y-R + X^{(-)}$$
(XXII)
Transition state

An explanation not easily distinguishable from the one involving resonance with a carbonium ion structure in the transition state is that the reactive species is an ion pair in equilibrium with the covalent molecule. This is quite likely in a solvent insufficiently polar to cause dissociation of the ion pairs. Examples of second order nucleophilic displacements accelerated by the sort of structural change that would stabilize a carbonium ion are of fairly frequent occurrence. Allyl chloride reacts with potassium iodide in acetone at 50° seventy-nine times as fast as does n-butyl chloride.[209] Another example is the reaction of 3,4-epoxy-1-butene with methoxide ion.[210]

$$CH_2\!\!-\!\!CH\!\!-\!\!CH = CH_2 + CH_3O^{(-)} \longrightarrow \begin{cases} CH_2\!\!-\!\!\overset{\displaystyle OH}{\underset{\displaystyle OCH_3}{CH}}\!\!-\!\!CH = CH_2 \\[2mm] CH_2\!\!-\!\!\overset{\displaystyle OCH_3}{\underset{\displaystyle OH}{CH}}\!\!-\!\!CH = CH_2 \end{cases}$$

The formation of the product by attack at the secondary carbon atom was not due to a concurrent S_n1 reaction since the isomer ratio was not affected by changes in methoxide ion concentration. Saturated epoxides differ from this example in that bimolecular attack always takes place at the less substituted carbon atom.

In order to overcome these difficulties a number of other kinds of supporting evidence for carbonium ion intermediates have been used. Even so, the status of many nucleophilic displacement reactions remains in doubt, and this type of reaction has probably been the subject of more mechanistic man hours of work than any other.[211,212]

[209] J. B. Conant, W. R. Kirner, and R. E. Hussey, *J. Am. Chem. Soc.*, **47**, 488 (1925).

[210] P. D. Bartlett and S. D. Ross, *J. Am. Chem. Soc.*, **70**, 926 (1948).

[211] S. Winstein, E. Grunwald, and H. W. Jones, *J. Am. Chem. Soc.*, **73**, 2700 (1951).

[212] C. K. Ingold, *Structure and Mechanism in Organic Chemistry*, Cornell University Press, Ithaca, New York, 1953.

The unresolved borderline cases have the solvent as one of the reagents and the order of the reaction with respect to the solvent is indeterminate. Their behavior resembles that of typical first order displacements in some ways and typical second order displacements in others.

Two explanations for the borderline solvolysis reactions may be considered:

(a) They are examples of concurrent unimolecular ionizations and bimolecular displacements by solvent molecules.

(b) They are examples of a reaction in which the solvent neither merely solvates the developing carbonium ion nor directly forms a covalent bond with it but instead interacts in a manner best described by a resonance hybrid transition state or intermediate, an unstable intermediate being hard to distinguish from a transition state.

$$\underset{H}{\overset{R}{\diagdown}}O + R'-X \longrightarrow \left[\underset{H}{\overset{R}{\diagdown}}\overset{(+)}{O}-R'\cdots X^{(-)} \longleftrightarrow \underset{H}{\overset{R}{\diagdown}}O\cdots R'^{(+)}\cdots X^{(-)} \right] \longrightarrow \underset{H}{\overset{R}{\diagdown}}\overset{(+)}{O}-R' + X^{(-)}$$

A transition state, perhaps an intermediate

There appears to be a consensus that all ionization reactions in solution involve solvation of both of the ions formed and of both parts of the transition state, and that there is no clear-cut division between electrostatic solvation of the incipient carbonium ion and the formation of a covalent bond between it and a solvent molecule.[211-213] That is, it is generally agreed that cases of type (b) should exist, although the assignment of this mechanism rather than mechanism (a) to any given reaction might be disputed. Most of the remaining differences of opinion concern matters of nomenclature or the degree of novelty to be attributed to some of these ideas.

The Rate-Product Criterion for Carbonium Ion Intermediates

As befits their status as compounds well-known to be in equilibrium with carbonium ions in suitable solvents, triphenylmethyl halides and related compounds give particularly unambiguous evidence of reaction involving ionic intermediates. In polar solvents they give

[213] C. G. Swain, *J. Am. Chem. Soc.*, **70**, 1119 (1948).

displacement reactions in which the rate is proportional solely to the concentration of the trityl halide and independent of the concentration, or even the nature, of the entering substituent.[214] These results clearly show that the initial slow and rate determining reaction is one not involving the entering substituent. In view of the known tendency of trityl halides to ionize, it must be the ionization.

$$\phi_3C{-}F \xrightarrow[\substack{50\% \text{ aqu. acetone at } 25°}]{k\,=\,7.6\,\times\,10^{-4}\,\text{sec.}^{-1}} \phi_3C^{(+)} \text{ solvated}) + F^{(-)} \text{ (solvated)}$$

$$\downarrow \substack{\text{solvent or} \\ \text{added reagent}} \; Y$$

$$\phi_3C{-}Y$$

The rate of the reaction is the same in the solvent alone as it is in the presence of sodium fluoride (up to $3 \times 10^{-3}\ M$), sodium hydroxide (up to $5 \times 10^{-3}\ M$), or sodium azide (up to $3 \times 10^{-3}\ M$). Yet sodium azide diverts the product from carbinol to a 90% yield of trityl azide even when sodium azide is present in as low a concentration as $1.3 \times 10^{-3}\ M$.

The addition of chloride ion to the medium in the case of the trityl chloride reaction reduces the net rate by virtue of the back reaction to regenerate trityl chloride. The product composition in the presence of various added reagents is a quantitative measure of the relative reactivity of the added reagents towards the carbonium ion. The results are summarized in Table VI.

TABLE VI

Relative Reactivities of Various Reagents toward Carbonium Ions[214]

Nucleophile	Cation			
	Trityl	p,p'-Dimethyl-benzhydryl	Benzhydryl	tertiary Butyl
Water	1	1	1	1
Acetate	1.1×10^3	–	–	–
Chloride	3.1×10^3	6.0×10^2	1.2×10^2	1.8×10^2
Bromide	–	–	3.3×10^2	–
Aniline	3.7×10^3	–	–	–
Azide	2.8×10^5	2.4×10^2	1.7×10^2	3.9
Hydroxide	5.3×10^4	–	7.7×10^3	–
Thiocyanate	1.3×10^4	–	–	–
Thiosulfate	1.9×10^4	–	–	3.4×10^2

[214] C. G. Swain, C. B. Scott, and K. H. Lohmann, *J. Am. Chem. Soc.*, **75**, 136 (1953).

Although some of the figures of Table VI are for different aqueous solvent mixtures or different temperatures and might well be somewhat different in a single standard solvent at a single temperature, it is clear that the rate of reaction of trityl cation with nucleophilic reagents is distinctly more sensitive to the nature of the nucleophilic reagent than are the rates for the other cations. The other cations are considerably less stabilized by resonance than is trityl cation, while the corresponding transition states for the combination with the anion are of more nearly the same free energy. Trityl ion will therefore react more slowly and more selectively. Although transition states for the ionization and its reverse reaction are somewhat like the carbonium ions, they are covalent enough to be less stabilized by resonance than the ions. They should also be less subject to steric inhibition of resonance. When the carbonium ion series is extended to still less stable carbonium ions the selectivity should vanish entirely. The successful reagent is then the first comer, but the kinetics are likely to become second order, the product determining and ionization reactions merging into a single bimolecular displacement.

Geometric Criteria for Carbonium Ion
Intermediates

The production of a tricovalent ion or radical with attendant re-hybridization or resonance stabilization may have certain geometric consequences that are diagnostic. The nature of the solvent or structural dependence of the rate will usually allow a choice between the alternative carbonium ion, carbanion, or radical intermediates. The disappearance of optical activity when the asymmetric atom bears the group to be displaced is one geometrical test for an intermediate of this type. A related test is the formation of a mixture of geometric isomers or an unexpected isomer rather than the single one predicted by the concerted mechanism. Still another is the inhibition of the reaction by structural features that interfere with the attainment of the optimum geometry required for the stabilization of the intermediate. Another test is the actual facilitation of the reaction by structural features, such as shielding of the back side, that would interfere with the bi-molecular process.

The ionization of an asymmetric alkyl halide, for example, leads to racemization, whereas the corresponding concerted or S_n2 process leads to inversion. Racemization is usually not complete, however, and this may be understood when the various parts of the ionization process are considered. First is the formation of a solvated ion pair such as XXIII. Even though the ion itself may have attained a planar and hence symmetrical configuration, the intimate ion pair as a whole is still asymmetric and less subject to attack on the side guarded by the anion. Inversion results if the bond to solvent becomes covalent at this stage. On the other hand, when the anion has departed to a more remote position, the carbonium ion becomes symmetrically solvated (XXIV). If it reacts at this stage the result is racemization. Since some of the carbonium ions react while still intimate ion pairs, the result is extensive but not complete racemization. The less stable the carbonium ion, the more likely it is to react before the stage of symmetrical solvation has been reached. The hydrolysis of secondary octyl bromide in aqueous ethanolic potassium hydroxide has a rate expression indicative of about 88% bimolecular reaction with hydroxide ions and about 12% spontaneous ionization: the steric result is 93% inversion of configuration.[215] On the other hand, without potassium hydroxide the reaction is solely a displacement by solvent molecules. Since the result is 66% inversion, it would seem that 66% of the intermediates or transition states, if not already covalently bonded, collapse to covalent, inverted product before becoming symmetrically solvated.

Inverted product   Racemized product

With α-phenylethyl chloride the tendency towards ionization is greater, and it is only in certain solvents that a second order, con-

[215] E. D. Hughes, C. K. Ingold, and S. Masterman, *J. Chem. Soc.*, **1937**, 1196.

certed reaction can be obtained.[216] In water the reaction is first order with or without added alkali and the extent of inversion is about 17% in both cases. This less reactive carbonium ion is usually able to persist long enough to become symmetrically solvated. A still lower proportion of inversion is observed if the water is diluted with acetone: evidently the decrease in the water concentration is more important than the probable decrease in the rate of ion pair dissociation. In the poorer ionizing solvent ethanol, the reaction with sodium ethoxide is largely second order and proceeds with inversion, but in ethanol alone the amount of inversion is low.

Effect of Structural Changes on Rate of Ionization

As a result of the inductive and hyperconjugative effects it is to be expected that tertiary carbonium ions will be more stable than secondary carbonium ions, which in turn will be more stable than primary ions. The stabilization of the corresponding transition states for ionization should be in the same order, since the transition state will somewhat resemble the ion. Thus the first order rate constant for the solvolysis of *tert*-butyl bromide in alkaline 80% aqueous ethanol at 55° is about 4000 times that of isopropyl bromide, while for ethyl and methyl bromides the first order contribution to the hydrolysis rate is imperceptible against the contribution from the bimolecular hydrolysis.[217] Formic acid is such a good ionizing solvent that even primary alkyl bromides hydrolyze at a rate nearly independent of water concentration. The relative rates at 100° are tertiary butyl, 10^8; isopropyl, 44.7; ethyl, 1.71; and methyl, 1.00.[218, 212] One α-phenyl substituent is about as effective in accelerating the ionization as two α-alkyl groups.[212] Thus the reactions of benzyl compounds, like those of secondary alkyl compounds, are of borderline mechanism, while benzhydryl compounds react by the unimolecular ionization mechanism.

[216] E. D. Hughes, C. K. Ingold, and A. D. Scott, *J. Chem. Soc.*, **1937**, 1201.
[217] L. C. Bateman, K. A. Cooper, E. D. Hughes, and C. K. Ingold, *J. Chem. Soc.*, **1940**, 925.
[218] L. C. Bateman and E. D. Hughes, *J. Chem. Soc.*, **1940**, 945.

It will eventually be desirable to replace discussion of the effect of structural changes on rates with a discussion of the effects on activation energy and entropy. It has usually been assumed, tacitly, that a higher rate is due to a lower activation energy. This is not always the case. In most reactions a structural change affects both the energy and entropy of activation and the effect on the relative rate may actually change from an increase to a decrease if the rates are compared at a different temperature. A qualitative change in the effect of a substituent is unlikely, however, when the substituent exerts a large effect. For example, the 4000-fold ratio between the solvolysis rates of *tert*-butyl bromide and isopropyl bromide in 80% ethanol at 55° is not likely to become less than unity at any temperature. On the other hand the small differences between isopropyl, ethyl, and methyl bromides in formic acid should perhaps be interpreted with the aid of activation energy data. Such data are available in the case of the hydrolysis of *p*-alkylbenzhydryl chlorides in 80% acetone and the rates at 0° are, in fact, in the reverse order of the activation energies.[219] The order of decreasing rate is methyl, ethyl, isopropyl, tertiarybutyl, hydrogen, which suggests that hyperconjugation between the ring and adjacent hydrogen atoms of the alkyl group stabilizes the carbonium ion-like transition state by lowering the potential energy. As an indication of the caution advisable in arriving at an interpretation of phenomena of this sort, it should be recalled that for the ionization *equilibrium* of triphenylmethyl chloride in sulfur dioxide, methyl and tertiary butyl were almost equal in their effect. It should also be recalled that under those conditions tertiarybutyl actually raised the enthalpy of ionization but nevertheless increased the extent of ionization by virtue of a more than counteracting entropy increase.

An example of solvolysis rates in which both the activation energy and entropy changes are important is the series:[220]

$$(CH_3)_3CBr \qquad (CH_3)_2\overset{\displaystyle COO^{(-)}}{\underset{}{C}}\text{—Br} \qquad CH_3\overset{\displaystyle COO^{(-)}}{\underset{\displaystyle COO^{(-)}}{\text{—}C\text{—Br}}}$$

[219] E. D. Hughes, C. K. Ingold, and N. A. Taher, *J. Chem. Soc.*, **1940**, 949.
[220] J. Gripenberg, E. D. Hughes, and C. K. Ingold, *Nature*, **161**, 480 (1948).

The source of some of the difficulties encountered in trying to explain the effects of structural changes on ionization rates may be due to the different parts played by the solvent, as for example, the sulfur dioxide of the trityl chloride equilibrium experiments and the aqueous acetone of the benzhydryl chloride rate data. The solvent is bound to modify the effect of a substituent, and although the solvent is usually ignored in discussing substituent effects this is because of a scarcity of usable data and not because the importance of the solvent is not realized: ". . . solvation energy and entropy are the most characteristic determinants of reactions in solution, and . . . for this class of reactions no norm exists which does not take primary account of solvation."[220] Precisely how best to take account of solvation is an unanswered problem that is the subject of much current research.

In the absence of an overriding steric effect, hydrogen on the beta carbon atom of a carbonium ion increase the rate of ionization. The fact that deuterium has a lesser effect than hydrogen probably means that the beta hydrogen or deuterium is less tightly bound in the transition state than in the ground state. Possible explanations are hyperconjugation and the formation of a non-classical ion in which the hydrogen atom bridges the alpha and beta carbon atoms. The amount of the isotope effect depends on the solvent. For example, in the solvolysis of 2-pentyl bromide the hydrogen compound is always faster than the deuterium compound but less so as the solvent becomes more nucleophilic, the effect decreasing in the order formic acid, acetic acid, 80% ethanol.[221] Apparently the more nucleophilic solvents take some of the burden of stabilizing the positive charge and decrease the importance of the substituent, in this case the β-hydrogen atoms. The same is true of the departing group: the more nucleophilic it is, the less positive charge is generated in the transition state for stabilization by substituents, and the less the isotope effect. In the case of the solvolysis of 2,3-dimethyl-2-chlorobutane in 80% ethanol, replacement of the hydrogen on carbon number three by deuterium slows down the solvolysis by virtue of an increase in activation energy. The increase in activation energy is partly counteracted, however, by a simultaneous

[221] E. S. Lewis and C. E. Boozer, *J. Am. Chem. Soc.*, **76**, 791 (1954).

increase in entropy of activation.[222] A similar effect is noted in the case of α-(p-tolyl)ethyl chloride, but when the isotopic substitution is carried out in the para methyl group instead of in the directly attached methyl group the change in rate is almost entirely due to a change in activation energy.[223]

Geometric Influences on Rate of Ionization

In the process of forming a carbonium ion from an alkyl halide or sulfonate the stretching of the bond between carbon and departing group is accompanied by a change in the geometry of the other bonds. Starting with the tetrahedral geometry characteristic of the ground state, the molecule goes through a transition state of some intermediate geometry to an ion pair in which the carbonium ion tends to be planar. The energy of all three states will depend on the extent to which steric factors allow an approximation to the optimum geometry for each particular state. Thus a crowded condition of the substituent groups, B (for back) strain, that may be a factor in the ground state is relieved in the ion and partially relieved in the transition state. On the other hand, anything that interferes with coplanarity raises the energy of the ion and, to a lesser degree, the transition state. An example of interference with coplanarity previously discussed is the failure of triptycyl bromide to ionize even under drastic conditions. The bridgehead alkyl bromides derived from bicyclo[2·2·2]octane and bicyclo[2·2·1]heptane exhibit a similar but lesser reluctance to ionize. The appearance potential of the ion from the bicyclooctane compound is somewhat less than that of the bicycloheptane compound, indicating that an easier or closer approach to coplanarity is possible in the case of the former ion.[224] Similarly, hydrolysis is much faster for the bicyclooctyl than for the bicycloheptyl bromide.[225]

Although the loss of beta hydrogens should decrease the stability of a carbonium ion or its related transition states, if enough of the beta

[222] V. J. Shiner, Jr., *J. Am. Chem. Soc.*, **76**, 1603 (1954).
[223] E. S. Lewis and G. M. Coppinger, *J. Am. Chem. Soc.*, **76**, 4495 (1954).
[224] J. L. Franklin and F. H. Field, *J. Chem. Phys.*, **21**, 550 (1953).
[225] W. von E. Doering, M. Levitz, A. Sayigh, M. Sprecher, and W. P. Whelan, Jr., *J. Am. Chem. Soc.*, **75**, 1008 (1953).

hydrogens are replaced by bulky groups the ionization is facilitated. In the series of alkyl chlorides of structure XXV there are small and irregular effects on the rate of ionization in 80% ethanol at 25° as R is progressively changed from methyl to ethyl to isopropyl, but a fairly large (20-fold) *increase* in rate when R is changed to tertiarybutyl.[226] Even greater rate increases are observed with still greater increase in the branching. The chlorides, unfortunately, are available only as mixtures prepared by treating the carbinol with hydrogen chloride. One component of the mixture may have the structure corresponding to that of the carbinol while the others have carbon skeletons of rearranged and unknown structure. There is no doubt that the unknown structures are still highly branched, however, and hence no doubt about the reality of a large increase in ionization rate associated with branching, an effect as great as a factor of 40,000.[227] Table VII gives the data for the first order elimination (ionization) reaction in 90% acetone at 25°.

$$CH_3—CH_2$$
$$|$$
$$R—C—Cl$$
$$|$$
$$CH_3—CH_2$$
$$(XXV)$$

One possible explanation for the effect of increased branching is the relief of B strain when the bonds connecting the central carbon atom to the substituent groups spread out on passing to a less tetrahedral and more nearly planar arrangement.[226]

Some doubt is thrown on B strain as the sole explanation of the branching effect by the observation that the tri-*tert*-butylboron-ammonia complex is actually less dissociated than the trimethylboron-ammonia complex.[227] Since the products of the ionization of these highly branched compounds contain large amounts of rearranged material, another effect may be operating. As will be discussed in the next section, many ionization reactions produce *directly* an ion of structure different from that of the covalent parent compound. The transition state presumably resembles the new ion or a non-classical

[226] H. C. Brown and R. S. Fletcher, *J. Am. Chem. Soc.*, **71**, 1845 (1949).
[227] P. D. Bartlett, *Bull. soc. chim. France*, **1951**, C100.

Parent carbinol	Relative rate constants of the chlorides prepared from the carbinol

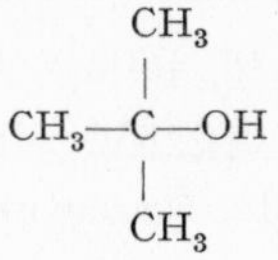

$$CH_3-\overset{\displaystyle CH_3}{\underset{\displaystyle CH_3}{\overset{|}{\underset{|}{C}}}}-OH$$

1

$$CH_3-\overset{H}{\underset{CH_3}{\overset{|}{\underset{|}{C}}}}-\overset{CH_3-CH-CH_3}{\underset{CH_3-\overset{|}{\underset{|}{C}}-CH_3}{\overset{|}{\underset{|}{C}}}}-OH$$
$$\underset{H}{}$$

250
5.5

$$\overset{CH_3}{\underset{CH_3}{\overset{|}{\underset{|}{CH}}}}-\overset{CH_3-\overset{CH_3}{\overset{|}{C}}-CH_3}{\underset{CH_3-CHCH_3}{\overset{|}{\underset{|}{C}}}}-OH$$

1300

$$CH_3-\overset{CH_3}{\underset{CH_3}{\overset{|}{\underset{|}{C}}}}-\overset{CH_3}{\underset{CH_3-\overset{|}{\underset{|}{C}}-CH_3}{\overset{|}{\underset{|}{C}}}}-OH$$
$$\underset{CH_3}{}$$

1600
25

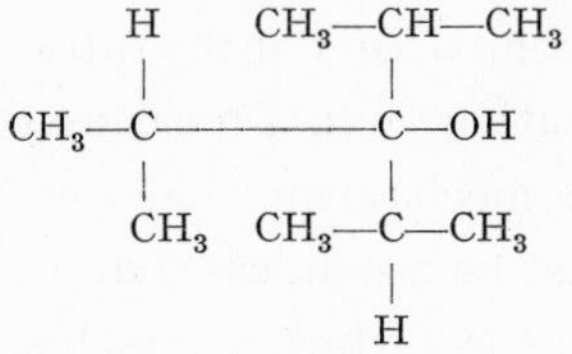

$$CH_3-\overset{CH_3}{\underset{CH_3}{\overset{|}{\underset{|}{C}}}}-\overset{CH_3-\overset{CH_3}{\overset{|}{C}}-CH_3}{\underset{CH_3-\overset{|}{\underset{|}{C}}-CH_3}{\overset{|}{\underset{|}{C}}}}-OH$$
$$\underset{H}{}$$

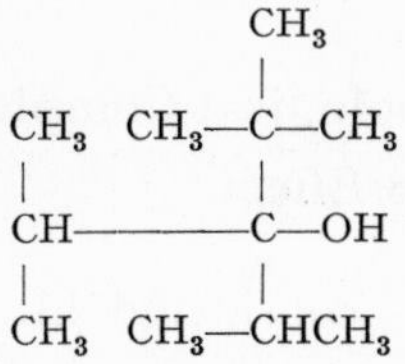

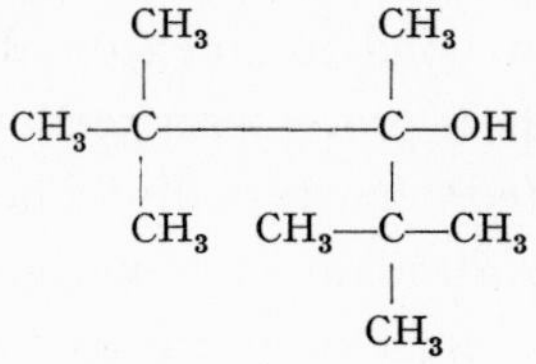

40,000
3,000
210

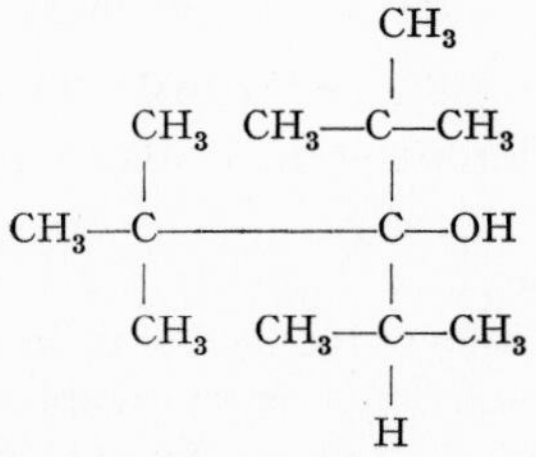

$$CH_3-\overset{CH_3}{\underset{CH_3}{\overset{|}{\underset{|}{C}}}}-\overset{CH_3-\overset{CH_3}{\overset{|}{C}}-CH_3}{\underset{CH_3-\overset{|}{\underset{|}{C}}-CH_3}{\overset{|}{\underset{|}{C}}}}-OH$$
$$\underset{CH_3}{}$$

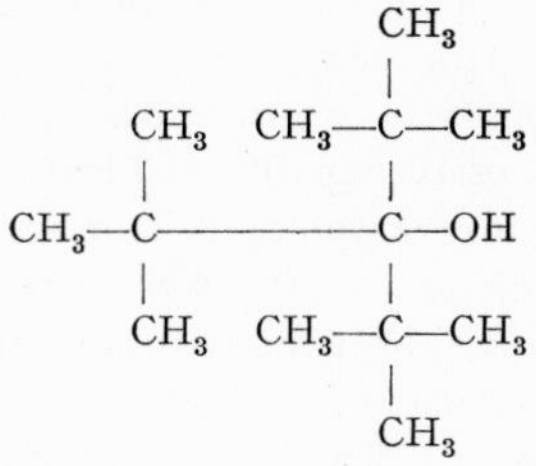

2600
130

structure intermediate between that of the new ion and the parent compound. It has been suggested that backside crowding may facilitate the production of the non-classical or partly rearranged transition state by forcing the migrating group into an optimum position very much like the one it occupies in the transition state for rearrangement.[227] If so, the comparison of the rates for the branched and less branched alkyl halides is a comparison of the rates of reactions of essentially different mechanism rather than a measure of the effect of structural changes on a single mechanism. The rate of simple ionization is then unknown, but must be much less than the measured rate of the reaction with which it unsuccessfully competes.

Ionization Reactions of Greater Topological Complexity: the Neighboring Group Effect

The ionization and related reactions considered hitherto have involved the breaking of only one bond in the organic substrate and sometimes the establishment of a new bond to an external displacing reagent. The central carbon atom in these processes is rendered electrophilic by the departure or the concerted departure of the negative ion. Its electrophilia may be quenched by attacking a new negative ion or solvent molecule, but in general by attacking any electron-rich or potentially electron-rich center. The center attacked may be part of the same molecule, in which case a ring is formed. Subsequent or concerted opening of the ring at a different point leads to a rearranged product.

Readers who do not feel entirely at home in the field of molecular psychology may replace the term "electron rich center" by "center capable of stabilizing a positive charge," thus avoiding the attribution of appetite or purpose to the electrophilic reagent. The point of attack of an electrophilic reagent will not always be at the center of the greatest electron density in any case; sometimes attack at that center produces a transition state or intermediate of higher free energy than attack at a center that is merely capable of furnishing bonding electrons on demand. The important feature of the transition state of lowest free energy is that it places the positive charge on an atom of reasonably low ionization potential or stabilizes the positive charge by additional resonance not offered by competing transition states. But to revert to the anthropomorphic terminology, it is not so much the supply of electrons directly available for satisfying electrophilia that determines the position attacked as it is the comparative electrofelicity of the corresponding transition state or product. The psychological state of electrofelicity, or electron-bliss, corresponds to the state of lowest free energy for the positive charge.

The numerous straightforward examples of internal displacement reactions leading to isolable cyclic products will not be discussed here, but only, for the most part, those ionization reactions in which a cyclic intermediate or transition state is deduced from the rearranged structure of the product. A well-known example is mustard gas and other alkyl chlorides with sulfur on the β-carbon atom. Although mustard gas is a primary and saturated alkyl chloride, its behavior is like that of a typical tertiary alkyl chloride. It reacts so fast by a first order ionization that the rate of the usual second order displacement reaction of primary alkyl halides is not measureable. Only the ultimate product, not the rate, is determined by the added reagent.[228] Since the effect of the sulfur is too large to be explicable in terms of a carbon sulfur dipole or similar explanation, a cyclic sulfonium ion has been proposed as an intermediate.

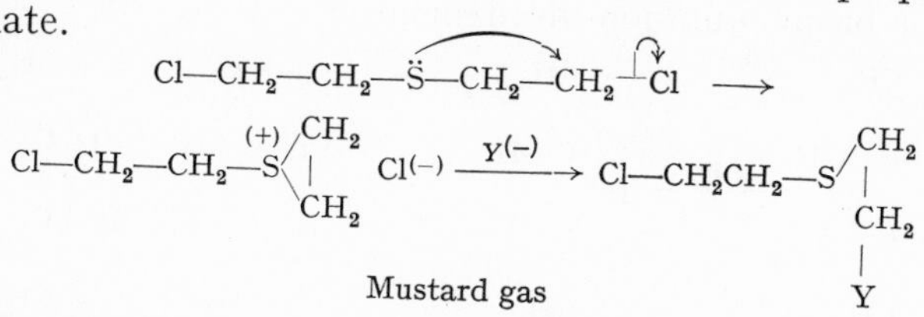

Mustard gas

The sulfur accelerates the ionization by direct participation as an internal displacing reagent. The reagent Y^- may attack the sulfonium ion at either of the ring carbon atoms, causing rearrangement in suitable derivatives:[229]

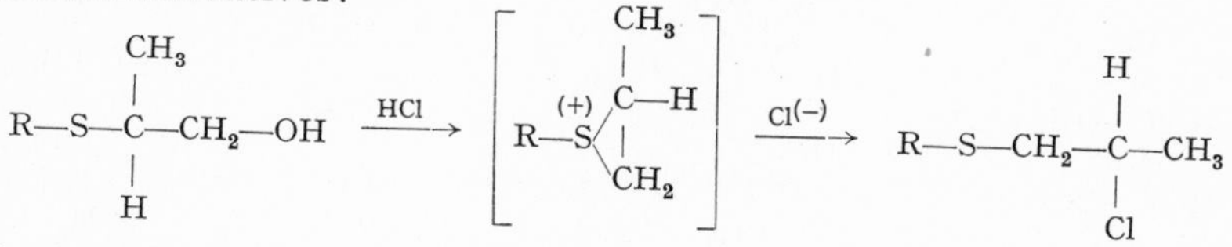

The behavior of β-aminoalkyl chlorides is similar.[230,231]

[228] P. D. Bartlett and C. G. Swain, *J. Am. Chem. Soc.*, **71**, 1406 (1949).
[229] R. C. Fuson, C. C. Price, and D. M. Burness, *J. Org. Chem.*, **11**, 475 (1946).
[230] S. D. Ross, *J. Am. Chem. Soc.*, **69**, 2982 (1947).
[231] P. D. Bartlett, S. D. Ross, and C. G. Swain, *J. Am. Chem. Soc.*, **71**, 1415 (1949).

The first cyclic intermediate of this type to be postulated involved bromine rather than sulfur or nitrogen and represented more of an extrapolation since the corresponding bimolecular reaction is unknown.

$$R_2S + R'-X \longrightarrow R_2R'S^{(+)}X^{(-)} \quad R_3N + R'X \longrightarrow R_3R'N^{(+)}X^{(-)}$$
$$RBr + R'-X \longrightarrow RR'Br^{(+)}X^{(-)}$$

The cyclic bromonium ion was first used to explain the stereochemistry and course of the bromination of olefins and later proposed as an intermediate in the displacement reaction:[232,233]

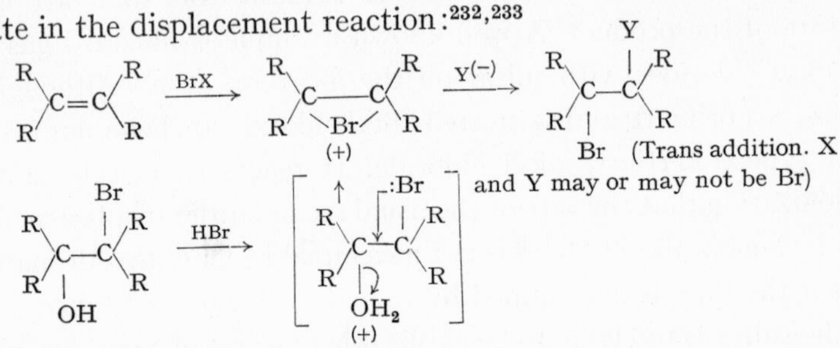

(Trans addition. X and Y may or may not be Br)

There are readily observable stereochemical consequences that serve as a test of the bromonium ion mechanism:

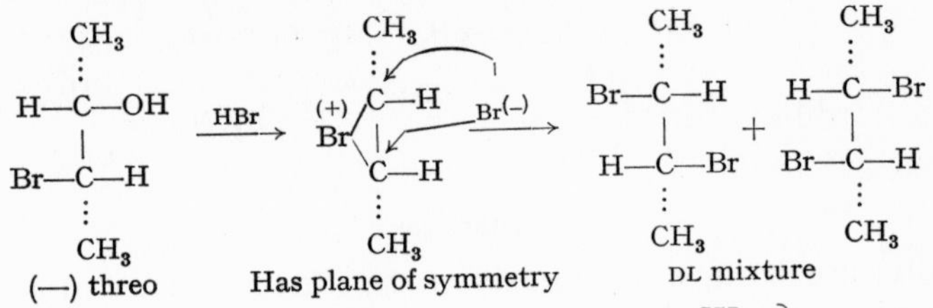

(—) threo   Has plane of symmetry   DL mixture

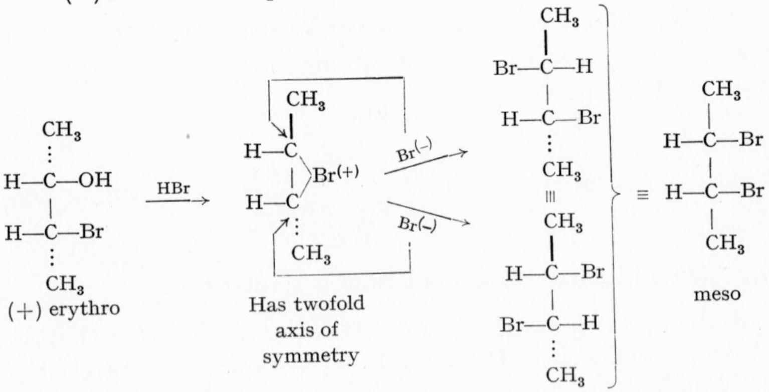

(+) erythro   Has twofold axis of symmetry   meso

[232] I. Roberts and G. E. Kimball, *J. Am. Chem. Soc.*, **59**, 947 (1937).
[233] S. Winstein and H. J. Lucas, *J. Am. Chem. Soc.*, **61**, 1576, 1581, 2845 (1939).

Because the product is reached by way of two Walden inversion reactions the result is retention of configuration, although not always retention of optical activity.

Since the pioneering work on the 3-bromo-2-butanol system similar observations have been made, not only with neighboring ether, ester, and thioether groups, but also with neighboring carbon.

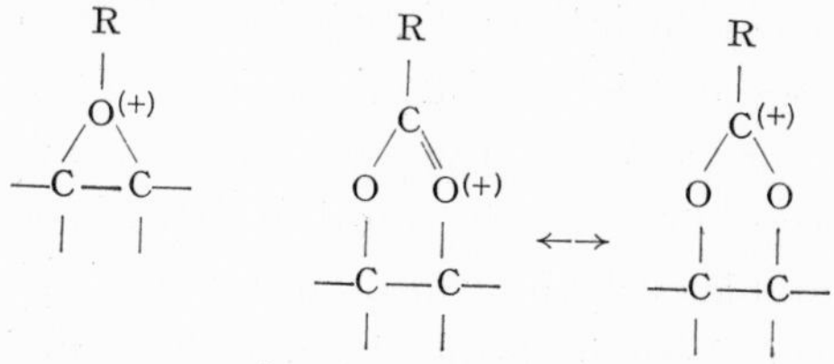

R   R   R
| | |
O(+)   C   C(+)
/\   / \   / \
—C—C—   O   O(+)   O   O
| | | | ←→ | |
                   —C—C—   —C—C—
                    | | | |

The rearrangement that often results from the cyclic intermediate or transition state is not the only sign of participation by a neighboring group. Such reactions can often be recognized by an unexpectedly rapid first order ionization. Thus a phenyl group in the β-position should, if anything, slow down a simple first order ionization reaction by virtue of its electron-withdrawing inductive effect, but instead this structural feature sometimes leads to a faster reaction. The same techniques that proved the participation of neighboring bromine were effective in the case of neighboring phenyl:[234]

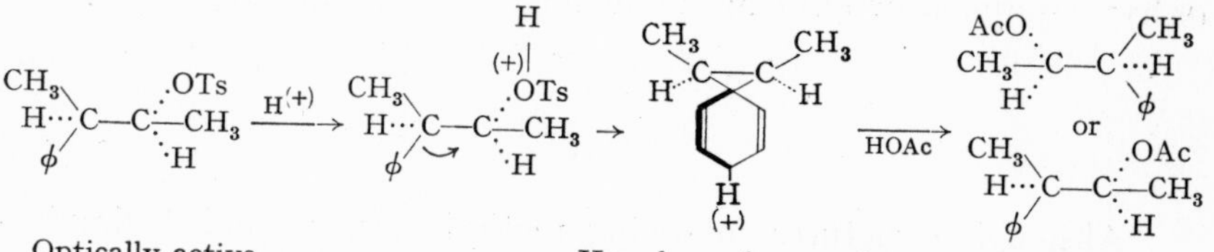

(chemical reaction scheme)

Optically active → Has plane of symmetry → DL pair

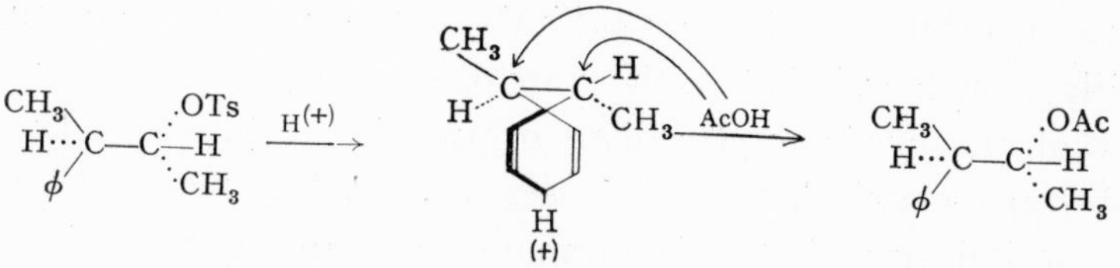

(chemical reaction scheme)

Optically active → No plane of symmetry, but has twofold axis of symmetry → Optically active. Attack at either ring carbon gives this product

[234] D. J. Cram, *J. Am. Chem. Soc.*, **71**, 3863 (1949).

It should be noted that participation by a neighboring group will always lead to a cyclic transition state but not necessarily to a cyclic *intermediate;* in some cases the cyclic transition state decays directly to an open chain product. Carbonium ion rearrangements can be classified into three types: (*a*) those in which an ion is produced and then rearranges; (*b*) those in which a rearranged ion is formed directly; (*c*) those in which a cyclic intermediate is formed directly. Reactions of the latter two types are distinguishable from the first by the acceleration of the ionization caused by the presence of the migrating group.[235] In reactions of type (*b*) a cyclic transition state corresponds to the somewhat more stable cyclic intermediate of type (*c*). There is no great difference between them in principle, and it is difficult to predict whether a given configuration will be an intermediate or metastable, that is, a transition state.

The same clue of abnormally fast ionization has lead to the postulation of transition states, if not intermediates, in which the participating electrons are σ-bonding electrons.[235] It will be recalled that in the case of neighboring bromine the participating electrons were believed to be the non-bonding electrons of the bromine atom, whereas in the case of neighboring phenyl they were believed to be the unsaturation electrons of the benzene ring. An example of the use of σ-bonding or hyperconjugation electrons is the migration of a methyl group:[236]

$$\underset{\substack{ \\ (+)}}{\overset{\substack{\phi. \qquad CH_3 \\ C-C \\ Et \qquad\qquad Et \\ CH_3}}{}}$$

Although structures involving methyl groups bonded simultaneously to two carbon atoms by means of an overlap between the hydrogen orbitals and the *p*-orbitals of the carbon atoms may be readily enough assimilated, the state of structural theory is such that most of the cyclic intermediate or transition state structures are dubbed non-classical. In many cases they are best depicted by molecular orbitals, usually by diagramming the component atomic orbitals in the best position for overlap. Since maximum overlap of the component atomic orbitals imposes certain geometric requirements, pre-

[235] S. Winstein and E. Grunwald, *J. Am. Chem. Soc.*, **70**, 828 (1948).
[236] D. J. Cram and J. D. Knight, *J. Am. Chem. Soc.*, **74**, 5839 (1952).

dictions can be made as to the relative stablity of various non-classical structures. The sterol-*i*-sterol system is an example of geometry favorable to the production of a non-classical ion. Maximum overlap is achieved only with the component *p*-orbitals parallel, and the rigidity of the sterol molecule prevents rotation into unfavorable skewed configurations.

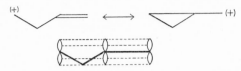

A similar explanation has been offered as an alternative to B strain: crowding at the backside may restrict a neighboring alkyl group to the position most favorable to interaction of its bonding atomic orbitals with the atomic orbital being vacated by the departing group.

The use of carbon-14 is bringing to light many unexpected topological complexities. It is a more subtle label, in spite of the existence of small isotope effects, than a substituent alkyl group. Any considerable substitution may alter the mechanism of a reaction from that of the unsubstituted compound, while carbon-14 is unlikely to do this. An example of newly discovered topological complexity is the ionization of *exo* and *endo*-norbornyl derivatives.

exo
(XXVI)

endo
(XXVII)

(XXVIII)

Ionization of either the exo (**XXVI**) or the endo (**XXVII**) derivative leads to substitution products with the exo configuration. The endo compounds solvolyze slowly, about like cyclohexyl derivatives, while the exo derivatives solvolyze as much as 350 times faster, indicating participation by neighboring carbon. Furthermore, optically active exo starting material gives racemic exo product. All of these results are consistent with the formation of the symmetrical ion **XXVIII**, in which carbon atoms 1 and 2 are indistinguishable.[237,238] But the ion **XXVIII**

[237] J. D. Roberts, C. C. Lee, and W. H. Saunders, Jr., *J. Am. Chem. Soc.*, **76**, 4501 (1954).

[238] S. Winstein and D. Trifan, *J. Am. Chem. Soc.*, **74**, 1147, 1154 (1952).

as the sole intermediate would predict that carbon-14 originally in the 2 and 3 positions would be found equally in the 1 and 7 positions of the product as well, and nowhere else. What is in fact observed is a distribution suggesting that at some stage the carbon bridges 1-7, 2-3, and 6-5 all become equivalent. This can be explained if, in addition to **XXVIII**, there is also formed an intermediate **XXIX** or its equivalent. The results could also be explained by an equilibrium between three ions of the type **XXVIII**, in which the extra hydrogen which differentiates carbon atom number 6 has migrated to carbon 1 or 2. Such a mixture would in effect have the same threefold symmetry as the single ion **XXIX**.

(XXIX)

Some Reactions of Carbonium Ions

On the basis of rearrangement reactions in which one group migrates in preference to another, "migration aptitudes" may be assigned to the various groups. The migration aptitude is a less useful concept than at first might be imagined as it is determined by several variable factors and is not independent of the nature of the departing group. Thus, when the departing group is formed by the action of nitrous acid on a primary amine, the migration aptitudes may be different from those observed in solvolysis reactions or in the pinacol rearrangement.[236,237,239] Both geometric and electronic factors are important in determining the course of the reaction, and both factors will depend to some extent on the nature of the departing group and on the detailed mechanism. Since the rearrangement is essentially an electrophilic displacement by a positively charged or partially positively charged carbon atom attacking the migrating group, the important electronic consideration is the degree to which the migrating group is able to accept and stabilize a positive charge in the intermediate or

[239] P. I. Pollak and D. Y. Curtin, *J. Am. Chem. Soc.*, **72**, 961 (1950).

transition state. Electronically, the reaction is closely analogous to electrophilic substitution:

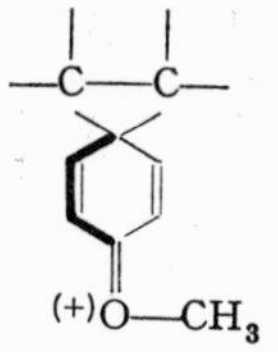

Intermediate in a
rearrangement

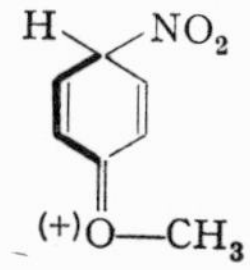

Intermediate in
an electrophilic
substitution

In cases where the pertinent configuration is a transition state rather than an intermediate, the importance of a charge-accepting structural feature will depend on the degree to which a charge is actually developed in the transition state. This means that even on electronic grounds alone it is not certain that migration aptitudes should be independent of the detailed mechanism. The other important factor is the geometry of the various transition states as compared with the ground state. When the rearrangement and departure of the the negative ion are concerted, the geometry must be appropriate to the occurrence of Walden inversion at the site of the departing negative ion or group. Some migrating groups will adapt themselves to this geometry more readily than others. On the other hand, the geometrical requirements will be quite different and probably less severe if the transition state for rearrangement is formed from an intermediate carbonium ion rather than from a molecule with departing group still attached. An example of a geometrically determined reaction is the at first sight anomalous migration of phenyl in preference to p-anisyl in the reaction of the amino alcohol **XXX** with nitrous acid.[239]

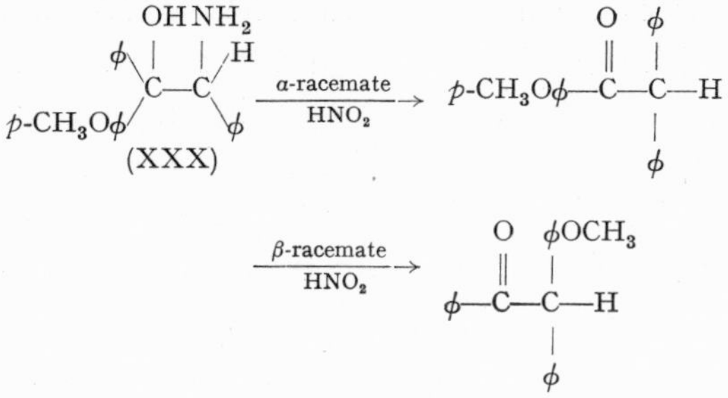

Another example is the migration of phenyl in preference to α-naphthyl in a similar reaction.[240]

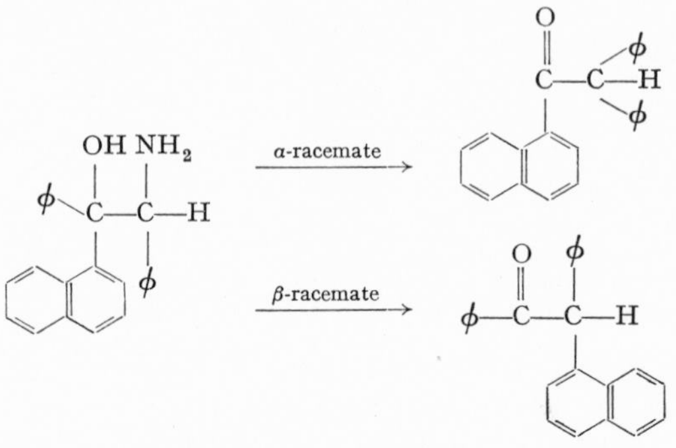

Just as the steric repulsion of adjacent groups of a substituted ethane may result in one of the staggered rotational configurations being more stable than the others, the various possible transition states also have different steric energies and these differences may be greater than the differences in electronic energy. The transition state for rearrangement should be intermediate in geometry between one of the staggered ground state configurations and a molecule with two covalent bonds to the migrating group.

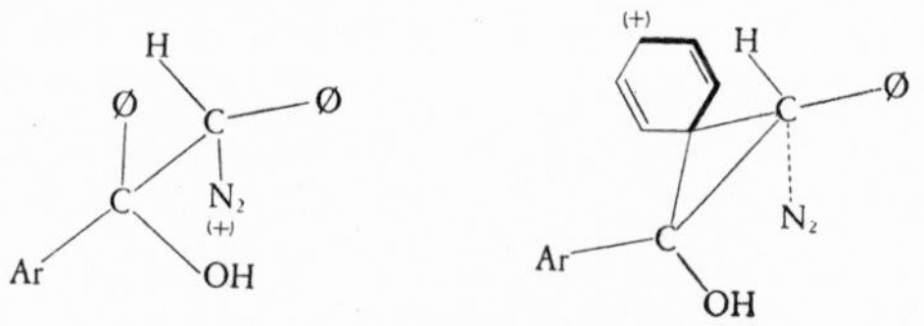

Transition state models
(XXXI)

If phenyl rather than the group Ar migrates in the rearrangement of the amino alcohols, it is presumably because the transition state has a lower steric energy with the migrating phenyl trans to the departing group than an alternative transition state with migrating Ar trans to departing nitrogen. Note that the configuration represented by structures XXXI and XXXII, with the phenyl group migrating, has the bulky aryl group eclipsing the space between the two smaller groups

[240] A. McKenzie and A. C. Richardson, *J. Chem. Soc.*, **123**, 79 (1923); A. McKenzie and W. S. Dennler, *ibid.*, **125**, 2105 (1924).

on the other carbon atom. On the other hand, if the aryl group were to migrate, the phenyl group would be oriented between the relatively bulky phenyl and diazonium groups on the other carbon atom. In the other geometric isomer these steric considerations are reversed, and a different group migrates. The diagrams XXXII-XXXV illustrate the configurations of the competing transition states.

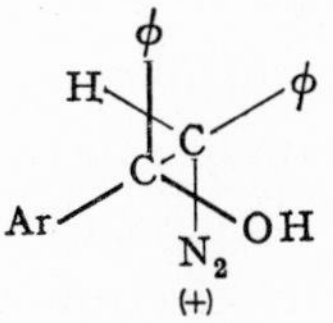

rather than

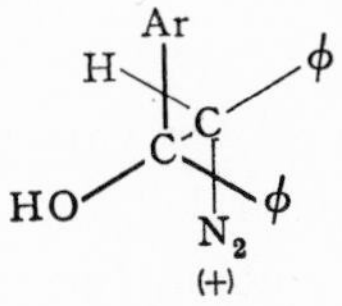

(XXXII)   (XXXIII)

For the other geometric isomer:

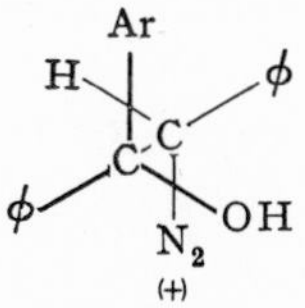

rather than

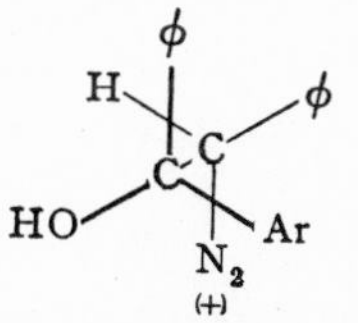

(XXXIV)   (XXXV)

Since it is not always known to what extent the departing group is still present at the rearrangement stage of the reaction, a detailed interpretation of migration aptitudes is difficult. The examples just discussed, however, should certainly not be compared with migration aptitudes within a fully formed carbonium ion.

The benzilic acid rearrangement, though catalyzed by hydroxide ion, probably belongs in the same category as carbonium ion rearrangements. Kinetic and isotopic exchange experiments show that there is a rapid reversible addition of hydroxide ion.[241,242]

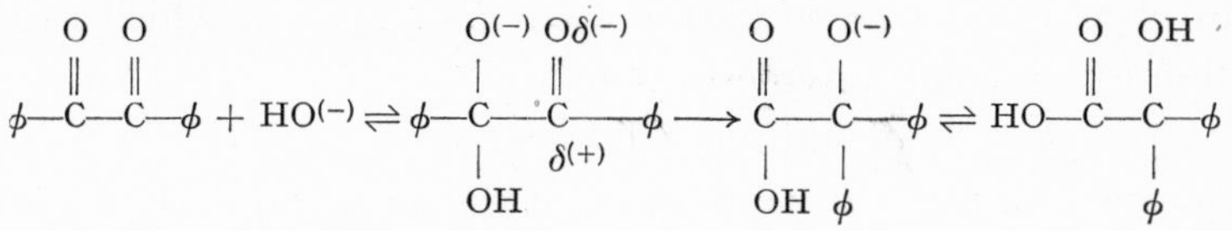

[241] F. H. Westheimer, *J. Am. Chem. Soc.*, **58**, 2209 (1936).
[242] I. Roberts and H. C. Urey, *J. Am. Chem. Soc.*, **60**, 881 (1938).

An irreversible reaction via a cyclic transition state has also been suggested:[242a]

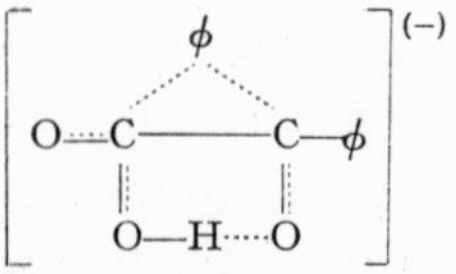

$$
\left[
\begin{array}{c}
\phi \\
O\text{---}C\text{--------}C\text{---}\phi \\
O\text{---}H\text{----}O
\end{array}
\right]^{(-)}
$$

Like the carbonium ion rearrangements, this is a purely internal electrophilic substitution reaction. The electrophilic reagent is the positive end of the carbonyl group and the site of substitution is the migrating phenyl group. The hydroxyl ion changes the substituent already present on the migrating ring from an electron-withdrawing carbonyl group to one more readily deprived of its bonding electrons.

A similar interpretation is possible for the Lobry de Bruyn rearrangement of glucose to fructose:

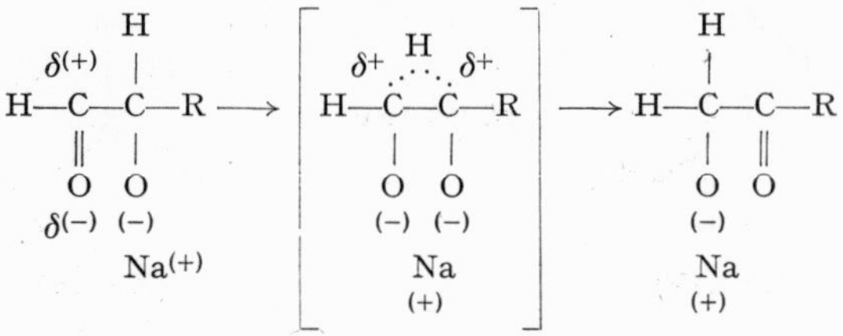

$$
\begin{array}{ccc}
\begin{array}{c}
\text{H} \\
\delta(+) \mid \\
\text{H---C---C---R} \\
\parallel \mid \\
\text{O O} \\
\delta(-)\ (-) \\
\text{Na}^{(+)}
\end{array}
&
\left[
\begin{array}{c}
\text{H} \\
\delta+\ \cdots\ \delta+ \\
\text{H---C---C---R} \\
\parallel \mid \\
\text{O O} \\
(-)\ (-) \\
\text{Na} \\
(+)
\end{array}
\right]
&
\begin{array}{c}
\text{H} \\
\uparrow \\
\text{H---C---C---R} \\
\mid \parallel \\
\text{O O} \\
(-) \\
\text{Na} \\
(+)
\end{array}
\end{array}
$$

Carbonium ions give external addition and displacement reactions as well as the internal rearrangements just discussed. As in the case of the rearrangment reaction, the question of whether the reaction is concerted or due to a genuinely free carbonium ion is one of the more difficult fine points. Addition of a carbonium ion to an unsaturated system leads to an intermediate carbonium ion that may stabilize itself by the loss of some positively charged atom or group other than the original carbonium ion as well as by reaction with a negative ion. Sometimes the ultimate stabilizing event takes place only after several cycles of addition to new unsaturated molecules, in which case the reaction is a cationic polymerization.

Some examples of addition followed by loss of a positive fragment are shown below. The decomposition of the diazonium salt XXXVI is

[242a] M. T. Clark, E. C. Hendley, and O. K. Neville, *J. Am. Chem. Soc.*, 77 3280 (1955).

considered to be a non-concerted process on the basis of the lack of effect of added chloride ion. Under acid conditions, to ensure the ionic mechanism, it gives fluorenone in high yield.[243]

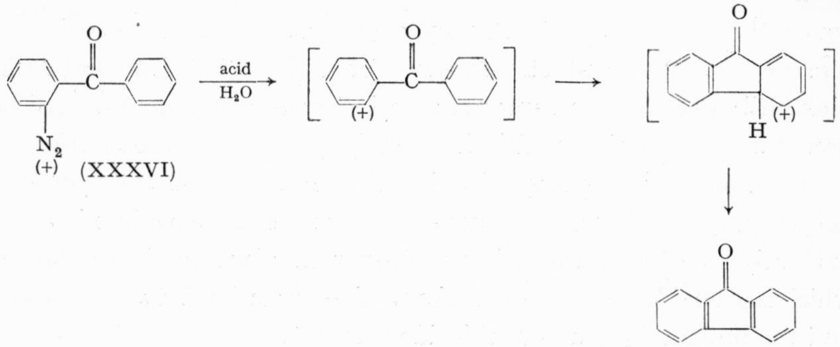

When the alcohol XXXVII is allowed to stand in ethanol in the presence of catalytic amounts of sulfuric acid, benzaldehyde and compound XXXVIII are formed in quantitative yield.[244]

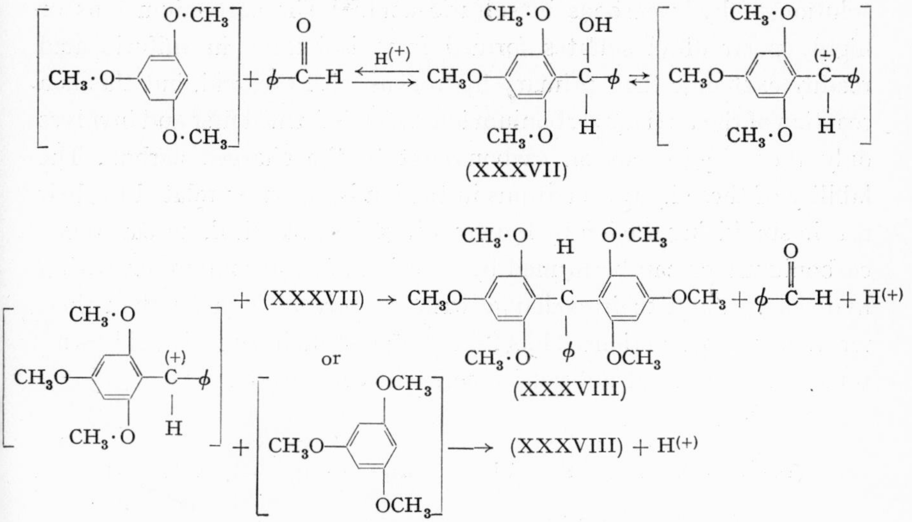

The Friedel-Crafts hydrocarbon synthesis appears to be a similar process in which (usually) a proton is displaced, but the actual reagent is

[243] D. F. De Tar and D. I. Relyea, *J. Am. Chem. Soc.*, **76**, 1680 (1954).
[244] J. Kenyon and R. F. Mason, *J. Chem. Soc*, **1952**, 4964.

as likely to be an alkyl halide-aluminum choloride complex as it is to be
a free carbonium ion.[245] That is, some of these reactions may be
analogous to the concerted type of "carbonium ion" rearrangement.
Aluminum chloride plus hydrogen chloride fails to give any considerable
concentration of ions under many conditions but does do so in the
presence of benzene which removes protons from the abundant complex $HCl \cdot AlCl_3$. Either n-propyl chloride or n-propyl alcohol may be
used for the aluminum chloride catalyzed propyldeprotonation of
benzene, but while n-propyl chloride gives both normal and isopropyl
benzenes, the alcohol gives only n-propyl benzene. Carbonium ions are
evidently free to rearrange in the former case but not in the latter,
which is probably best represented as a direct reaction between benzene
and the propanol aluminum chloride complex.

A reaction of carbonium ions analogous to the internal migration
of a hydrogen atom is the removal of a hydrogen atom, which must be
tertiary, from an external hydrocarbon molecule. This reaction occurs
in reaction mixtures of interest to the petroleum industry, such as a
solution of hydrocarbons in sulfuric acid.[246] The carbonium ions or
highly polar alkyl sulfates formed from isobutane in sulfuric acid
readily exchange their primary hydrogens with the acid, but this is a
reaction of the tertiary carbonium ion which is formed first and involves
only those hydrogens on carbon next to the charged carbon. The
lability of these hydrogen atoms in the ion is probably related to their
role in stabilizing the ion by hyperconjugation. Classical, unrearranged
carbonium ions can be formed by reaction of a carbonium ion with a
hydrocarbon and their exchange with the solvent is faster than their
rearrangement reactions. Thus 2-methylpentane in sulfuric acid forms
some deuterated but not yet isomerized hydrocarbon.

$$CH_3-\underset{\underset{H}{|}}{\overset{\overset{CH_3}{|}}{C}}-CH_2-CH_2-CH_3 + R^{(+)} \longrightarrow CH_3-\underset{(+)}{\overset{\overset{CH_3}{|}}{C}}-CH_2-CH_2-CH_3 + RH$$

(R+ from traces of olefin)

[245] H. C. Brown, L. P. Eddy, and R. Wong, *J. Am. Chem. Soc.*, **75,** 6275 (1953).
[246] P. D. Bartlett, F. E. Condon, and A. Schneider, *J. Am. Chem. Soc.*, **66**
1531 (1944); J. W. Otvos, D. P. Stevenson, C. D. Wagner, and O. Beeck,
ibid., **73,** 5741 (1951); D. P. Stevenson, C. D. Wagner, O. Beeck, and J. W.
Otvos, *ibid.*, **74,** 3269 (1952).

$$
\begin{array}{ccc}
\overset{\displaystyle CH_3}{\underset{(+)}{\overset{|}{CH_3-C-CH_2-CH_2-CH_3}}} & \xrightarrow{\;D_2SO_4\;} & \overset{\displaystyle CD_3}{\underset{(+)}{\overset{|}{CD_3-C-CD_2CH_2CH_3}}}
\end{array}
$$

$$
\overset{\displaystyle CD_3}{\underset{(+)}{\overset{|}{CD_3-C-CD_2-CH_2-CH_3}}} + \overset{\displaystyle CH_3}{\underset{\displaystyle H}{\overset{|}{CH_3-C-CH_2CH_2CH_3}}} \longrightarrow
$$

$$
\longrightarrow \overset{\displaystyle CD_3}{\underset{\displaystyle H}{\overset{|}{CD_3-C-CD_2CH_2CH_3}}} + \overset{\displaystyle CH_3}{\underset{(+)}{\overset{|}{CH_3-C-CH_2CH_2CH_3}}} \quad \text{etc.}
$$

Solvent Effects on Rate of Ionization

A very rough generalization is that solvents of higher dielectric constant give faster ionizations just as they give more extensive ionizations in cases where it is possible to measure the equilibrium. Behind the generalization lies a model of the transition state and solvent consisting of a dipole imbedded in a continuous dielectric. Even aside from the reactions in which the the solvent forms an actual covalent bond to carbon in concert with the ionization, the continuous dielectric has been on the whole a rather unsatisfactory model for the solvent.[247] It does not adequately reflect the specific chemical interactions of the ground state and both ends of the developing dipole with the solvent. Returning to the generalization about the effect of a more polar solvent, such solvents usually accelerate the ionization reaction but not necessarily because of a lowered activation energy as might perhaps be thought. The more usual effect of a polar solvent is to increase the entropy of activation.[185]

A further complication in the action of the solvent is connected with the possibility that the original ions will recombine and reverse the ionization reaction even before they can escape from the cage formed by the surrounding solvent molecules. This return of the original departing group to its parent molecule is called "internal return" or the

[247] H. Sadek and R. M. Fuoss, *J. Am. Chem. Soc.*, **76**, 5897 (1954).

Hardy effect.[248,249] The internal return part of the ionization equilibrium is particularly hard to detect since it is almost completely independent of the concentration of anything in the bulk of the solution outside of the solvent cage. The extent of internal return will depend on the reactivity of the cage walls and their resistance to the escape of either ion. Unless internal return has been eliminated by the use of an extremely reactive cage wall, the measured rate is not that of the ionization but the lesser rate of ion pair dissociation. In the case of the acetolysis of α, α-dimethylallyl chloride (XXXIX), internal return is detectable by virtue of the fact that the chloride ion can return to either of two allylic carbon atoms.[248]

$$
\begin{array}{ccc}
CH_3 & CH_3 & CH_3 \\
| & | \;\;(+) & | \\
CH_3-C-CH=CH_2 \;\rightleftharpoons\; & CH_3-C^{\cdots}CH^{\cdots}CH_2 \;\rightleftharpoons\; & CH_3-C=CH-CH_2Cl \\
| & & \\
Cl & Cl^{(-)} & \\
\end{array}
$$

(XXXIX)

The acetolysis reaction is slower than the isomerization because the latter reaction makes greater use of intimate ion pairs as well as free ions.

Another detectable example of internal return is afforded by the solvolysis of exo-norbornylbromobenzenesulfonate (XL): it racemizes from 40 to 240% faster than it produces bromobenzenesulfonic acid, yet both reactions are strictly first order. The racemization reaction is kinetically independent of bulk bromobenzenesulfonate concentration but its rate is dependent on the nature of the solvent, pyridine being less effective than alcohol, acetic acid, or aqueous acetone.[238] The behavior of 3-phenyl-2-butyl-p-toluenesulfonate is similar.[250]

(XL)	Symmetrical ion pair	Racemic exo-norbornyl-bromobenzenesulfonate
Optically active exo-norbornylbromobenzene-sulfonate		

Solvent ROH

Exo solvolysis product plus
p-bromobenzenesulfonic acid

[248] W. G. Young, S. Winstein, and H. L. Goering, *J. Am. Chem. Soc.*, **73**, 1958 (1951).

[249] T. Hardy, *The Return of the Native.*

[250] S. Winstein and K. C. Schreiber, *J. Am. Chem. Soc.*, **74**, 2165 (1952).

The effect of solvent changes on the rates of solvolysis and racemization are closely enough parallel to support the idea that racemization is due to the internal collapse of the same ion pair whose separation by diffusion or attack by solvent leads to solvolysis.[250] Winstein has reported, however, that some but not all reactions exhibiting "internal return" exhibit an unusual salt effect.[251] This suggests that there are two kinds of ion pair, a truly intimate one enclosed in a solvent cage and a solvent-separated ion pair. The solvent-separated ion pair is still likely to give the Hardy effect or return of the original negative ion to reconstitute the molecule, but it is more susceptible to interference by other reagents. With the reactions believed to involve intimate ion pairs, lithium perchlorate exerts only the normal effect of a dissolved salt on a reaction that is developing a strong dipole, and an intimate ion pair can be considered to be merely a strong dipole. This normal effect is an increase in log k for the reaction proportional to the concentration of dissolved lithium perchlorate. The reactions believed to involve solvent-seperated ion pairs, on the other hand, show an initial large acceleration with low concentrations of lithium perchlorate followed by a lesser and linear increase in log k at higher lithium perchlorate concentrations. The initial large increase in rate with low lithium perchlorate concentrations is probably due to a rather specific and short range interaction of the salt with the solvent-separated ions of the ion pair. The specific or chemical interaction is an effect that soon reaches saturation and is followed by the normal linear increase in rate with higher salt concentrations. The intimate ion pairs do not show the large initial effect because they are already stabilized internally and less subject to strong interaction with foreign ions. A similar non-linear salt effect has been observed by S. K. Liu in the author's laboratory for a molecule whose probable structure is a zwitterion with more charge separation than in a really intimate ion pair.

Acylium Ions

Acylium ions are formed by the departure of a negative ion or group from an acyl compound. Just as in the case of other carbonium

[251] S. Winstein, E. Clippinger, A. H. Fainberg, and G. C. Robinson, *J. Am. Chem. Soc.*, **76**, 2597 (1954).

ions, the ionization is facilitated by polar solvents and catalysts capable of accepting the departing group. As with the alkyl compounds, it is not always clear whether an acylium ion is really involved as an intermediate in a given reaction or whether its formation and destruction are concerted. Thus in the Friedel-Crafts ketone synthesis the reagent might be the acylium ion XLI or the complex XLII. The possibility that XLI may be the actual reagent, at least in some cases, is strengthened by the fact that halogen exchange and the Friedel-Crafts reaction both go even with compounds having hindered carbonyl groups.[252] On the other hand, there is evidence indicating that most of the acylium ions are tied up in some way in the presence of suitable reagents. Unless there is an excess of aluminum chloride present, benzophenone added to the reaction mixture prevents the reaction of benzoyl chloride with anisole. This could, of course, be due to the removal of the aluminum chloride as a complex with the benzophenone, yet benzophenone does not prevent the halogen exchange reaction. It has been suggested that the failure of the reaction is due to the trapping of the acylium ion as the complex XLIII.

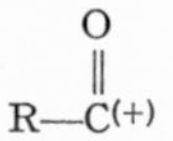

$$
\begin{array}{cc}
\overset{\displaystyle O}{\underset{\displaystyle \;}{\overset{\parallel}{R-C^{(+)}}}} & \overset{\displaystyle O}{\underset{\displaystyle \;}{\overset{\parallel}{R-C-Cl\cdots AlCl_3}}} \\
(XLI) & (XLII)
\end{array}
$$

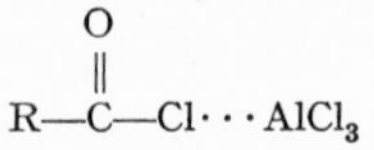

$$
R-\overset{\displaystyle O}{\overset{\parallel}{C}}-O-\overset{\displaystyle \phi}{\underset{\displaystyle \phi}{C^{(+)}}}
$$

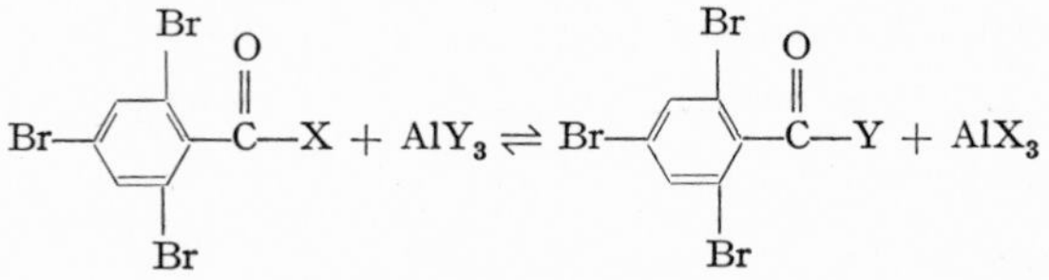

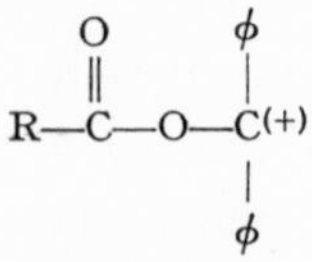

$$(XLIII)$$

It is not out of the question that a complex of the general character of XLIII should function as an acylating agent itself. It will be recalled that the position of acylation of naphthalene is often determined by the

[252] G. Baddeley and D. Voss, *J. Chem. Soc.*, **1954**, 418.

solvent used. Possibly the reagent in the presence of ketones or nitro-benzene is a bulky complex like XLIII. This would explain avoidance of the reactive but hindered α-position of naphthalene.

Sometimes acylium ions lose carbon monoxide to generate an ordinary carbonium ion. It will be recalled that free acyl radicals exhibit similar behavior at high temperatures. Whether or not the loss of carbon monoxide takes place seems to depend on the stability of the resulting carbonium ion and on the speed with which the acylium ion is removed by competing reactions. Thus no decarbonylation is observed in Friedel-Crafts reactions of benzoyl chloride, the phenyl cation being rather unstable. But attempts to make pivaloyl benzene by the Friedel-Crafts reaction produce *tert*-butyl benzene instead. With compound XLIV cyclization competes with decarbonylation, but this competition is not successful in the case of compound XLV in which the ring is deactivated.[253]

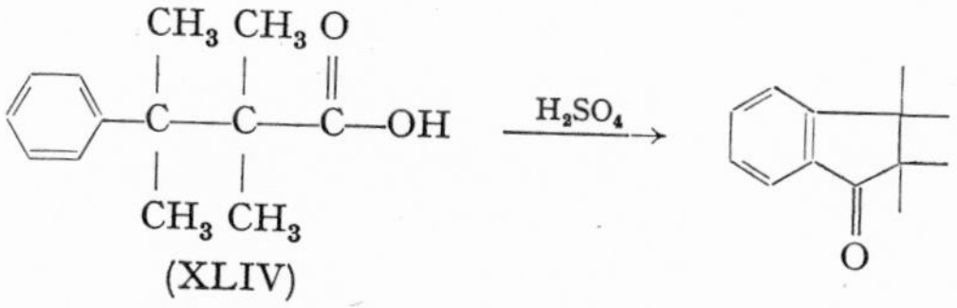

(XLIV)

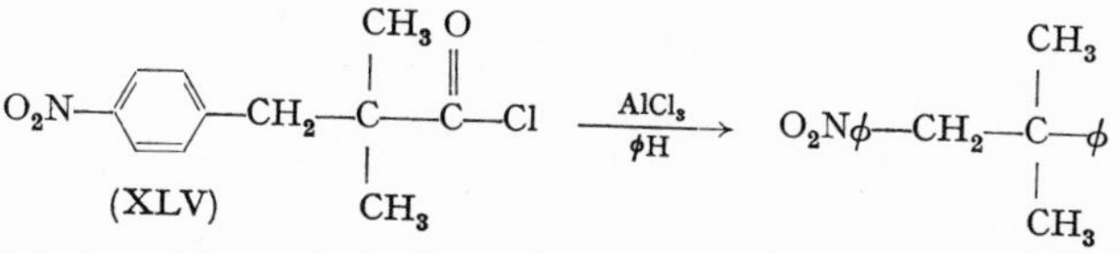

(XLV)

Although substituted benzoic acids give esters when their acylium ion-containing solutions in sulfuric acid are poured into alcohol, the sort of acylium ion that loses carbon monoxide gives an ether instead.[254]

The reaction of carboxylic acids with hydrazoic acid in concentrated sulfuric acid to give amines is faster with acids whose i-factor equals 4.

[253] E. Rothstein and R. W. Saville, *J. Chem. Soc.*, **1949**, 1946.
[254] H. A. Smith and R. J. Smith, *J. Am. Chem. Soc.*, **70**, 2400 (1948).

Mesitoic acid, for example, will give the amine at 0°, while benzoic acid requires a temperature of 35° for the reaction to go at a convenient rate. Presumably the higher concentration of acylium ion in the former case reacts more rapidly than a lower concentration or a less reactive source of acyl groups in the latter case.[255]

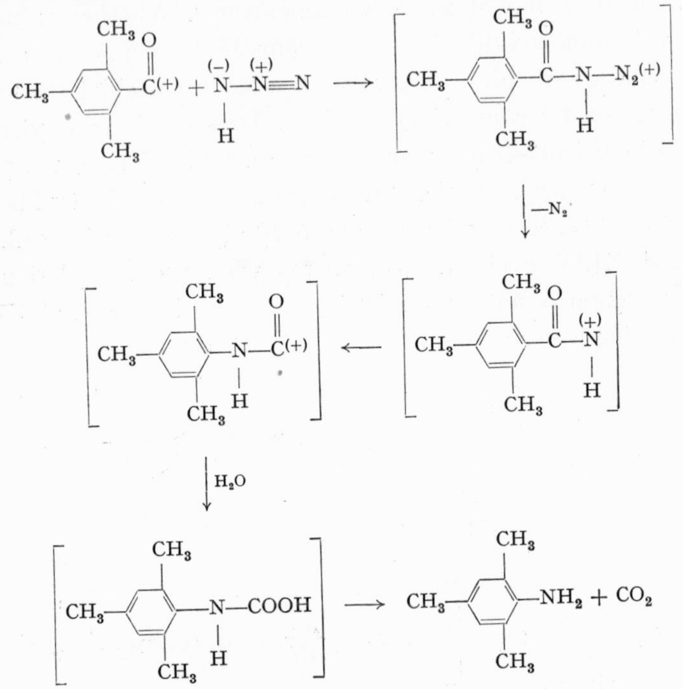

The loss of nitrogen and migration of the mesityl group very likely constitute a single concerted process although they have been written here as two separate steps.

Not only water and alcohols, but also other oxygen compounds, are able to react covalently with acylium ions. In the case of hydroxy compounds the product is stabilized by loss of the proton from the hydroxyl group, but certain ethers give an analogous reaction in which the product is stabilized by loss of a carbonium ion.[256] Using acetyl chloride with silver perchlorate in nitromethane as the source of acetyl

[255] M. S. Newman and H. L. Gildenhorn, *J. Am. Chem. Soc.*, **70**, 317 (1948).
[256] H. Burton and P. F. G. Praill, *J. Chem. Soc.*, **1951**, 522.

cations, benzyl phenyl ether is converted partly into phenyl acetate and partly into *p*-benzylphenyl acetate.

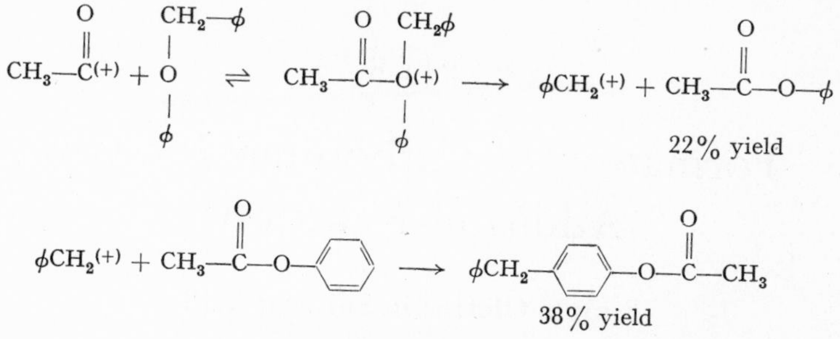

$$CH_3-\overset{\overset{\displaystyle O}{\|}}{C}{}^{(+)} + \overset{\overset{\displaystyle CH_2-\phi}{|}}{\underset{\underset{\displaystyle \phi}{|}}{O}} \rightleftharpoons CH_3-\overset{\overset{\displaystyle O}{\|}}{C}-\overset{\overset{\displaystyle CH_2\phi}{|}}{\underset{\underset{\displaystyle \phi}{|}}{O}}{}^{(+)} \longrightarrow \phi CH_2{}^{(+)} + CH_3-\overset{\overset{\displaystyle O}{\|}}{C}-O-\phi$$

$$22\% \text{ yield}$$

$$\phi CH_2{}^{(+)} + CH_3-\overset{\overset{\displaystyle O}{\|}}{C}-O-\!\!\left\langle\!\!\bigcirc\!\!\right\rangle \longrightarrow \phi CH_2-\!\!\left\langle\!\!\bigcirc\!\!\right\rangle\!\!-O-\overset{\overset{\displaystyle O}{\|}}{C}-CH_3$$

$$38\% \text{ yield}$$

Anisole under the same conditions gives only *p*-methoxyacetophenone, even though the acetyl cation undoubtedly reacts faster with the methoxy group than with the benzene ring. Since no stabilizing carbonium ion is split off the former reaction remains reversible and ineffective, while the nuclear substitution is pushed to completion by the removal of a proton.

CHAPTER VII

Formation of Carbonium Ions by Addition Reactions

Simple Olefins in Sulfuric Acid

Olefins are soluble in concentrated sulfuric acid, but only by virtue of a chemical reaction.

$$C{=}C + H_2SO_4 \rightleftharpoons H{-}C{-}C{-}OSO_3H \rightleftharpoons H{-}C{-}C^{(+)} + HSO_4^{(-)}$$

The alkyl hydrogen sulfate is in part dissociated into carbonium and bisulfate ions, to an extent that depends on the structure of the olefin. The quantitative study of the protonation of the olefin in concentrated sulfuric acid is made difficult by the occurrence of polymerization and oxidation reactions, although the former reaction is in itself evidence favoring the existence of carbonium ions.[257] Ethylene itself is exceptional among the simple olefins in that the ethyl hydrogen sulfate formed is quite stable in sulfuric acid. It is largely undissociated however. Experiments with diluted sulfuric acid show that olefins which could form classical tertiary carbonium ions or tertiary bisulfates dissolve in less concentrated acid or dissolve more rapidly in acid of a given concentration than olefins which can form only secondary carbonium ions or secondary bisulfates. "Secondary" olefins in turn undergo addition more readily than ethylene. Although dilution of solutions of the less substituted olefins produces secondary alkyl bisulfates, the more substituted olefins yield tertiary alcohols on dilution, very probably because of the rapidity with which the tertiary alkyl bisulfates are hydrolyzed. The formation of the tertiary addition compound in preference to the secondary, and the secondary in preference

[257] R. J. Gillespie and J. A. Leisten, *Quart. Revs. (London)*, **8**, 40 (1954)

to the primary (Markownikoff's rule) would seem to reflect the greater stability of the more highly substituted carbonium ions, except that the major species present in sulfuric acid appears to be the neutral bisulfate ester. The ester is therefore regarded as existing as ion pairs or at least in a highly polar form.

Olefins in Aqueous Acid

Olefins dissolved in aqueous acid are in rapid reversible equilibrium with a carbonium ion formed by addition of a proton.[258] This rapidly and reversibly formed carbonium ion has to be a non-classical one in view of the behavior of the isomeric pentenes XLVI and XLVII.[259] Both pentenes react with dilute nitric acid to give the same tertiary carbinol. If the reaction is interrupted when half of the olefin has been converted to carbinol, the remaining olefin has its original structure in both cases. The first product of protonation of the olefin is therefore of such a structure that loss of a proton gives only the original olefin. The reversibly formed carbonium ion can not therefore be the classical one.

$$H_3\text{-}C\text{=}CH\text{-}CH_3 + H^{(+)} \rightleftharpoons CH_3\text{-}\overset{\overset{\displaystyle H^{(+)}}{\uparrow}}{C}\overset{+}{\text{=}}CH\text{-}CH_3$$

(XLVI), with CH_3 substituent

$$H_3\text{-}C\text{-}CH_2\text{-}CH_3 + H^+ \rightleftharpoons CH_3\text{-}C\text{-}CH_2\text{-}CH_3$$

(XLVII), with CH_2 substituent, $\mathbin{+\!\!\!+} \rightarrow H^{(+)}$

$$CH_3\overset{(+)}{\text{-}}C\text{-}CH_2\text{-}CH_3 \longrightarrow CH_3\overset{\displaystyle OH}{\text{-}}C\text{-}CH_2CH_3$$

with CH_3 substituents

The reversibly formed π-complexes precursor to the hydration of olefins have the proton imbedded in the π-electron cloud of the double bond somewhere between the two carbon atoms. They are therefore

[258] R. W. Taft, Jr., *Abstract, Joint Symposium on Mechanisms of Homogeneous and Heterogeneous Hydrocarbon Reactions*, Kansas City, Missouri, 1954; E. L. Purlee, *Doctoral Dissertation*, The Pennsylvania State University, June, 1954; R. W. Taft, Jr., *J. Am. Chem. Soc.*, **74**, 5372 (1952).
[259] J. B. Levy, R. W. Taft, Jr., and L. P. Hammett, *J. Am. Chem. Soc.*, **75**, 1253 (1953); J. B. Levy, R. W. Taft, Jr., D. Aaron, and L. P. Hammett, *ibid.*, **75**, 3955 (1953).

reasonable intermediates to expect in reactions in which a rearranged carbonium ion is formed and the migrating group is hydrogen. It is more likely, however, that the half-way position of the hydrogen in the rearrangement corresponds to a transition state rather than an intermediate, and that the bonds to hydrogen are of the σ rather than the π-type. In the treatment of labeled ethylamine with nitrous acid the product is mostly ethanol with the label unrearranged.[260]

$$
\overset{*}{CH_3}CH_2-NH_2 \xrightarrow[NaNO_2]{HClO_4} \left[\overset{*}{CH_3}CH_2{}^{(+)} \right] \longrightarrow \overset{*}{CH_3}CH_2-OH \text{ (mostly)}
$$

$$
\left[\underset{(+)}{CH_2}-\overset{*}{CH_3} \right] \longrightarrow \overset{*}{CH_3}-CH_2OH \ (1.5\%)
$$

This means that the ionization and rearrangement need not be concerted and that symmetrical protonated ethylene can not be a major intermediate in the reaction. A similar experiment with isobutylamine and nitrous acid in heavy water gave products that contained no carbon-deuterium bonds. Since it is known that the π-complex formed from isobutylene and acid is in rapid equilibrium with protons from the solvent, none of this can be formed in the nitrous acid induced deamination. This in turn makes it probable that the transition state for the hydrogen migration is of the sigma rather than the π-bonded type.[261]

In contrast to the simple olefins, aryl-substituted olefins dissolve in sulfuric acid to give comparatively stable carbonium ions, as is shown by the i-factors, the spectra, and the recovery of the olefin on dilution.[262] In some cases it is neccessary to extrapolate the freezing point depression to zero time owing to a slow sulfonation. Because of the similarity in the spectra it is believed that these carbonium ions have the classical structures shown below.[263]

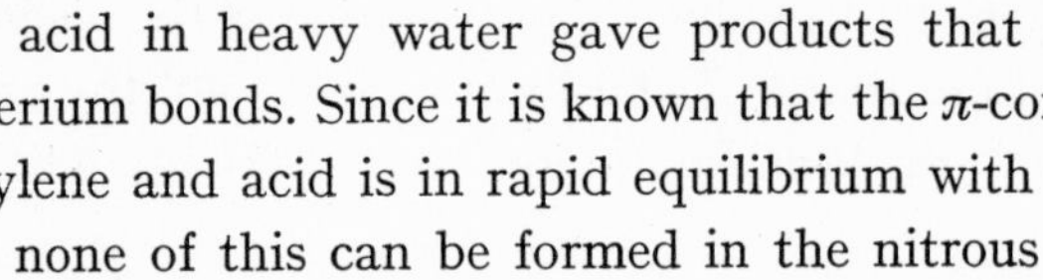

Classical structures

[260] J. D. Roberts and J. A. Yancey, *J. Am. Chem. Soc.*, **74**, 5943 (1952).
[261] L. G. Cannell and R. W. Taft, Jr., private communication.
[262] V. Gold, B. W. V. Hawes, and F. L. Tye, *J. Chem. Soc.*, **1952**, 2167.
[263] V. Gold and F. L. Tye, *J. Chem. Soc.*, **1952**, 2172.

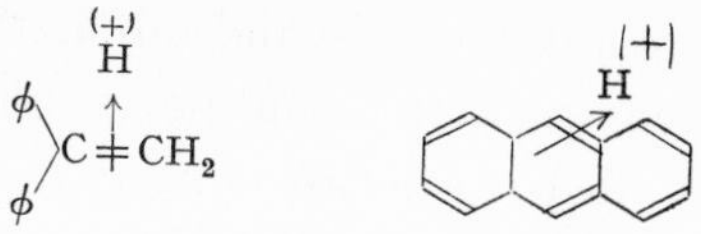

Non-classical structures

It is difficult to see why the spectra of the ions from diphenylethylene and triphenylethylene should resemble that of the ion from anthracene if the ions have the non-classical protonated double bond structure.

The relative basicities of the hydrocarbons may be determined from the result of partition between aqueous sulfuric acid and cyclohexane, the reasonable assumption being made that the degree of conversion to conjugate acid, rather than the distribution coefficient of the neutral olefin, is the major factor determining the overall distribution. The resulting order of basicities is:

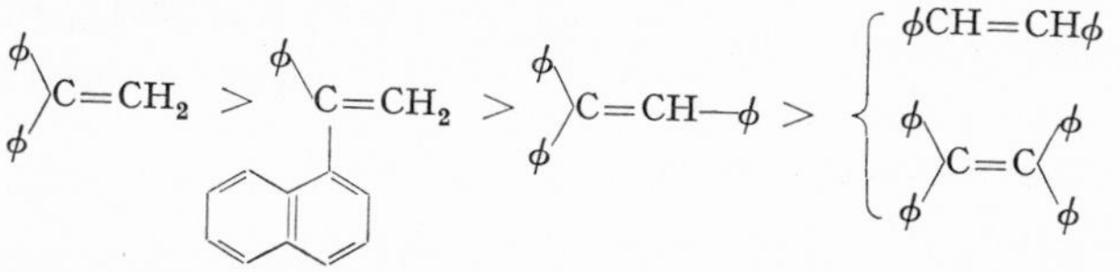

The differences between the aryl-substituted olefins may be interpreted as the result of two opposing resonance stabilizations, that of the olefin and that of the carbonium ion. The carbonium ion is stabilized when the positive charge is placed on a carbon atom adjacent to two aromatic rings, but, on the other hand, in tetraphenylethylene this stabilization of the positive charge by one pair of phenyl groups is not sufficient to counteract the loss of the resonance energy due to the interaction of the central double bond with all four benzene rings. Although this explanation may be correct, it is not known experimentally that the relative stabilities are in fact due to energy effects alone and that considerations of entropy may be neglected.

The quasi-aromatic azulenes dissolve in 50–60 % sulfuric acid, a property used in their isolation. The sulfuric acid solutions are yellow to orange rather than blue like the parent hydrocarbon, and they are

[264] P. A. Plattner, E. Heilbronner, and S. Weber, Helv. Chim. Acta, 32, 574 (1949).

[265] W. Herz and J. L. Rogers, J. Am. Chem. Soc., 75, 4498 (1953).

somewhat susceptible to autoxidation and sulfonation. The blue hydrocarbon is reprecipitated when the solution is diluted to about 20%
acid.[264] Distribution coefficients between an inert solvent and aqueous
sulfuric acid are linear in H_0, the parameter that measures the tendency
of the sulfuric acid solution to donate a proton to the hydrocarbon.
Another type of reactivity distinguishing the azulenes is the formation
of very stable and very dark-colored molecular complexes with
aromatic nitro compounds.[265] Both properties are indicative of an
unusual basicity for azulene. Azulene is unique in possessing within a
single molecule both the cycloheptatriene and cyclopentadiene structures. These structures are complementary in their electronic properties
as is shown by the stability of the ionic tropyllium bromide on the one
hand and the ionic (or at least highly polar) sodium salt of cyclopentadiene on the other. The remarkable stability of the complexes
and perhaps the color of the azulenes may be associated with a dipolar
structure, more important in the excited states, and one that makes
use of the specific electronic properties of the two rings.

Azulene

Azulene conjugate acid

Protonation of Aromatic Hydrocarbons

The more basic of the polynuclear benzenoid hydrocarbons dissolve
in concentrated sulfuric acid, probably with the formation of simple
carbonium ions.[263] Benzene itself is only slightly soluble, but exchanges
hydrogen with D_2SO_4.[266] Benzene and toluene will dissolve in a mixture
of hydrogen fluoride and boron trifluoride.[267,268] Pyrene in hydrogen

[266] C. K. Ingold, *Structure and Mechanism in Organic Chemistry*, Cornell,
1953, p. 303.
[267] M. Kilpatrick and F. E. Luborsky, *J. Am. Chem. Soc.*, **5**, 577 (1953).
[268] C. Reid, *J. Am. Chem. Soc.*, **76**, 3264 (1954).

fluoride-boron trifluoride solution is initially yellow-orange but is converted into a green substance, possibly a tautomeric ion, on irradiation.[268]

An aromatic hydrocarbon of most unusual basicity and color is the Z-shaped molecule zethrene synthesized by Clar and the object of quantum mechanical calculations by Coulson.[269] Zethrene is green and only sparingly soluble in neutral solvents but readily soluble in acetic acid. The solutions in acetic acid and in other acids are violet. The zethrene is recovered unchanged on neutralization.

Zethrene

The effect of alkyl substituents on the basicity of benzene is that to be expected from the ability of alkyl substituents to stabilize a positive charge. Hydrogen chloride, which probably hydrogen-bonds to aromatic hydrocarbons, is increasingly soluble in a dilute solution of the aromatic compound in n-heptane as the aromatic compound is changed from chlorobenzene to toluene, to p-xylene, to m-xylene, to mesitylene.[270] This order of increasing basicity parallels the order of increasing reactivity towards electrophilic reagents in general.

Two structures are possible for the interaction of aromatic hydrocarbons with acids.[270] In the σ-structures a covalent bond is established between the acidic reagent and a particular carbon atom of the benzene ring. The σ-structures are essentially classical carbonium ions. In the π-structures a non-classical bond is established, not to any particular atom, but to the π-electron cloud in general. It is quite likely that both types of structure are represented by actual examples. Thus m-xylene interacts more strongly with hydrogen chloride than does o-xylene, but the difference between the two hydrocarbons is much more pronounced when their interactions with a boron trifluoride-hydrogen fluoride mixture are compared. This is readily understandable

[269] C. A. Coulson and C. M. Moser, *J. Chem. Soc.*, **1953**, 1341.
[270] H. C. Brown and J. D. Brady, *J. Am. Chem. Soc.*, **74**, 3570 (1952).

if the hydrogen chloride complexes are of the π-type and the hydrogen fluoride-boron trifluoride complexes are of the σ-type.

π-Complexes (colorless)

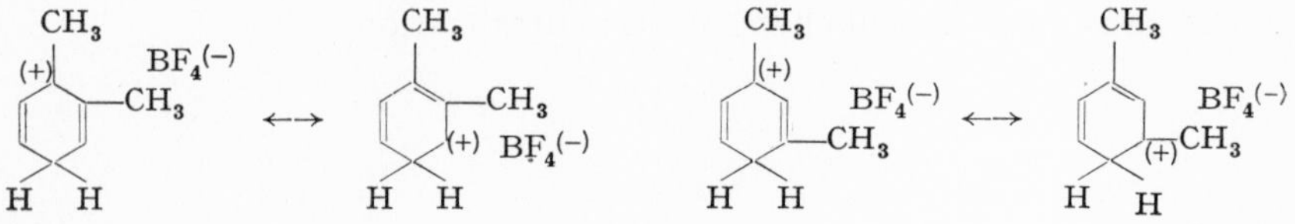

σ-Complexes (colored)

In the σ-complex a meta location of the two methyl groups is particularly favorable because it allows both methyl groups to interact effectively with the positive charge. In the π-complex the location of the methyl groups makes less difference.

Another anomaly that is removed by the possible existence of more than one kind of complex is the order methyl < ethyl < isopropyl < tertiarybutyl for the basicities of the alkyl benzene toward hydrogen chloride. This contrasts with precisely the reverse order for the reactivities in nuclear halogenation. If the intermediate in halogenation is of the σ-type it should be more stabilized by hyperconjugation than by the inductive effect, while the π- or hydrogen chloride type of complex might be more stabilized by the inductive effect. Since para methyl and tertiarybutyl are about the same in the stabilization of the triphenylcarbonium ion in sulfur dioxide, it may be tentatively concluded that both hyperconjugation and the inductive effect are important in that ion. It should be remembered, however, that the stabilizing effect of the tertiarybutyl group in triphenylcarbonium ion was an entropy effect. In the hydrolysis of p-alkylbenzhydryl chlorides in aqueous acetone, methyl accelerates the reaction more than tertiarybutyl in agreement with the hyperconjugation order found for σ-complexing. One of several possible explanations is that the σ-type of interaction of the charge with the substituent ring (resonance) is hampered more by non-coplanarity in the triphenylcarbonium ion than it is in the benzhydryl chloride transition state. The favorable entropy effect of the tertiarybutyl group in triphenylcarbonium ion might then be due to the fact that the inductive effect has less stringent geometrical requirements than does resonance.

Aromatic hydrocarbons will interact even with relatively weak proton donors, although very likely in the pi rather than the sigma-fashion. For example, the dipole moment of phenol is considerably higher in benzene than in cyclohexane.[271] The infrared spectrum of phenol in benzene has a double peak, indicating that the solvent can take up two orientations with respect to the OH dipole, each of very different energy.[272] One of these orientations presumably corresponds to a hydrogen bond to the benzene. A similar but internal hydrogen bond effect is shown by o-hydroxybiphenyl in which the hydroxyl group interacts with the other benzene ring of the same molecule.

Protonation of Carbonyl Compounds

The addition of protons to the carbonyl group is an important process because of the role it plays in the acid catalyzed reactions of many types of carbonyl compounds. Because of the difference in electronegativity, it is likely that the proton is associated specifically with the oxygen rather than with the carbonyl group as a whole.

$$\begin{array}{ccc} \overset{(+)}{O}{-}H & & O{-}H \\ \| & & | \\ R{-}C{-}R & \longleftrightarrow & R{-}\underset{(+)}{C}{-}R \end{array}$$

In some cases spectroscopic evidence for such species exists. Thus the ultraviolet spectrum of acetophenone in aqueous sulfuric acid changes markedly as the concentration of acid is increased.[273] In concentrated sulfuric acid simple aldehydes and ketones exists completely in the conjugate acid form. Unsaturated ketones give colored solutions in sulfuric acid and have i-factors greater than two. The higher i-factors

[271] R. L. Schupp and R. Mecke, Z. Elektrochem., 52, 54 (1948).
[272] W. Lüttke and R. Mecke, Z. Elektrochem., 53, 241 (1949).
[273] L. A. Flexser, L. P. Hammett, and A. Dingwall, J. Am. Chem. Soc., 57, 2103 (1935).

are due to sulfonation rather than multiple protonation, however.[274] The major species present before sulfonation in the case of dibenzyl-ideneacetone probably has its single proton on the oxygen atom.

In less polar solvents, complexes in which an acid or alcohol is loosely attached to the oxygen of the carbonyl group by a hydrogen bond also betray their presence by spectroscopic effects. The catalytic effect of a molecule hydrogen-bonded to a carbonyl group is also like that of a covalently attached proton, the difference being one of degree. An example in which the proton might or might not be covalently attached is the formation of cyanohydrin catalyzed by optically active amine hydrocyanides. The kinetics fit the scheme shown below in which the proton on oxygen facilitates the attack of cyanide ion on carbon.[275,276] Ion pairs rather than free ions are indicated because the solvent, chloroform, is a relatively non-polar one.

$$
\begin{array}{c}
\overset{\displaystyle O}{\overset{\displaystyle \|}{R-C-H}} + \overset{*}{BH^{(+)}CN^{(-)}} \underset{}{\overset{\text{fast}}{\rightleftharpoons}} R-C=O\cdots\overset{(+)}{H}-\overset{*}{B}\ CN^{(-)} \\
\qquad\qquad\qquad\qquad\qquad\qquad\qquad | \\
\qquad\qquad\qquad\qquad\qquad\qquad\qquad H
\end{array}
$$

$$
\begin{array}{c}
\overset{(+)*}{H}-B\ CN^{(-)} \\
\vdots \\
\overset{\displaystyle O}{\overset{\displaystyle \|}{R-C-H}} \overset{\text{slow}}{\longrightarrow} \quad R-\overset{*|}{\underset{|}{C}}-H + \overset{(+)*}{HB}\ CN^{(-)} + \overset{*}{B} \\
\vdots \qquad\qquad\qquad\quad CN \\
^{(-)}CN \\
\overset{(+)*}{B}-H
\end{array}
$$

with OH above the middle carbon.

The asymmetric synthesis achieved when the base is an optically active one is proof that the base is present in a transition state with the carbonyl and not just an agent for removal of protons from hydrogen cyanide. It has further been shown that asymmetric synthesis is still achieved even if the only optically active molecules present are *quaternary* ammonium compounds, i.e., positive ions without any protons to donate. This probably means that the important thing is to have some positive ion near the carbonyl oxygen, an actual covalent

[274] R. J. Gillespie and J. A. Leisten, *J. Chem. Soc.*, **1954**, 1; *ibid.*, **1954**, 7.
[275] H. Albers and E. Albers, *Z. Naturforsch.*, **9b**, 122 (1954).
[276] V. Prelog and M. Wilhelm, *Helv. Chim. Acta*, **37**, 1634 (1954).

bond to the oxygen being unnecessary. The catalytic role of the quaternary ammonium salt is confirmed by the fact that the asymmetric synthesis is suppressed by the use of an excess of inactive quaternary ammonium salt.[276] The inactive salt competes with the active salt in catalyzing the reaction but is not stereospecific.

$$
\begin{array}{c}
\text{R}\\
\overset{*}{\text{R}}\text{—N}\overset{|\ \text{R}}{\underset{(+)}{\angle}}\text{R}\quad \text{Y}^{(-)}\\
\underset{\text{O}}{\overset{}{}}\\
\parallel\\
\text{R—C—H}
\end{array}
\quad\xrightarrow{\ \text{BH}^{(+)}\text{CN}^{(-)}\ }\quad
\begin{array}{c}
\text{O}^{(-)}\quad \text{R}_4\overset{*}{\text{N}}^{(+)}\quad \text{Y}^{(-)}\\
\overset{*}{|}\\
\text{R—C—H}\ +\ \text{BH}^{(+)}\\
|\\
\text{CN}
\end{array}
$$

Other reactions in which cations other than protons are catalytically effective are esterification and acetal formation, catalyzed by calcium salts,[277] and the bromination of ethyl cyclopentanone-2-carboxylate, catalyzed by magnesium, calcium, cupric, and nickel, but not by sodium or potassium ions.[278] One interpretative difficulty, of course, is the separation of catalysis from the less specific salt effects. The boundary line between salt effects (medium effects) and salt effects (catalysis) is not sharp either in concept or experimentally.

Addition of Other Cations to Hydrocarbons

From the solubilities of aromatic hydrocarbons in aqueous silver nitrate it is clear that there is an interaction with the silver ion to give monoargentated and, to a lesser extent, diargentated hydrocarbons. The bond to silver ion is probably of the π-type, since the differences in the association constants for the complex with the three isomeric xylenes are small and since a single methyl group stabilizes the complex almost as much as two.[279]

The argentation of olefins at 25° is more nearly complete than is the argentation of aromatic hydrocarbons and also differs in that alkyl substituents decrease rather than increase the stability of the com-

[277] W. Langenbeck, Z. Elektrochem., 54, 393 (1950).
[278] K. J. Pedersen, Acta Chem. Scand., 2, 385 (1948).
[279] L. J. Andrews and R. M. Keefer, J. Am. Chem. Soc., 71, 3644 (1949).

plex.[280] The destabilization by alkyl substituents is very likely a steric effect. It is not known whether the effect is the same at other temperatures. Alkyl groups increase the rate of the addition of acids to olefins.[281] It may be that the argentate is a π-complex while the proton in the transition state for acid addition is σ-bonded, as is the proton in reactions in which a proton migrates in a carbonium ion. A circumstance that tends to confirm the view that the argentates are π-complexes is the fact that no polymerization of the olefin is initiated.

A cyclic complex derivable by addition of positive bromine to a double bond has already been discussed as an example of the neighboring group effect. The same intermediate, except perhaps for the nature of the bonds to bromine, is formed in the addition of bromine to olefins and is responsible for the stereochemistry of the addition reaction and the nature of the by-products.[232]

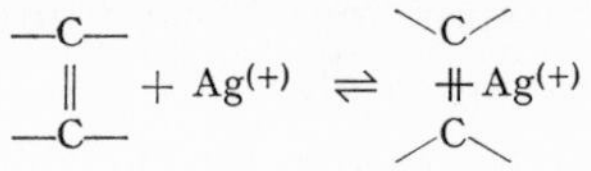

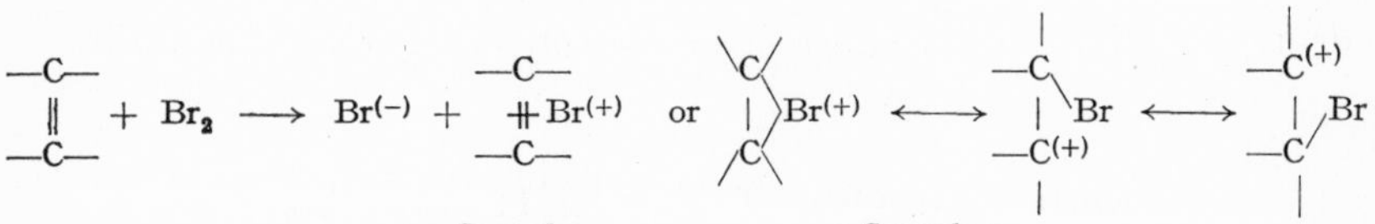

π-Complex σ-Complex

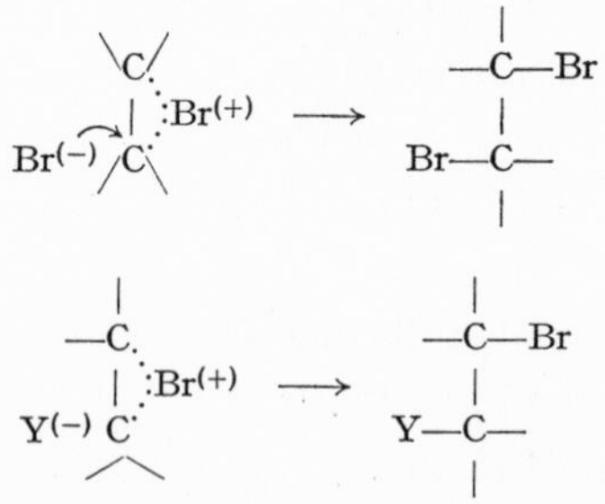

Competition with the bromide ion by solvent and by other ions for the intermediate bromonium ion explains the formation of such by-

[280] S. Winstein and H. J. Lucas, *J. Am. Chem. Soc.*, **60**, 836 (1938).
[281] R. J. Gillespie and J. A. Leisten, *Quart. Rev, (London)*, **8**, 40 (1954).

products as the bromohydrin and bromoacetate. The trans addition is due to opening of the bromonium ring by backside attack at one of the carbon atoms.

No product has as yet been isolated that is believed to have the bromonium ion ring intact, but some closely related ionic compounds are known. The latter compounds could have the bromonium and iodonium structure but their colors and the probable stability of the alternative carbonium ion make it unlikely.[282]

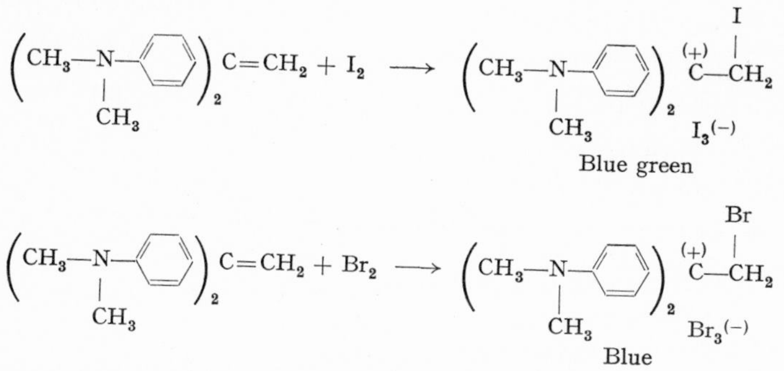

Blue green

Blue

A detailed spectroscopic examination should settle the question of whether the ion has the open or the cyclic structure. In general halochromic salts lose their color when a covalent bond is established to the central carbon atom, but the bromonium ion might resemble the carbonium ion. Compounds of similar color but which are certainly not cyclic halonium ions are also known:

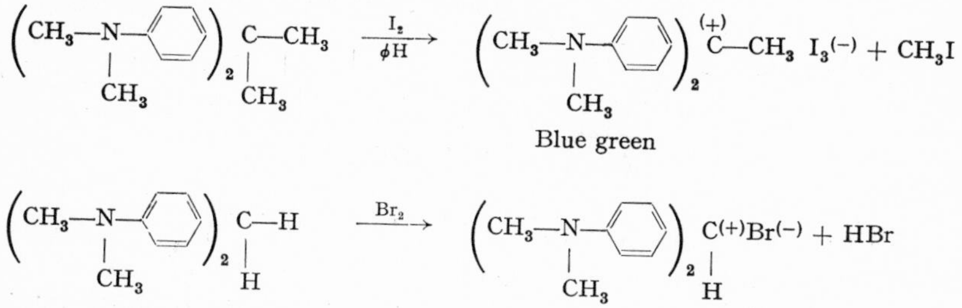

Blue green

It should perhaps be mentioned that the addition of halogens to the double bond takes place by a multiplicity of mechanisms and

[282] R. Wizinger and R. Gross, Helv. Chim. Acta, 35, 411 (1952).

various kinetic orders, usually higher than the second.[283] The reaction is not always homogeneous nor is it always polar.

The neat picture of a single cyclic intermediate produced by the addition of cations to olefins and by the solvolysis reaction with participation of a neighboring group will not be complete so long as it contains only the probable example of the bromonium ion. There should exist other reactions analogous to the formation of the cyclic bromonium ion by addition to the olefin to balance the other neighboring group reactions. Perhaps the formation of epoxides from peracids and olefins is such a reaction. The fact that the olefin is more reactive towards peracids if it has electron-releasing groups favors such an interpretation, but the fact that the reaction goes quite well in non-polar solvents is rather against it.

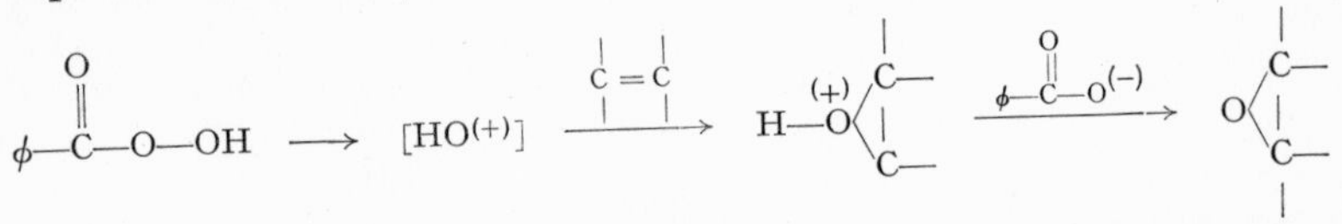

The least polar and most acceptable version of the mechanism involves a concerted formation, addition, and deprotonation of the hydroxyl cation, a process that amounts simply to the direct transfer of an oxygen atom.[284]

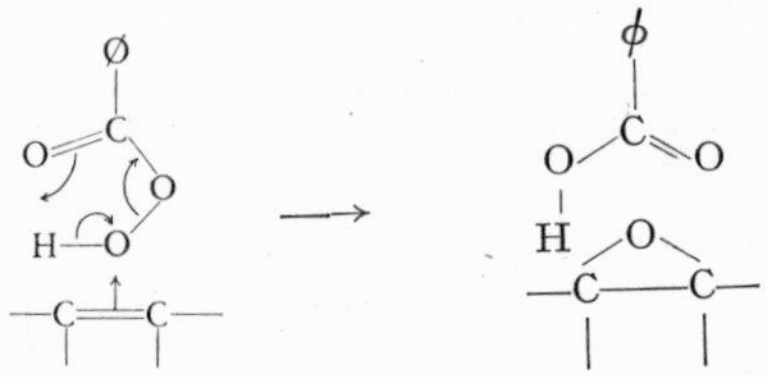

Aromatic Substitution

In aromatic substitution of the electrophilic type, a cation or potential cation attacks the benzene ring. The transition state or intermediate, whichever it may be, has largely covalent bonds holding

[283] P. W. Robertson, N. T. Clare, K. J. McNaught, and G. W. Paul, *J. Chem. Soc.*, **1937**, 335.
[284] D. Swern, *J. Am. Chem. Soc.*, **69**, 1692 (1947); P. D. Bartlett, *Record Chem. Progr.*, **11**, 47 (1950).

both the departing hydrogen and the entering cation. It is therefore very much like a classical carbonium ion, although one of fairly high energy relative to the aromatic reagent and product. In the nitration of toluene it is found that the rate is nearly the same whether tritium or hydrogen is the displaced species.[285] This means *at the very least* that the transition state for the rate-determining reaction still has the carbon to hydrogen bond in essentially the covalent condition characteristic of the ground state.[286] In addition to this minimum conclusion it is highly probable that the first product following the essentially covalent transition state is also one in which the hydrogen or tritium is still attached.

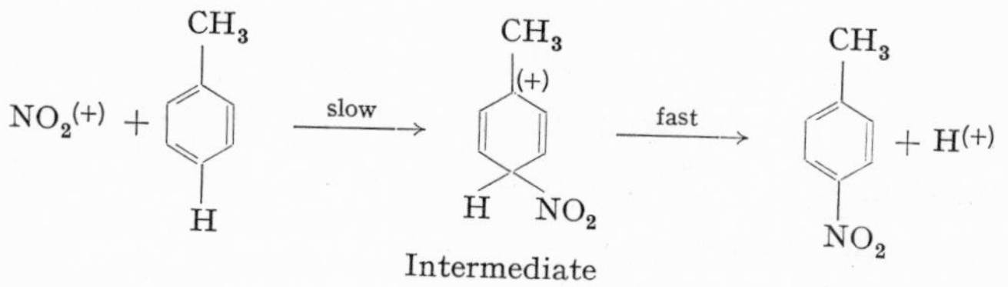

Intermediate

In sulfonation on the other hand, a tritium isotope effect is observed.[287] Sulfonation is a reversible reaction and the fact that it is less exothermic is compatible with a slow, rate-determining dissociation of the inter- mediate. The transition state for the slow second step has a less covalent carbon-hydrogen bond than the ground state and hence the reaction is faster for deprotonation than for detritonation.

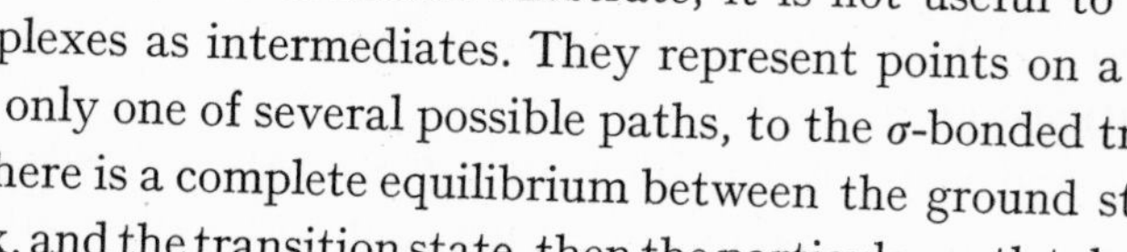

Although an electrophilic reagent should and probably does form π-complexes with the aromatic substrate, it is not useful to consider such complexes as intermediates. They represent points on a possible path, but only one of several possible paths, to the σ-bonded transition state. If there is a complete equilibrium between the ground state, the π-complex, and the transition state, then the particular path taken by the

[285] L. Melander, *Nature,* **163**, 599 (1949).
[286] G. S. Hammond, *J. Am. Chem. Soc.,* **77**, 334 (1955).
[287] L. Melander, *Arkiv Kemi,* **2**, 213 (1950).

system in going from the ground to the transition state can have no kinetic or other experimental consequences. Of course, if a π-complex is highly associated it may be important by virtue of lowering the free energy of the ground state, making the complex and the ground state one and the same thing. Otherwise it may be neglected. This does not mean that some substance other than the substituting reagent might not be catalytically active by virtue of forming a π-complex, but only that the interaction between the substituting reagent and the aromatic ring in the transition state does not partake of the nature of a π-complex.

An indication of the nature of the transition state in aromatic substitution is provided by the existence of some extrathermodynamic relationships among rate and acid-base equilibrium constants. Thus a simple linear relationship exists between the logarithms of the relative rates of halogenation of the methylbenzenes and the logarithms of the relative basicities of the hydrocarbons toward HF-BF$_3$ (σ-complex equilibrium).[288,270] A similar relationship with the basicities toward HCl (π-complex equilibrium) is much less precise. The π-complex is therefore a poorer model for the substitution transition state than is the σ-complex.

The influence of a substituent in the selection of the position of attack of a second entering substituent is best explained in terms of transition state theory. The reaction may be regarded as three independent competing reactions leading to ortho, meta, and para substitution. The problem thus reduces to one of comparing reaction rates, in case the reaction is irreversible, or equilibrium constants in case it is reversible. The rate is in turn determined by the difference in free energy between the ground and transition states. A useful simplification of the problem is then possible because *the ground states for all three reactions are identical.* This means that in comparing the rates considerations of ground state resonance, ground state inductive effects, ground state electron densities, ground state dipole moments, etc. cancel out and are completely irrelevant. If a high energy ground state resonance structure such as XLVIII is at all important for

288 F. E. Condon, *J. Am. Chem. Soc.*, **74**, 2528 (1952).

anisole, the fact that this may seem to predict para substitution is merely a coincidence.

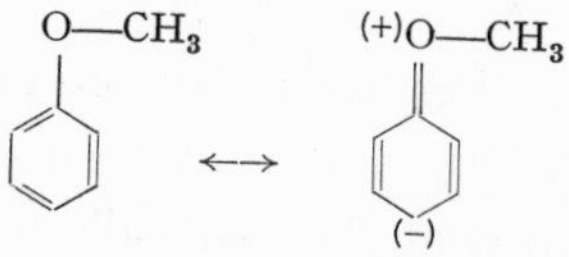

(XLVIII)

In any case the electrophilic reagent can attack the oxygen atom of anisole directly, and probably does, but reversibly and without leading to further reaction. The success of the electrostatic and free valency approaches is due to the degree to which their predictions happen to correlate with those of the transition state theory and is not a good test of the correctness of their basic premises.[289] Thus, corresponding to the irrelevant resonance structure XLVIII, there is a relevant transition state-stabilizing structure XLIX. To the extent that such correlations exist, the ground state electrostatic theory works.

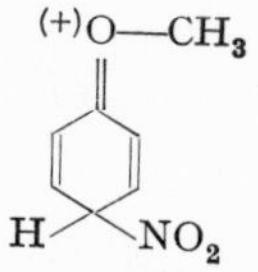

(XLIX)

Where they do not hold, it breaks down. For example, recent work has provided new data on isomer distribution that fails to fit the previous correlations with the dipole moment of the reagent aromatic compound.[290]

The effect of a substituent on the aromatic substitution reaction is similar to its effect on electrophilic side chain reactions, but not precisely parallel. Thus the Hammett relationship using the usual sigma or substituent constants gives considerable scatter when applied to aromatic substitution. The scatter is probably due to an increased importance of resonance effects in the nuclear substitution reaction as compared with the side chain reactions.

[289] M. J. S. Dewar, *J. Am. Chem. Soc.*, **74**, 3355 (1952).
[290] J. D. Roberts, J. K. Sanford, F. L. J. Sixma, H. Cerfontain, and R. Zagt, *J. Am. Chem. Soc.*, **76**, 4525 (1954).

Cationic Polymerization

The addition of a cation to an olefin to produce a carbonium ion or ion pair need not end there but may go through many cycles of olefin addition before the chain is eventually terminated by neutralization of the end carbonium ion. Simple addition to the double bond is essentially the same reaction stopped at the end of the first cycle. The addition of mineral acids to produce alkyl halides or sulfates, for example, may be prolonged into a polymerization reaction. However, simple addition or dimerization is the usual result with olefins and hydrogen acids. The polymerization which occurs with α-methylstyrene and sulfuric acid or styrene and hydrochloric acid at low temperatures in polar solvents is exceptional.[291] Polymerization may also be initiated by a carbonium ion formed by the dissociation of an alkyl halide as in the reaction of octyl vinyl ether with trityl chloride in ionizing solvents.[292]

$$\phi_3C\text{—}Cl \ \rightleftharpoons \ \phi_3C^{(+)} + Cl^{(-)} \quad \text{or} \quad \phi_3C^{(+)}Cl^{(-)}$$

$$\phi_3C^{(+)}Cl^{(-)} + C_8H_{17}\text{—}O\text{—}CH\text{=}CH_2 \ \longrightarrow \ [\phi_3C\text{—}CH_2\text{—}\overset{Cl^{(-)}}{\underset{}{\overset{(+)}{C}H}}\text{—}O\text{—}C_8H_{17}]$$

$$\longrightarrow \ \phi_3C\text{—}(CH_2\text{—}CH)_n\text{—}CH\text{=}CH\text{—}O\text{—}C_8H_{17}$$
$$\underset{O\text{—}C_8H_{17}}{|}$$

Another probable example of initiation by carbonium ions is the polymerization in alkyl bromides as solvents, in which the alkyl group is found at the end of the polymer chain.[291]

The most commonly used catalysts for cationic polymerization are the Lewis acids BF_3, $AlCl_3$, $SnCl_4$, $FeCl_3$, etc. There are two plausible modes of action for a Lewis acid. One of these, and rather a doubtful one, is the formation of a zwitterion and the growth at the positive end of the zwitterionic chain.

$$\underset{|\ \ |}{\overset{|\ \ |}{C\text{=}C}} + AlCl_3 \ \longrightarrow \ \overset{|\ \ |}{\underset{|\ \ |}{(+)C\text{—}C\text{—}AlCl_3}}^{(-)} \ \xrightarrow{\ \ \overset{|\ \ |}{\underset{|\ \ |}{C\text{=}C}}\ \ } \ \overset{|\ \ |\ \ |\ \ |}{\underset{|\ \ |\ \ |\ \ |}{(+)C\text{—}C\text{—}C\text{—}C\text{—}AlCl_3}}^{(-)} \text{ etc.}$$

291 *Symposium on Cationic Polymerization*, Heffer, Cambridge, England, 1953.
292 D. D. Eley and A. W. Richards, *Trans. Faraday Soc.*, **45**, 425 (1949).

The main objection to the zwitterion scheme is that as the chain grows there must either be increased charge separation with attendant increase in the free energy or a meeting of the chain ends with considerable ring formation. The barrier to the formation of rings of from eight to eleven carbon atoms might help to favor the polymerization, of course, but there should still be considerable formation of six-membered rings. The other mode of action of a Lewis acid is by way of a co-catalyst. Just as the mixture hydrogen fluoride-boron trifluoride is more acidic than either constituent alone, the addition of a hydrogen acid, an alkyl halide, or even a nitro compound enhances the power of a Lewis acid as a polymerization initiator.

$$HF + BF_3 \longrightarrow HF \cdots BF_3$$

$$HF \cdots BF_3 + \overset{|}{\underset{|}{C}}=\overset{|}{\underset{|}{C}} \longrightarrow H-\overset{|}{\underset{|}{C}}-\overset{|}{\underset{|}{C}}{}^{(+)}BF_4{}^{(-)} \xrightarrow{\overset{|}{\underset{|}{C}}=\overset{|}{\underset{|}{C}}} H-\overset{|}{\underset{|}{C}}-\overset{|}{\underset{|}{C}}-\overset{|}{\underset{|}{C}}-\overset{|}{\underset{|}{C}}{}^{(+)}BF_4{}^{(-)} \text{ etc.}$$

$$RX \; \rightleftharpoons \; R^{(+)}X^{(-)}$$

$$RX + AlClX_3 \; \rightleftharpoons \; R-X \cdots AlX_3 \; \rightleftharpoons \; R^{(+)}AlX_4{}^{(-)}$$

$$RX \cdots AlX_3 + \overset{|}{\underset{|}{C}}=\overset{|}{\underset{|}{C}} \longrightarrow R-\overset{|}{\underset{|}{C}}-\overset{|}{\underset{|}{C}}{}^{(+)}AlX_4{}^{(-)} \xrightarrow{\overset{|}{\underset{|}{C}}=\overset{|}{\underset{|}{C}}} R-\overset{|}{\underset{|}{C}}-\overset{|}{\underset{|}{C}}-\overset{|}{\underset{|}{C}}-\overset{|}{\underset{|}{C}}{}^{(+)}AlX_4{}^{(-)} \text{ etc.}$$
(or $R^{(+)}$)

Usually the stronger acids are also the more effective co-catalysts, but exceptions to this rule are known. Trichloroacetic acid, but not the equally strong picric acid, will co-catalyze the system isobutene-titanium tetrachloride in hexane.[293] Some Lewis acid-olefin systems will not polymerize at all in the absence of a co-catalyst, an example being isobutene with boron trifluoride.[294] This fact, together with the markedly slower reaction usual with carefully dried materials, has nourished the current suspicion that a co-catalyst may be necessary in every Lewis acid-olefin polymerization. It is very difficult to eliminate small traces of water which could act as a co-catalyst or generate mineral acid, and it may well be that the reactions which are slower when drier would not go at all if they could be made completely dry.

[293] P. H. Plesch, Nature, 160, 868 (1947).
[294] A. G. Evans and G. W. Meadows, Trans. Faraday Soc., 46, 327 (1950).

Generally speaking, a monomer with electron-releasing groups will be more rapidly polymerized by cationic initiators. Anionic initiators polymerize olefins with electron-withdrawing groups more rapidly. A more sensitive test of the nature of the reaction is the behavior of a mixture of two such monomers in copolymerization in which they compete for the intermediate. This will be discussed in more detail in Chapter XII on polar versus radical mechanisms.

CHAPTER VIII

Analogs of Carbonium Ions

Carbonium ions have several structural and behavioral analogs. The chemistry of the analogs has been less thoroughly investigated than that of the carbonium ions, and plausible reasoning based on the analogy serves as a temporary substitute for the missing observations. The important structural feature of the carbonium ions and their analogs is not the charge nor the valence, but the possession of more low energy orbitals than electrons to fill them. Neutral tricovalent boron or aluminum compounds, tricovalent silicon compounds with a positive charge on silicon, unicovalent oxygen compounds with a positive charge on oxygen, neutral unicovalent nitrogen compounds, and dicovalent nitrogen compounds with a positive charge on nitrogen may all be regarded as carbonium ion analogs. In three of these cases the ground state may or may not be a diradical (triplet state). The analogy is not entirely spoiled by this possibility since either the singlet or the triplet ground state could give rise to transition states of either multiplicity. The neutral carbon diradical might well be added to the list.

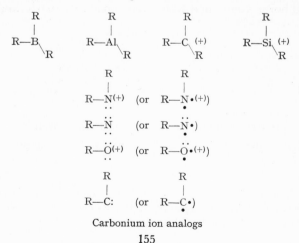

Carbonium ion analogs

One of the most striking of chemical analogies is the parallelism between the rearrangement reactions of the carbonium ion and its various analogs. Like the "carbonium ion" rearrangements, the analogous hetero rearrangements may be concerted and need not involve the corresponding intermediate in a free state. The field of hetero rearrangements is one that has as yet been only partially explored. Some of the more obvious possibilities have not been realized at all, while in no case will the available evidence allow the analysis of the mechanisms with the richness of detail prevalent in the carbonium ion field. Richness of detail is desirable because it lends an air of verisimilitude to an otherwise bald and unconvincing narrative.

The term *hetero rearrangement* is not limited to those reactions in which only the initially electron-deficient atom is something other than carbon, but may be applied to rearrangements in which any of the carbon atoms of formula L have been replaced with other elements.

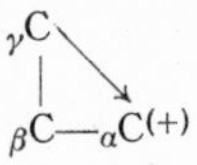

$$_{\gamma}C \diagdown \\ | \\ _{\beta}C - _{\alpha}C^{(+)}$$

(L)

The reader will no doubt have realized that the γ-hetero rearrangement is well-known, being none other than the familiar neighboring group effect. The α-hetero rearrangement is known for all of the elements mentioned but boron, aluminum, and silicon. Perhaps a suitably constituted boron compound would rearrange to a zwitterionic product as follows:

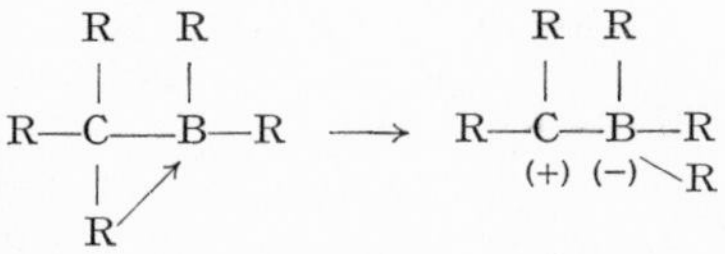

$$\begin{matrix} R & R & & R & R \\ | & | & & | & | \\ R-C-B-R & \longrightarrow & R-C-B-R \\ | \nearrow & & (+) \; (-)\diagdown R \\ R \end{matrix}$$

The β-hetero rearrangement is known only for silicon in contrast to the variety of instances of the reverse reaction, the α-hetero rearrangement.[295]

[295] F. C. Whitmore, L. H. Sommer, and J. R. Gould, *J. Am. Chem. Soc.*, **69**, 1976 (1947); L. H. Sommer, D. L. Bailey, J. R. Gould, and F. C. Whitmore, *ibid.*, **76**, 801 (1954).

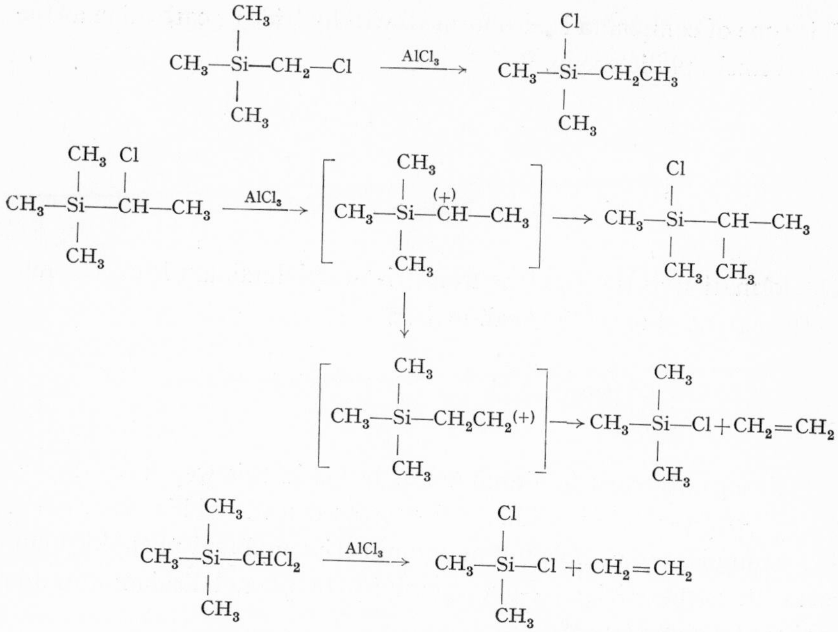

$$CH_3-\underset{\underset{CH_3}{|}}{\overset{\overset{CH_3}{|}}{Si}}-CH_2-Cl \xrightarrow{AlCl_3} CH_3-\underset{\underset{CH_3}{|}}{\overset{\overset{Cl}{|}}{Si}}-CH_2CH_3$$

$$CH_3-\underset{\underset{CH_3}{|}}{Si}-\overset{\overset{Cl}{|}}{CH}-CH_3 \xrightarrow{AlCl_3} \left[CH_3-\underset{\underset{CH_3}{|}}{\overset{\overset{CH_3}{|}}{Si}}-\overset{(+)}{CH}-CH_3 \right] \longrightarrow CH_3-\underset{\underset{CH_3\ CH_3}{|\ \ |}}{\overset{\overset{Cl}{|}}{Si}}-CH-CH_3$$

$$\downarrow$$

$$\left[CH_3-\underset{\underset{CH_3}{|}}{\overset{\overset{CH_3}{|}}{Si}}-CH_2CH_2^{(+)} \right] \longrightarrow CH_3-\underset{\underset{CH_3}{|}}{\overset{\overset{CH_3}{|}}{Si}}-Cl+CH_2=CH_2$$

$$CH_3-\underset{\underset{CH_3}{|}}{\overset{\overset{CH_3}{|}}{Si}}-CHCl_2 \xrightarrow{AlCl_3} CH_3-\underset{\underset{CH_3}{|}}{\overset{\overset{Cl}{|}}{Si}}-Cl + CH_2=CH_2$$

Some examples of β-hetero rearrangement in silicon compounds

Boron and Aluminum Compounds

The analogy between the trivalent boron compounds and carbonium ions extends to the geometry. Although our arguments for a preferred planar structure in carbonium ions are indirect, there is electron diffraction evidence for the planar structure of boron trimethyl and the boron trihalides.[296] Like carbonium ions, the boron and aluminum analogs readily form a fourth covalent bond to atoms having the requisite non-bonding electrons. Examples are the compounds with ammonia, ether, and fluoride ion.[297]

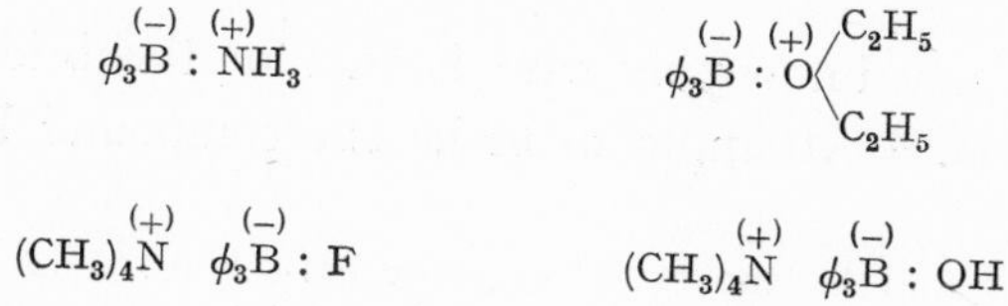

$$\overset{(-)}{\phi_3B} : \overset{(+)}{NH_3} \qquad\qquad \overset{(-)}{\phi_3B} : \overset{(+)}{O}\!\!\begin{array}{c}C_2H_5\\C_2H_5\end{array}$$

$$(CH_3)_4\overset{(+)}{N} \quad \overset{(-)}{\phi_3B} : F \qquad\qquad (CH_3)_4\overset{(+)}{N} \quad \overset{(-)}{\phi_3B} : OH$$

[296] H. A. Lévy and L. O. Brockway, *J. Am. Chem. Soc.*, **59**, 2085 (1937).
[297] D. L. Fowler and C. A. Kraus, *J. Am. Chem. Soc.*, **62**, 1143 (1940).

This type of compound is also formed with hydride or carbanion as the added nucleophilic group.[298]

$$\phi_3B + LiH \longrightarrow \overset{(+)}{Li} \overset{(-)}{\phi_3BH}$$

$$\phi_3B + LiBu \longrightarrow \overset{(+)}{Li} \overset{(-)}{\phi_3BBu}$$

The formation of the etherate from tri-p-tolylaluminum is exothermic to the extent of about 20 kcal./mole.[299]

$$(p\text{-}CH_3\phi)_3Al + Et_2O \longrightarrow (p\text{-}CH_3\phi)_3\overset{(-)}{Al} : \overset{(+)}{O}\overset{Et}{\underset{Et}{\diagdown}}$$

Groups attached to aluminum or boron in this way have the expected increased electrophilic and decreased nucleophilic reactivities. For example, the complex of aluminum triphenyl and phenyl lithium lacks the usual Grignard-like reactivity of phenyl lithium towards carbonyl compounds.[300]

$$\phi_3Al + \phi Li \longrightarrow \overset{(-)}{\phi_4Al} \overset{(+)}{Li}$$

An instance of increased electrophilic reactivity is the behavior of complexed tetrahydrofuran.[298, 300]

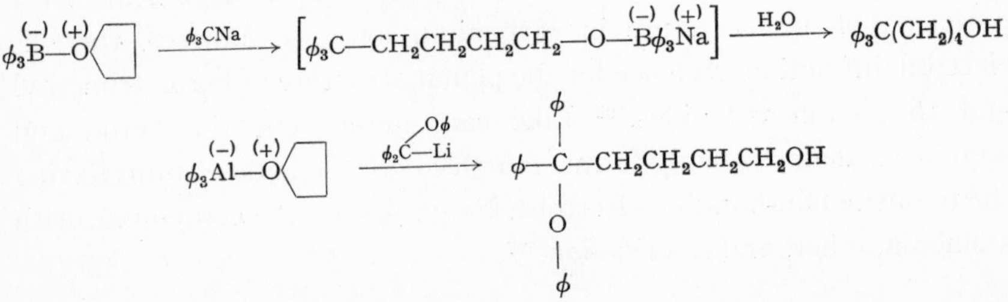

A particularly interesting case is that of the bridgehead compounds of boron.[301] Attempts to make the compound LI gave only

[298] G. Wittig and A. Rückert, *Ann.*, **566**, 101 (1950).
[299] E. Krause and P. Dittmar, *Ber.*, **63B**, 2401 (1930).
[300] G. Wittig and O. Bub, *Ann.*, **566**, 113 (1950).
[301] H. C. Brown and E. A. Fletcher, *J. Am. Chem. Soc*, **73**, 2808 (1951).

polymeric ester, indicating a considerable degree of strain for configurations in which the bonds to boron can be neither coplanar nor double.

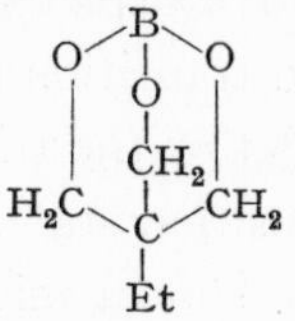

(LI)

Compound LII, on the other hand, can be made readily. It can have either the planar tricovalent boron structure or the "triptych" tetracovalent structure. In the latter structure the nitrogen is attached to boron and should be considerably less basic and nucleophilic than usual. It does in fact react unusually slowly with methyl iodide and with acids. The neutralization reaction with acids in water is not only slow but of zero order with respect to the acid. It is believed to have a rate-determining transformation from the triptych to the more basic form as the first step.

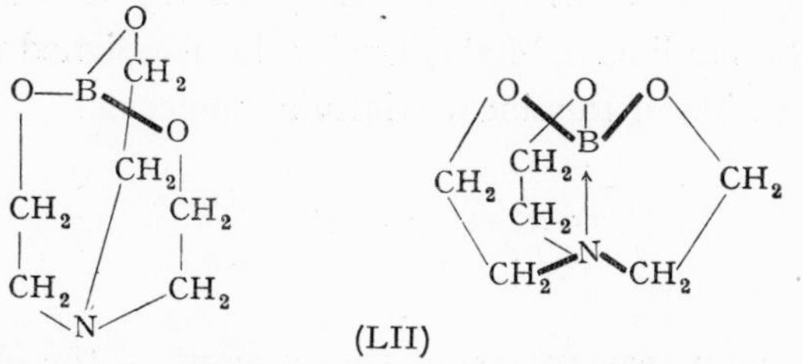

(LII)

Although it does not concern us here, it should be mentioned that organoboron and organoaluminum compounds exhibit anionoid (Grignard) and free radical reactivity as well as their behavior as carbonium ion analogs.

The Nitrogen Analogs

The possible nitrogen analogs of carbonium ions are the cation LIII and its conjugate base LIV.

(LIII)   (LIV)

The assignment of these intermediates to any given reaction is made doubtful not only by the possibility of radical chain mechanisms, but also by the alternative diradical or triplet state favored by Hundt's rule. For most of the reactions the transition state could be either singlet or triplet, and either the singlet or the triplet intermediate could give either of the two types of transition state. Thus the fact that many of the reactions considered have shown migration aptitudes paralleling those of carbonium ion rearrangements suggests, but does not prove, that the intermediates and transition states are singlet states as well as electron deficient. Pertinent evidence might be obtained by studying the type of copolymerization initiated by the reaction or by observing the catalysis or lack of catalysis by paramagnetic substances.

The simplest intermediate of the nitrogen cation type is the nitronium ion, the active species in most aromatic nitration reactions. There is both cryoscopic and spectroscopic (Raman and infrared) evidence for its existence.[302] On the other hand, it has a structure with quaternary rather than electron deficient nitrogen, a structure compatible with the centrosymmetric geometry demanded by the spectra. The Raman line at 1400 cm.$^{-1}$ has been assigned to the totally symmetric vibration of the linear triatomic molecule.

$$O=\underset{(+)}{N}=O \quad \text{not} \quad {}^{(+)}N{\displaystyle\mathop{<}_{O}^{O}}$$

The Beckmann rearrangement shows many of the characteristics of the concerted type of carbonium ion rearrangement. The migrating and displaced groups are trans, the reaction is accelerated by electron releasing substituents in the migrating group, and the reaction is catalyzed by Lewis acids and other reagents capable of stabilizing a

$$\underset{\substack{\downarrow \\ \rightarrow N \frown X}}{\overset{R—C—R'}{\underset{\parallel}{}}} \longrightarrow \begin{bmatrix} {}^{(+)}C—R' \\ \parallel \\ R—N\ X^{(-)} \end{bmatrix} \longrightarrow \begin{bmatrix} X—C—R' \\ \parallel \\ R—N \end{bmatrix} \xrightarrow{H_2O} \underset{\substack{| \\ H}}{\overset{\overset{\displaystyle O}{\overset{\parallel}{R—N—C—R'}}}{}}$$

Beckmann rearrangement

[302] R. J. Gillespie, J. Graham, E. D. Hughes, C. K. Ingold, and E. R. A. Peeling, *J. Chem. Soc,*. 1950, 2504; D. J. Millen, *ibid* , 1950, 2589, 2600, 2612, 2620.

departing negative ion. The reaction will go without a catalyst if the oxime esters of picric acid rather than the oximes themselves are used.[303] A closely analogous reaction is triggered by the nitrous acid deamination of benzophenone hydrazone. Under ordinary conditions the hydrazone is merely hydrolyzed to the ketone, but in concentrated sulfuric acid it is quantitatively converted to benzanilide.[304]

$$
\begin{array}{c}
\text{N—NH}_2 \\
\parallel \\
\phi\text{—C—}\phi
\end{array}
\xrightarrow{\text{HNO}_2}
\left[
\begin{array}{c}
\curvearrowright\text{N}\overset{\curvearrowleft}{}\text{N}_2^{(+)} \\
\parallel \\
\phi\text{—C—}\phi
\end{array}
\right]
\longrightarrow
\left[
\begin{array}{c}
(+) \\
\phi\text{—N}=\text{C—}\phi
\end{array}
\right]
\longrightarrow
\begin{array}{c}
\text{O} \\
\parallel \\
\phi\text{—NH—C—}\phi
\end{array}
$$

The Schmidt reaction of ketones with hydrazoic acid is believed to be a similar rearrangement, again with concerted trans migration and elimination of nitrogen.

$$
\begin{array}{c}
\text{O} \\
\parallel \\
\text{R—C—R}' + \text{HN}_3
\end{array}
\longrightarrow
\left[
\begin{array}{c}
\curvearrowright\text{N}\overset{\curvearrowleft}{}\text{N}_2^{(+)} \\
\parallel \\
\text{R—C—R}'
\end{array}
\right]
\longrightarrow
\left[
\begin{array}{c}
\text{R—N} \\
\parallel \\
(+)\text{C—R}'
\end{array}
\right]
\longrightarrow
\begin{array}{c}
\text{O} \\
\parallel \\
\text{R—NH—C—R}'
\end{array}
$$

Schmidt reaction

When the two groups of the ketone are para-substituted phenyls, the product of the Schmidt reaction is usually a nearly equimolecular mixture of the two isomeric amides.[305] This result, obtained instead of a preferential migration of the more electron-releasing group, is consistent with a mechanism in which the formation of the intermediate rather than its rearrangement is rate determining.

In the reaction of hydrazoic acid with carboxylic acids the amine is probably formed by way of an intermediate identical with that

$$
\text{ArCOOH}
\xrightarrow[\text{Schmidt}]{\text{HN}_3}
\left[
\begin{array}{c}
\text{O} \\
\parallel \\
\text{Ar—C—N}\underset{|}{\overset{(+)}{—}}\text{N}{\equiv}\text{N} \\
\text{H}
\end{array}
\right]
\xleftarrow[\text{Curtius}]{\text{H}^{(+)}}
\begin{array}{c}
\text{O} \\
\parallel \\
\text{Ar—C—N}_3
\end{array}
$$

$$
\left[
\begin{array}{c}
(+) \\
\text{Ar—N}=\text{C}=\text{O} \\
| \\
\text{H}
\end{array}
\right]
\xrightarrow[-\text{CO}_2]{\text{H}_2\text{O}}
\text{ArNH}_2
$$

[303] A. W. Chapman and F. A. Fidler, *J. Chem. Soc.*, **1936**, 448; A. W. Chapman and C. C. Howis, *ibid*, **1933**, 806; A. W. Chapman, *ibid.*, **1934**, 1550.

[304] D. E. Pearson and C. M. Greer, *J. Am. Chem. Soc.*, **71**, 1895 (1949).

[305] P. A. S. Smith and J. P. Horwitz, *J. Am. Chem. Soc.*, **72**, 3718 (1950).

formed by adding a proton to an acyl azide. The decomposition of acyl azides (Curtius reaction) is in fact acid catalyzed.[306]

The rate of the Schmidt reaction of para-substituted benzoic acids is governed by the electron-releasing character of the substituent, the value of the Hammett ρ parameter being the same as that needed to correlate product ratios in the related reaction of 1,1-diarylethylenes.[307] The latter reaction is believed to go by a similar mechanism.

$$\underset{Ar'}{\overset{Ar}{>}}C=CH_2 \;\underset{\longleftarrow}{\overset{H(+),HN_3}{\longrightarrow}}\; \left[\begin{array}{c} Ar \\ Ar' \end{array} \overset{CH_3}{\underset{\underset{(+)}{N}}{\overset{|}{C}}} \overset{|}{N} \right] \longrightarrow \left[\underset{\underset{H}{\overset{|}{N}}\diagdown Ar'}{Ar-\overset{(+)}{C}-CH_3} \right] \overset{H_2O}{\longrightarrow} \begin{array}{c} O \\ \| \\ Ar-C-CH_3 \\ + \\ Ar'NH_2 \end{array}$$

The product ratio $ArCOCH_3/Ar'COCH_3$ is in this case determined by the ability of the migrating groups to accept a positive charge rather than by geometrical factors. The migration aptitudes are the same as in those carbonium ion rearrangements in which geometrical factors can be neglected.

The decomposition of alkyl azides, N-alkylhydroxylamines, and N-chloro or N-bromoamines often requires more drastic conditions than the reactions discussed heretofore, and the resemblance to carbonium ion rearrangements is less pronounced.

$$\phi_3C-N\underset{OH}{\overset{H}{<}} \xrightarrow{-H_2O} \phi_3C-\ddot{N} \longrightarrow \phi_2C=N-\phi$$

$$\phi_3C-N\underset{Br}{\overset{H}{<}} \xrightarrow{-HBr} \phi_3C-\ddot{N} \longrightarrow \phi_2C=N-\phi$$

$$\phi_3C-N_3 \xrightarrow{-N_2} \phi_3C-\ddot{N} \longrightarrow \phi_2C=N-\phi$$

In the mildest of these reactions the hydroxylamine is refluxed in ether over phosphorus pentachloride and the same order of migration aptitudes is observed as in the pinacol rearrangement. The range in

[306] M. S. Newman and H. L. Gildenhorn, *J. Am. Chem. Soc.*, **70**, 317 (1948).
[307] W. E. McEwen and N. B. Mehta, *J. Am. Chem. Soc.*, **74**, 526 (1952).

migration aptitude is much less, however, p-anisyl being only about nine times as good a migrator as phenyl.[308]

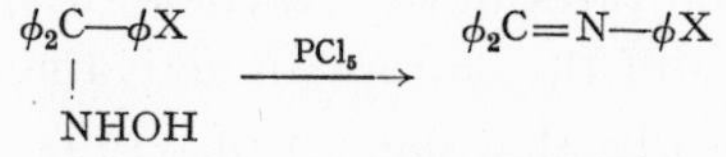

$$\phi_2C\!-\!\phi X \quad \xrightarrow{\text{PCl}_5} \quad \phi_2C\!=\!N\!-\!\phi X$$
$$\underset{\text{NHOH}}{|}$$

Substituent	Migration aptitude
p-methoxy	9.1
p-chloro	0.55
p-nitro	0.38 to 0.18
none	1

The results for some reactions that require more drastic conditions are shown below: [309–312].

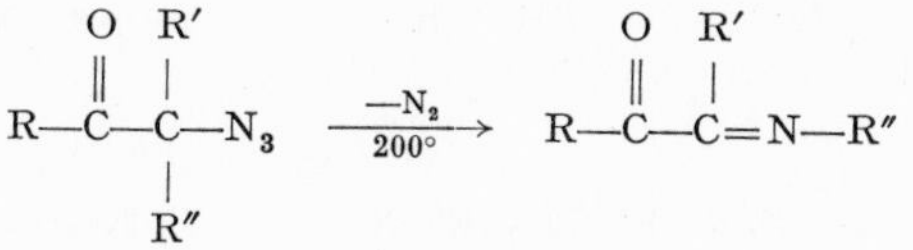

$$\underset{\underset{R''}{|}}{\overset{\overset{O}{\|}}{R\!-\!C}}\!-\!\overset{\overset{R'}{|}}{C}\!-\!N_3 \quad \xrightarrow[200°]{-N_2} \quad \overset{\overset{O}{\|}}{R\!-\!C}\!-\!\overset{\overset{R'}{|}}{C}\!=\!N\!-\!R''$$

Migration aptitudes: $H > \phi > CH_3$

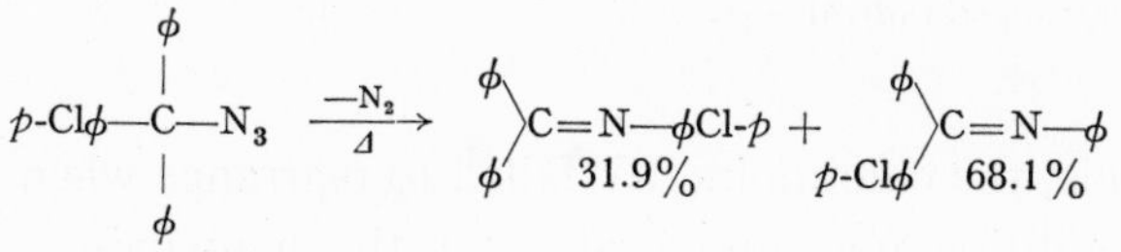

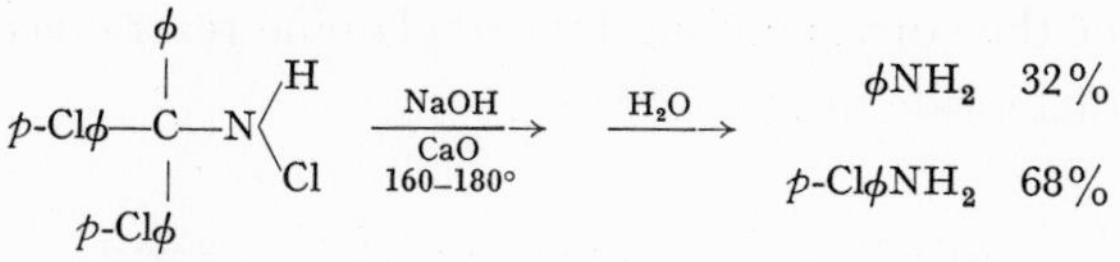

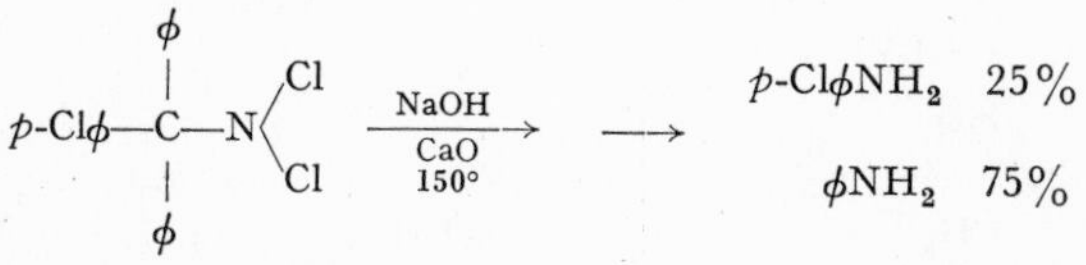

$$p\text{-Cl}\phi\!-\!\overset{\overset{\phi}{|}}{\underset{\underset{\phi}{|}}{C}}\!-\!N_3 \quad \xrightarrow[\Delta]{-N_2} \quad \overset{\phi}{\underset{\phi}{}}\!\!\!C\!=\!N\!-\!\phi\text{Cl-}p \;+\; \overset{\phi}{\underset{p\text{-Cl}\phi}{}}\!\!\!C\!=\!N\!-\!\phi$$
$$31.9\% \qquad 68.1\%$$

$$p\text{-Cl}\phi\!-\!\overset{\overset{\phi}{|}}{\underset{\underset{p\text{-Cl}\phi}{|}}{C}}\!-\!N\!\!\!\overset{H}{\underset{Cl}{\diagdown}} \quad \xrightarrow[\substack{CaO \\ 160-180°}]{NaOH} \quad \xrightarrow{H_2O} \quad \begin{array}{l} \phi NH_2 \quad 32\% \\[4pt] p\text{-Cl}\phi NH_2 \quad 68\% \end{array}$$

$$p\text{-Cl}\phi\!-\!\overset{\overset{\phi}{|}}{\underset{\underset{\phi}{|}}{C}}\!-\!N\!\!\!\overset{Cl}{\underset{Cl}{\diagdown}} \quad \xrightarrow[\substack{CaO \\ 150°}]{NaOH} \quad \longrightarrow \quad \begin{array}{l} p\text{-Cl}\phi NH_2 \quad 25\% \\[4pt] \phi NH_2 \quad 75\% \end{array}$$

In at least the first three of the high temperature reactions the migration aptitudes are not quite those to be expected of the analogous

[308] M. S. Newman and P. M. Hay, *J. Am. Chem. Soc.*, **75**, 2322 (1953).
[309] J. H. Boyer and D. Straw, *J. Am. Chem. Soc.*, **75**, 1642 (1953).
[310] J. K. Senior, *J. Am. Chem. Soc.*, **38**, 2718 (1916).
[311] A. F. Morgan, *J. Am. Chem. Soc.*, **38**, 2095 (1916).
[312] I. Vosburgh, *J. Am. Chem. Soc.*, **38**, 2081 (1916).

reactions at lower temperature. In the first reaction it may be that hydrogen is removed by a radical chain reaction. In the others it may be that the migration rates have been more nearly equalized by the increased importance of the entropy of activation at the higher temperature. It may also be that one set of results represents migration aptitudes in a triplet state mechanism while the other corresponds to a singlet state mechanism.

Quite often the Hofmann and Stieglitz rearrangements fail for molecules not having hydrogen attached to the nitrogen. The hydrogen is necessary either for a radical chain reaction or for the electron-deficient nitrogen mechanism in which the nitrogen is unicovalent.

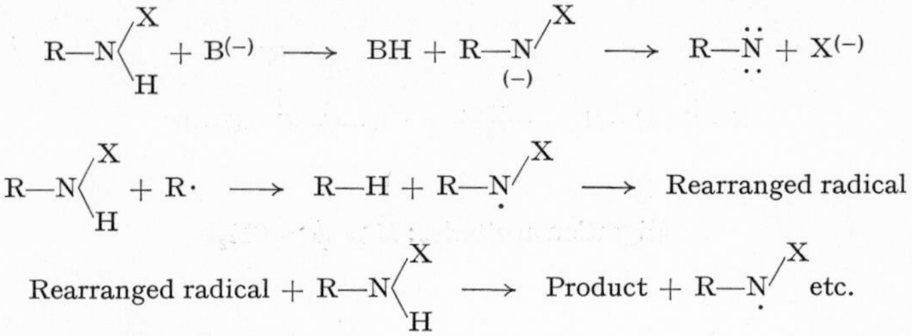

$$R-N\langle^{X}_{H} + B^{(-)} \longrightarrow BH + R-N\Big/^{X}_{(-)} \longrightarrow R-\ddot{N} + X^{(-)}$$

$$R-N\langle^{X}_{H} + R\cdot \longrightarrow R-H + R-\overset{X}{\underset{\cdot}{N}} \longrightarrow \text{Rearranged radical}$$

$$\text{Rearranged radical} + R-N\langle^{X}_{H} \longrightarrow \text{Product} + R-\overset{X}{\underset{\cdot}{N}} \quad \text{etc.}$$

For example, the chloramine LV failed to rearrange when heated with base, a condition not unfavorable for the non-chain radical mechanism.[312] Yet the corresponding hydroxylamine rearranged with phosphorus pentachloride in ether.[313]

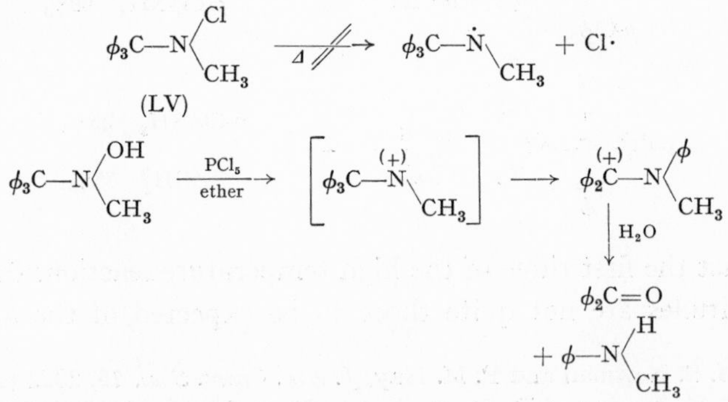

$$\phi_3C-N\langle^{Cl}_{CH_3} \xrightarrow{\;\;\Delta\;\;} \phi_3C-\dot{N}\langle_{CH_3} + Cl\cdot$$
(LV)

$$\phi_3C-N\langle^{OH}_{CH_3} \xrightarrow[\text{ether}]{PCl_5} \Big[\phi_3C-\overset{(+)}{N}\langle_{CH_3} \Big] \longrightarrow \phi_2\overset{(+)}{C}-N\langle^{\phi}_{CH_3}$$

$$\Big\downarrow H_2O$$

$$\phi_2C=O$$
$$+ \phi-N\langle^{H}_{CH_3}$$

The reaction with phosphorus pentachloride failed in the case of the

[313] J. Stieglitz and B. A. Stagner, *J. Am. Chem. Soc.*, **38**, 2046 (1916).

analogous amides, whose nitrogen is less able to tolerate a positive charge:[313]

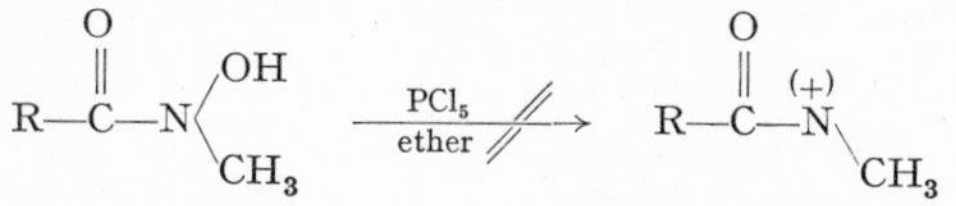

$$R-\overset{\overset{\displaystyle O}{\|}}{C}-N\overset{\displaystyle OH}{\underset{\displaystyle CH_3}{\Big\langle}} \xrightarrow[\text{ether}]{PCl_5} \quad R-\overset{\overset{\displaystyle O}{\|}}{C}-\overset{(+)}{N}\overset{}{\underset{\displaystyle CH_3}{\Big\langle}}$$

The Hofmann reaction of an amide with bromine and alkali apparently goes by way of the N-bromoamide and unicovalent electron-deficient nitrogen.

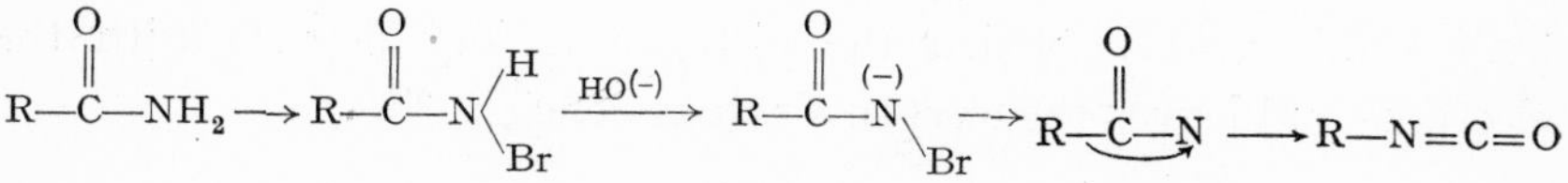

$$R-\overset{\overset{\displaystyle O}{\|}}{C}-NH_2 \longrightarrow R-\overset{\overset{\displaystyle O}{\|}}{C}-N\overset{\displaystyle H}{\underset{\displaystyle Br}{\Big\langle}} \xrightarrow{HO(-)} R-\overset{\overset{\displaystyle O}{\|}}{C}-\overset{(-)}{N}\overset{}{\underset{\displaystyle Br}{\Big\backslash}} \longrightarrow R-\overset{\overset{\displaystyle O}{\|}}{C}-N \longrightarrow R-N=C=O$$

$$R-N=C=O + H_2O \longrightarrow RNH_2 + CO_2$$

Evidence supporting a step analogous to a carbonium ion rearrangement is the accelerating effect of electron-releasing substituents in the migrating group.[314] The mechanism shown above has been expanded for the sake of clarity and is not meant to imply that the rearrangement can not be concerted with the departure of the bromide ion.

As in the case of carbonium ion rearrangements, mechanisms in which the migrating group is set free may be discarded. In those cases where the stereochemistry has been investigated it is found that an asymmetric group migrates with retention of its original configuration. The rearrangements are internal substitution reactions rather than dissociation reactions followed by recombination at a new site.

The Lossen rearrangement of an hydroxamic acid under basic conditions is a variant of the Hofmann reaction in which the aroyloxy group fills the role of the bromine.[314]

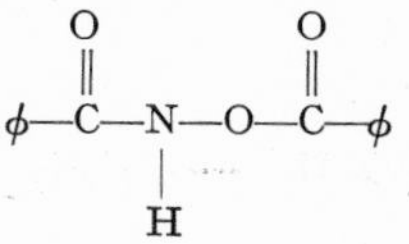

$$\phi-\overset{\overset{\displaystyle O}{\|}}{C}-\underset{\underset{\displaystyle H}{|}}{N}-O-\overset{\overset{\displaystyle O}{\|}}{C}-\phi$$

Benzhydroxamic acid

In neutral media the decomposition of hydroxamic acids may be a

[314] C. R. Hauser and W. B. Renfrow, Jr., *J. Am. Chem. Soc.*, **59**, 121 (1937); W. B. Renfrow, Jr., and C. R. Hauser, *ibid.*, **59**, 2308 (1937); R. D. Bright and C. R. Hauser, *ibid.*, **61**, 618 (1939).

cyclic one in which the hydrogen and carboxylate group depart together.

$$\phi-\overset{\overset{\textstyle O}{\|}}{C}-\overset{\overset{\textstyle H\cdots\cdots O}{|}}{N}\underset{\diagdown O\diagup}{\overset{\overset{\textstyle O}{\|}}{C}}-\phi \longrightarrow \phi-\overset{\overset{\textstyle O}{\|}}{C}-N + HO-\overset{\overset{\textstyle O}{\|}}{C}-\phi$$

This decomposition is somewhat analogous to the polar decomposition of suitably unsymmetrical diacyl peroxides. However, it has not been possible to force the complementary mode of decomposition of a hydroxamic acid in which the nitrogen moiety departs with the electrons and leaves the oxygen electron-deficient.[315]

$$O_2N\phi-\overset{\overset{\textstyle O}{\|}}{C}-\overset{\overset{\textstyle H}{|}}{N}-O-\overset{\overset{\textstyle O}{\|}}{C}-\phi OCH_3 \:\:\not\longrightarrow\:\: O_2N\phi-\overset{\overset{\textstyle O}{\|}}{C}-\overset{\overset{\textstyle H}{|}}{N} \underset{(-)\:\:(+)}{O}-\overset{\overset{\textstyle O}{\|}}{C}-\phi OCH_3$$

Since the analogous peroxides usually decompose by a free radical mechanism, it is noteworthy that this hydroxamic acid is not sensitive to the action of free radicals from anisoyl peroxide. A radical chain mechanism like that shown below can therefore be ruled out for this compound.

$$O_2N\phi-\overset{\overset{\textstyle O}{\|}}{C}-\overset{\overset{\textstyle H}{|}}{N}-O-\overset{\overset{\textstyle O}{\|}}{C}-\phi OCH_3 \:\:\not\longrightarrow\:\: O_2N-\phi-\overset{\overset{\textstyle O}{\|}}{C}-\overset{\overset{\textstyle H}{|}}{N}\bullet + \bullet O-\overset{\overset{\textstyle O}{\|}}{C}-\phi OCH_3$$

$$O_2N\phi-\overset{\overset{\textstyle O}{\|}}{C}-\underset{\overset{\textstyle |}{H}}{N}-O-\overset{\overset{\textstyle O}{\|}}{C}-\phi OCH_3 + \bullet O-\overset{\overset{\textstyle O}{\|}}{C}-\phi OCH_3 \:\:\not\longrightarrow$$

$$CH_3O\phi COOH + O_2N\phi-\overset{\overset{\textstyle O}{\|}}{C}-\underset{\bullet}{N}-O-\overset{\overset{\textstyle O}{\|}}{C}-\phi OCH_3$$

$$O_2N\phi-\overset{\overset{\textstyle O}{\|}}{C}-\underset{\bullet}{N}-O-\overset{\overset{\textstyle O}{\|}}{C}-\phi OCH_3 \longrightarrow O_2N\phi-\overset{\overset{\textstyle O}{\|}}{C}-N + \bullet O-\overset{\overset{\textstyle O}{\|}}{C}-\phi OCH_3$$

The Oxygen Analogs

Organic peroxides can decompose either homolytically into a pair of oxygen radicals or heterolytically to give an oxygen cation and

[315] J. E. Leffler, *J. Am. Chem. Soc.*, **72**, 4294 (1950).

anion.[316] Unsymmetrical substitution of the peroxide, a polar medium, groups of superior migration aptitude, and acid catalysts favor the latter mode of reaction. The evidence that the reaction is indeed polar rather than radical consists of migration aptitudes (like those in carbonium ion reactions), differences in the products, and appropriate medium effects. The conclusion is strengthened by the fact that in some cases one and the same peroxide will decompose by either mechanism and give quite different products, depending on the reaction conditions. Examples of the dual mechanisms are to be found among hydroperoxides, diacyl peroxides, and per-esters.

The thermal decomposition of p-nitrotriphenylmethyl hydroperoxide in benzene gives p-nitrophenol 32%, phenol 9%, p-nitrotriphenylcarbinol 23%, p-nitrobenzophenone 14%, and no benzophenone; the decomposition in ether plus sulfuric acid gives p-nitrobenzophenone 94% and phenol 81%.[317] The latter reaction is very probably:

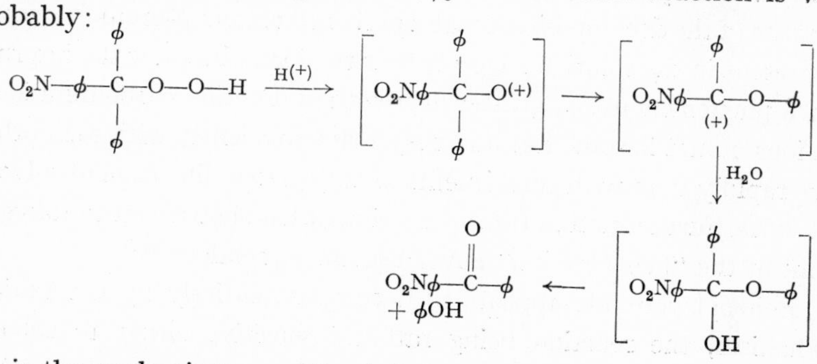

Again the mechanism as written is not meant to imply a completely free oxygen cation as the intermediate. A concerted ionization and rearrangement seems more likely.

A similar mechanism is probable for the decomposition of decalyl perbenzoate.[318]

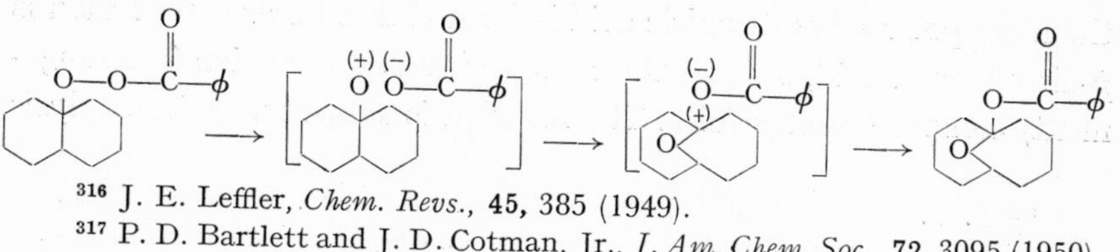

[316] J. E. Leffler, Chem. Revs., 45, 385 (1949).
[317] P. D. Bartlett and J. D. Cotman, Jr., J. Am. Chem. Soc., 72, 3095 (1950).
[318] R. Criegee, Ann., 560, 127, (1948); R. Criegee and H. Dietrich, Ann. 560, 135 (1948).

The reaction goes faster in more polar solvents (a range of 10^5 in the rate constant) and parallels carbonium ion rearrangements in that respect. The effect of substituents in the para position of the benzoate group also suggests that the rate-determining step is the formation of an initial ion pair. The reaction is faster with the nitro than with the methoxyl substituent.[319, 320] The Hammett ρ value is 1.34. The activation parameters are not known for any but the unsubstituted member of the series however, and hence it is not known to what extent the relative rates depend upon the temperature.

The initial ion pair in the decalyl perbenzoate rearrangement may well be the rearranged or bridged ion. Thus the failure of *tert*-butyl perbenzoates to show any signs of a polar decomposition suggests that the nature of the group involved in a concerted migration may be an important factor in bringing about the ionic rather than the radical reaction. Finally, the absence of any considerable interchange between benzoate of the decomposing decalyl perbenzoate and *p*-bromobenzoate ion present in the solution suggests that the ion pairs show the internal return phenomenon to a greater degree than do other carbonium ions. The ions do not become free and they react covalently with each other more rapidly than with constituents of the surrounding cage of solvent molecules. Furthermore, a tracer experiment has shown that the oxygen atoms of the "benzoate ion" never become equivalent.[320a]

Benzoyl peroxide appears to decompose entirely by the radical mechanism, the reaction being rather insensitive either to solvent changes or to the addition of acid catalysts. The unsymmetrical peroxide, *p*-methoxy-*p'*-nitrobenzoyl peroxide, behaves quite differently. It will decompose either by the polar mechanism or by the radical mechanism.[321] The radical mechanism prevails in benzene and the acids produced are *p*-nitrobenzoic and anisic in equal amounts. In the more polar solvents anisic acid is formed to a lesser extent than is *p*-nitrobenzoic acid, because the carboxy inversion reaction (rearrangement) competes successfully. The reaction is subject to acid catalysis

319 P. D. Bartlett, and J. L. Kice, *J. Am. Chem. Soc.*, **75**, 5591 (1953).
320 H. L. Goering and A. C. Olson, *J. Am. Chem. Soc* , **75**, 5853 (1953).
320a D. B. Denney, *J. Am. Chem. Soc.*, **77**, 1706 (1955).
321 J. E. Leffler, *J. Am. Chem. Soc.*, **72**, 67 (1950).

and is also faster in the more polar solvents, the ratio of the decomposition rate constants in nitrobenzene and benzene being about eight at 70°. The ratio of the rates of the polar reaction alone in the two solvents must be much greater since the polar reaction is completely masked by the radical reaction in benzene and accounts for a negligible part of the rate in that solvent. In thionyl chloride the intermediate responsible for the extensive decarboxylation of the anisoyloxy part of the molecule is easily isolable, and the reaction leading to it is called the carboxy inversion reaction because the overall effect is to turn the carboxy group end for end in the molecule.

$$O_2N-\phi-\overset{\overset{\displaystyle O}{\|}}{C}-O-O-\overset{\overset{\displaystyle O}{\|}}{C}-\phi OCH_3 \xrightarrow{\text{benzene}} O_2N\phi-\overset{\overset{\displaystyle O}{\|}}{C}-O\cdot + CH_3O-\phi-\overset{\overset{\displaystyle O}{\|}}{C}-O\cdot$$

$$\left.\begin{array}{c} O_2N\phi-\overset{\overset{\displaystyle O}{\|}}{C}-O\cdot \\[3mm] CH_3O\phi-\overset{\overset{\displaystyle O}{\|}}{C}-O\cdot \end{array}\right\} + RH \longrightarrow R\cdot + \left.\begin{array}{c} O_2N\phi-\overset{\overset{\displaystyle O}{\|}}{C}-OH \\[3mm] CH_3O\phi-\overset{\overset{\displaystyle O}{\|}}{C}-OH \end{array}\right\} \text{Equal amounts}$$

$$O_2N-\phi-\overset{\overset{\displaystyle O}{\|}}{C}-O-O-\overset{\overset{\displaystyle O}{\|}}{C}-\phi OCH_3 \xrightarrow{SOCl_2} \left[O_2N\phi-\overset{\overset{\displaystyle O}{\|}}{C}-O\underset{\text{(+)}}{\overset{\text{(-)}}{}}\overset{\text{(+)}}{O}-\overset{\overset{\displaystyle O}{\|}}{C}-\phi OCH_3 \right]$$

$$\downarrow$$

$$O_2N\phi-\overset{\overset{\displaystyle O}{\|}}{C}-O-\overset{\overset{\displaystyle O}{\|}}{C}-O-\phi OCH_3 \longleftarrow \left[O_2N\phi-\overset{\overset{\displaystyle O}{\|}}{C}-\underset{\text{(+)}}{O}\,\overset{\text{(-)}}{}\overset{\overset{\displaystyle O}{\|}}{C}-O-\phi OCH_3 \right]$$

Although benzoyl peroxide will initiate the polymerization (by a radical chain reaction) of either styrene or acrylonitrile, p-methoxy-p'-nitrobenzoyl peroxide will not initiate polymerization efficiently in the latter monomer because it is too rapidly destroyed by the polar decomposition. Acrylonitrile, but not styrene, causes the polar decomposition to predominate, and the intermediates of the polar decomposition are not catalysts for the polymerization of acrylonitrile.

The reactions of per-acids and hydrogen peroxide with carbonyl compounds can be formulated as the result of addition to the carbonyl group followed by the decomposition of the new peroxide thus formed.[316] Although the initial rate-determining addition to the carbonyl group is undoubtedly a polar reaction,[322] the subsequent decomposition of the resulting hydroperoxide may be either radical or polar, probably depending on the reaction conditions.

$$
\begin{array}{ccccc}
 & & \text{OH} & & \text{OH} \\
\text{O} & & | & & | \\
\| & & \text{R—C—R}' & & \text{R—C—R}' \\
\text{R—C—R}' + \text{R''OOH} & \longrightarrow & | & \longrightarrow & \text{O}\bullet & \longrightarrow & \text{R—C—O—R} \\
 & & \text{O} & & \\
 & & | & & \text{OH} \\
 & & \text{O} & & | \\
 & & | & & \text{or R—C—R}' \\
 & & \text{R''} & & \text{O}^{(+)}
\end{array}
$$

As is predicted by the mechanism in which the oxygen radical or cation rearranges (rather than cleaves), labeled oxygen in the carbonyl group of the ketone is found in the carbonyl of the product, and migrating groups retain their original configuration.[323-325]

$$
\overset{O^{18}}{\underset{}{\overset{\|}{\phi\text{—C—}\phi}}} + \overset{O}{\underset{}{\overset{\|}{\phi\text{—C—O—OH}}}} \longrightarrow \overset{O^{18}}{\underset{}{\overset{\|}{\phi\text{—C—O—}\phi}}}
$$

$$
\overset{O}{\underset{|}{\overset{\|}{CH_3\text{—C}}}}\overset{H}{\underset{\phi}{\overset{*|}{\text{—C—CH}_3}}} \xrightarrow[\text{CHCl}_3]{\phi\text{—C—OOH}} \overset{O}{\underset{|}{\overset{\|}{CH_3\text{—C—O}}}}\overset{H}{\underset{\phi}{\overset{*|}{\text{—C—CH}_3}}} \text{ (retention)}
$$

cis   cis

The migration aptitudes in the reaction of ketones with peracetic acid in acetic acid as a solvent are in the order p-anisyl > phenyl > p-nitro-phenyl.[326] Cyclohexyl and phenyl are about equal in migration aptitude

[322] S. L. Friess, *J. Am. Chem. Soc.*, **71**, 2571 (1949).
[323] W. von E. Doering and E. Dorfman, *J. Am. Chem. Soc.*, **75**, 5595 (1953).
[324] K. Mislow and J. Brenner, *J. Am. Chem. Soc.*, **75**, 2318 (1953).
[325] R. B. Turner, *J. Am. Chem. Soc.*, **72**, 878 (1950).
[326] W. von E. Doering and L. Speers, *J. Am. Chem. Soc.*, **72**, 5515 (1950).

under these rather polar conditions[326] while, with perbenzoic acid in the less polar solvent chloroform, cyclohexyl out-migrates phenyl 5 to 1.[327] In general the migration aptitudes are not so clean-cut as to rule out considerable radical as well as polar decomposition of the intermediate peroxide.

Another reaction in which an oxygen cation is plausible as an intermediate is in the ozonization of olefins. Ozonides are now known to have many structures, but the molozonide precursor of the "classical" or most common ozonide is believed to have a four-membered, cyclic structure. Criegee and the author have independently proposed a mechanism in which heterolytic fission of the cyclic peroxide bond leads to an intermediate that can rearrange either to the classical ozonide or to an "abnormal" ozonide:[316, 328]

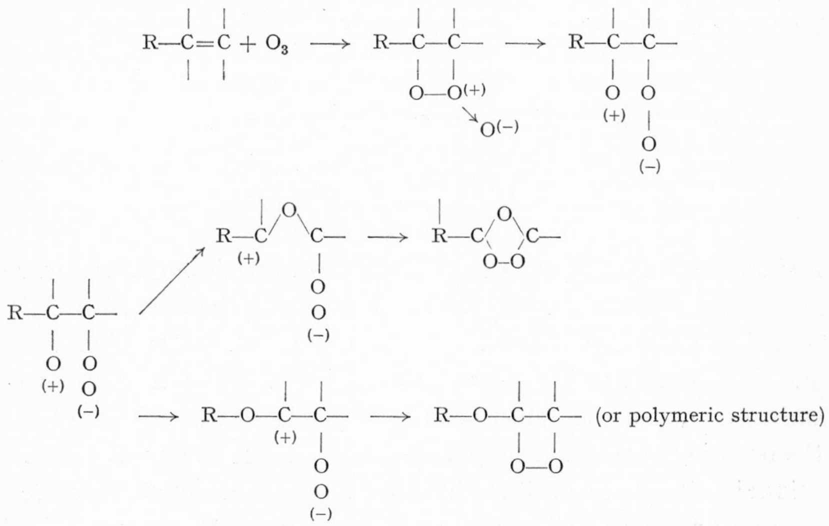

Hydrolysis, or better, hydrogenolysis of the normal ozonide leads to the cleavage of the original carbon-carbon double bond with formation of carbonyl groups. The abnormal ozonide usually decomposes before it reaches room temperature and both the double bond and the adjacent carbon-carbon single bond are found to have cleaved.

[327] S. L. Friess and N. Farnham, *J. Am. Chem. Soc.*, **72**, 5518 (1950).
[328] R. Criegee, *Ann.*, **560**, 127 (1948).

$$R-\overset{|}{\underset{|}{C}}\overset{O}{\diagdown}\overset{|}{\underset{|}{C}}- \longrightarrow R-\overset{|}{\underset{|}{C}}\overset{O}{\diagdown}\overset{|}{\underset{|}{C}}- \longrightarrow R-\overset{|}{\underset{||}{C}}- + H_2O + O=\overset{|}{C}-$$

$$R-O-\overset{|}{\underset{|}{C}}\mathrel{\vdots}\overset{|}{\underset{|}{C}}- \longrightarrow R-O-\overset{|}{\underset{||}{C}}- + \overset{|}{\underset{||}{C}}-$$

The abnormal ozonolysis is chiefly observed when the group R is one that shows a high migration aptitude in carbonium ion rearrangements.

The formation of an intermediate with electron-deficient oxygen is also one of the possible paths for the oxidation of alcohols. An intermediate such as LVI, or the chromate ester LVII which might behave in similar fashion, could rearrange to give "abnormal" products or lose a proton to give the usual, expected product.[329-332]

$$ROH \xrightarrow[\text{acid}]{\text{chromic}} RO^{(+)} \quad \text{or} \quad R-O-\overset{O}{\underset{O}{\overset{||}{\underset{||}{Cr}}}}-OH$$

$$\text{(LVI)} \qquad\qquad\qquad \text{(LVII)}$$

A simple removal of hydrogen from the hydroxyl group, however, can not be the rate-determining step in the case of the oxidation of isopropyl alcohol to acetone, since the 2-deuterated alcohol is oxidized only one sixth as fast as is isopropyl alcohol itself.[333] The breaking of the carbon-hydrogen bond must be at least concerted with, if not prior to, the breaking of the oxygen-hydrogen bond. Some examples of chromic acid oxidation products (other than the expected ketone) attributable to the rearrangement of an oxygen cation are shown on the next page. It will be understood by the indulgent reader that, as usual, the equations are not meant to imply anything with regard to the degree of concertedness of the indicated steps.

[329] W. A. Mosher and F. C. Whitmore, *J. Am. Chem. Soc.*, **70**, 2544 (1948).
[330] W. A. Mosher and E. O. Langerak, *J. Am. Chem. Soc.*, **71**, 286 (1949).
[331] W. A. Mosher and K. A. Neidig, *J. Am. Chem. Soc.*, **72**, 4452 (1950).
[332] W. A. Mosher and E. O. Langerak, *J. Am. Chem. Soc.*, **73**, 1302 (1951).
[333] F. H. Westheimer and N. Nicolaides, *J. Am. Chem. Soc.*, **71**, 25 (1949).

$$\underset{\substack{CH_3 \\ |}}{\overset{\substack{CH_3 \quad OH \\ | \quad\quad |}}{CH_3-C-\!\!-C-CH_3}} \;\longrightarrow\; \left[\underset{\substack{CH_3 \\ |}}{\overset{\substack{CH_3 \quad \overset{(+)}{O} \\ | \quad\quad \nearrow|}}{CH_3-C-\!\!-C-CH_3}}\right] \;\longrightarrow\; \underset{\substack{CH_2 \\ | \\ CH_3}}{CH_3-C-OH} \;(7\%\ \text{yield})$$

(with CH_2, H, CH_3 branches)

$$\underset{\substack{CH_3 \quad H}}{\overset{\substack{CH_3 \quad OH}}{CH_3-C-\!\!-C-CH_3}} \;\longrightarrow\; \left[\overset{\substack{CH_3 \quad \overset{(+)}{O}}}{CH_3-C-\!\!-C-CH_3}\right] \;\longrightarrow\; \underset{\substack{CH_3}}{\overset{\substack{CH_3}}{CH_3-C-OH}} \;(6\%\ \text{yield})$$

$$\underset{\substack{Et \quad H}}{\overset{\substack{CH_3 \quad OH}}{H-C-\!\!-C-Et}} \;\longrightarrow\; \left[\overset{\substack{CH_3 \quad \overset{(+)}{O}}}{H-C-\!\!-C-Et}\right] \;\longrightarrow\; \underset{\substack{Et}}{\overset{\substack{CH_3}}{H-C-OH}} \;(1\%\ \text{yield})$$

$$\underset{\substack{CH_3 \quad H}}{\overset{\substack{CH_3 \quad OH}}{I_3-C-\!\!-C-CH_2CH_2CH_3}} \;\rightarrow\; \left[\overset{\substack{CH_3 \quad \overset{(+)}{O}}}{CH_3-C-\!\!-C-CH_2CH_2CH_3}\right] \;\rightarrow\; \left[\underset{\substack{CH_3 \quad H}}{\overset{\substack{CH_3}}{CH_3-C-O-\overset{(+)}{C}-CH_2CH_2CH_3}}\right]$$

$$\Big\downarrow H_2O$$

$$\left[\underset{\substack{CH_3 \quad H}}{\overset{\substack{CH_3 \quad OH}}{CH_3-C-O-C-CH_2CH_2CH_3}}\right]$$

$$(4\%\ \text{yield}) \begin{cases} \underset{\substack{CH_3}}{\overset{\substack{CH_3}}{CH_3-C-OH}} \quad\longleftarrow \\[2em] \overset{O}{\overset{\|}{CH_3CH_2CH_2-C-H}} \end{cases}$$

$$\underset{\substack{H}}{\overset{\substack{OH}}{\phi_3C-C\!\!-\!\!\phi}} \;\longrightarrow\; \left[\underset{\substack{H}}{\overset{\substack{\overset{(+)}{O}}}{\phi_3C-C\!\!-\!\!\phi}}\right] \;\longrightarrow\; \phi_3C^{(+)} + \overset{O}{\overset{\|}{\phi-C-H}} \;(6\%\ \text{yield})$$

$$\Big\downarrow H_2O$$

$$\phi_3COH \;(\mathbf{22\%}\ \text{yield})$$

$$(2\%\ \text{yield})$$

CHAPTER IX

The Formation of Carbanions

Conductivity of Organometallic Compounds

One of the obstacles to the proof of the formation of carbanions by the dissociation of organometallic compounds is the scarcity of solvents that are of high dielectric constant yet not too acidic or otherwise reactive. Diethyl ether is sufficiently inert but has so low a dielectric constant that ion clusters are formed extensively as well as single ions and ion pairs. Thus the equivalent conductance of sodium triphenylmethyl in ether passes through a minimum at a concentration of about 2×10^{-3} M.[334, 335] At concentrations higher than this most of the conductivity is due to ion aggregates, while at lower concentrations the dependence of the conductivity on the concentration suggests simple ionization. The equilibrium constant for the simple dissociation into two ions at 25° is estimated to be about 10^{-12}.[334] The equilibrium constants for sodium phenylxenyl-α-naphthylmethyl and sodium diphenyl-α-naphthylmethyl are about 10^{-13} and 10^{-12}.[336] The extent of ionization in ether is not very sensitive to temperature changes, so the low value of the ionization constants is due to an unfavorable entropy of ionization, probably corresponding to the high degree of orientation of ether molecules in the neighborhood of an ion as contrasted with their lack of orientation in ether itself.

The low degree of ionization in ether does not necessarily mean that triarylmethyl sodium compounds are largely covalent in that solvent. They may still be highly polar. Lithium iodide, for example, is also a poor conductor in ether although a good one in water. The conductivity of triphenylmethyl sodium in pyridine is very much

---

[334] E. Swift, *J. Am. Chem. Soc.*, **60**, 1403 (1938).
[335] K. Ziegler and H. Wollschitt, *Ann.*, **479**, 123 (1930).
[336] N. B. Keevil and H. E. Bent, *J. Am. Chem. Soc.*, **60**, 193 (1938).

greater than in ether. The color of triphenylmethyl sodium in pyridine is also much deeper than in ether and, in fact, pyridine added to ethereal triphenylmethyl sodium precipitates a red and rather insoluble pyridine complex. The deeper color in pyridine does not of course prove that the compound is covalent in ether, since it might be the result of the complex formation or of a shift in the position of an absorption band rather than the result of a decrease in the proportion of the material in the covalent form. The effect of changing the concentration of the triphenyl-methyl sodium on the conductivity in pyridine is like that in the case of triphenylmethyl perchlorate in sulfur dioxide. Thus even an unsub-stituted sodium triphenylmethide is a strong electrolyte in pyridine, as are potassium triphenylmethide, sodium tris-(p-nitrophenyl)-methide, and the potassium salts of diphenylmethane, fluorene, and indene.[335] Triphenylmethyl sodium in ether reacts with tetramethylammonium chloride to form triphenylmethyl tetramethylammonium, a red sub-stance that is a good conductor in pyridine and is hardly likely to have any covalent character for quantum mechanical reasons in view of the reluctance of nitrogen to expand its octet.

Triphenylmethyl sodium and triphenylmethyl potassium conduct in liquid ammonia although they slowly react with that solvent.[337, 338] When the liquid ammonia is allowed to evaporate from a solution of triphenylmethyl sodium in ammonia, the residue is a colorless mixture of sodamide and triphenylmethane. The sodium-tin and sodium-germanium compounds analogous to sodium triphenylmethide are also strong electrolytes in liquid ammonia. Sodium acetylide in liquid ammonia is dissociated to about the same extent as sodium acetate in water.[339]

Diethyl zinc is another solvent in which organo-alkali compounds conduct, doubtless as complex ions containing diethyl zinc. Ethyl sodium, ethyl lithium, ethyl potassium, and methyl, phenyl, and benzyl lithium all form conducting solutions in that solvent. In general the higher the melting point, the higher the conductivity and the lower the solubility. These properties are presumably associated with a greater

[337] C. A. Kraus and R. Rosen, J. Am. Chem. Soc., 47, 2739 (1925).
[338] C. A. Kraus and W. H. Kahler, J. Am. Chem. Soc., 55, 3537 (1933).
[339] C. B. Wooster, Chem. Revs., 11, 1 (1932).

degree of ionic bond character. Benzyl lithium, for example, is a good conductor while phenyl lithium is a poor one.[339] Presumably the difference is due to the resonance stabilization of the anion in the case of benzyl lithium. Methyl sodium is a white powder that will not melt or dissolve in any known solvent without decomposition. It reacts explosively with air. None of its properties seem well chosen for the convenience of chemists who might wish to study it. Most alkyl lithium compounds, on the other hand, have properties appropriate to a covalent carbon-lithium bond. They can be distilled and are soluble in non-polar solvents. The dipole moment of *n*-butyl lithium in benzene is only 0.97 D.[340] Electrolysis of ethyl sodium in diethyl zinc gives products at the anode suggestive of oxidation of the carbanion to the free radical; these products include ethane, ethylene, and with a lead anode, tetraethyl lead.[339]

Grignard reagents also behave in a complicated way in conductivity experiments. The aromatic Grignard reagents form colloidal rather than tiue solutions in ether. An additional complication is the disproportronation of the Grignard reagent into dialkyl magnesium and magnesium bromide. The extent of this disproportionation is only inaccurately measured by the dioxane precipitation technique and therefore can not be corrected for. Although nothing quantitative can be said about the relation between the structure of the Grignard reagent and its tendency to ionize, it seems likely from the conductance data that the migrating ion is the complex LVIII rather than a free carbanion.[341]

$$\underset{(-)}{\overset{\overset{\displaystyle R}{|}}{R\!-\!Mg\!-\!X}}$$

(LVIII)

Electrolysis of Grignard reagents in ether produces the saturated and unsaturated hydrocarbons to be expected if the anode oxidizes a real or potential carbanion to the corresponding free radical.

$$R^{(-)} \longrightarrow R\bullet + e$$

or $$R_2MgX^{(-)} \longrightarrow R\bullet + e + RMgX$$

[340] M. T. Rogers and A. Young, *J. Am. Chem. Soc.*, **68**, 2748 (1946).
[341] W. V. Evans and R. Pearson, *J. Am. Chem. Soc.*, **64**, 2865 (1942).

Color and Spectrophotometry of Organometallic Compounds

Unlike the carbon acids of simpler structure, the triarylmethanes form colored salts. No quantitative results are available, but the appearance of the color has been used qualitatively as an indication of the formation of the ions and ion pairs. Table VIII gives the colors of some organometallic compounds.

TABLE VIII

Compound	Color
Sodium, potassium, or tetramethyl-ammonium triphenylmethide	Red
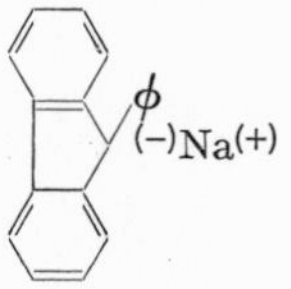	Orange red
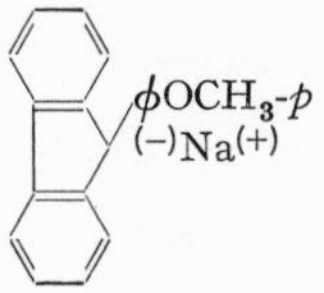	Red
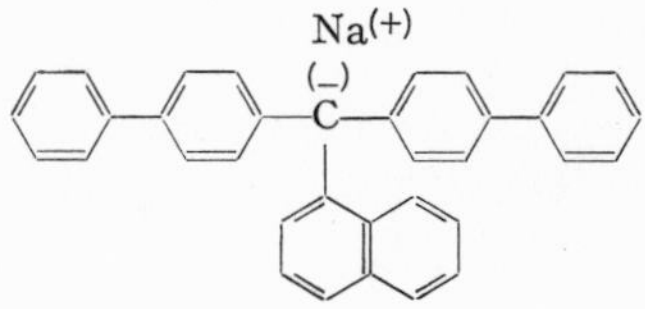	Dark violet
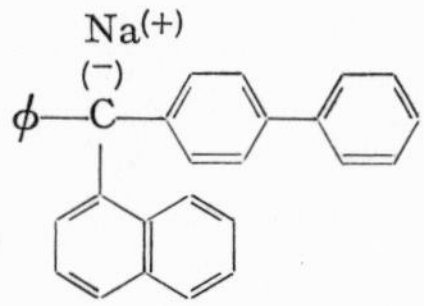	Blue violet

(Table continued)

TABLE VIII *(continued)*

Compound	Color
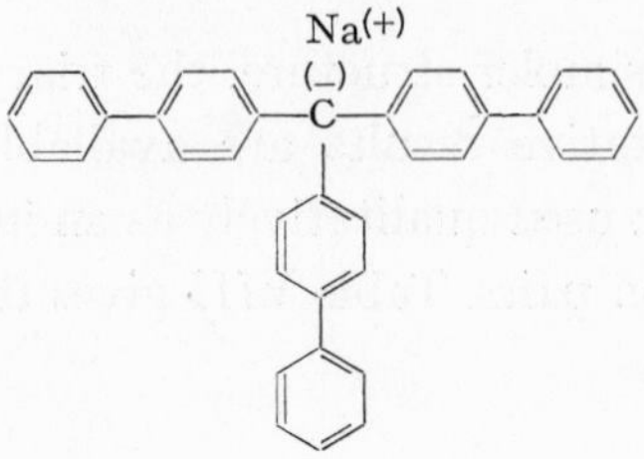	Blue
$\phi_2CH^{(-)}Na^{(+)}$	Orange red
$CH_3^{(-)}Na^{(+)}$	White
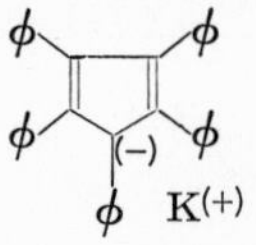	Colorless
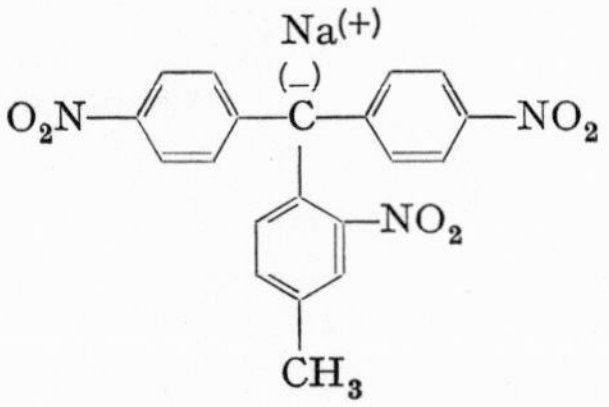	Red violet
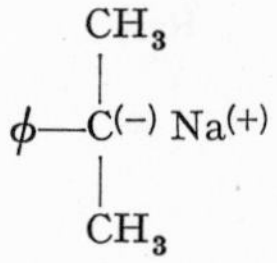	Red
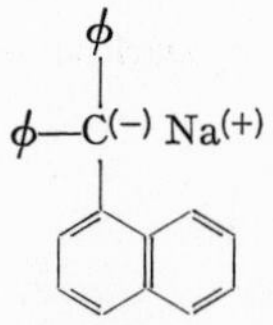	Green
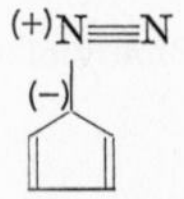	Red
$(p\text{-}O_2N\phi)_3\,C^{(-)}Na^{(+)}$	Blue

Acid Dissociation of the Carbon-Hydrogen Bond

Because the salts have different colors, it is easy to tell whether the reaction of a salt with a given carbon acid goes to completion in either direction.

$$R—H + R'—Na \rightleftharpoons RNa + R'H$$

This has been used to rank hydrocarbons in a series of increasing acidity in the solvent ether:[342]

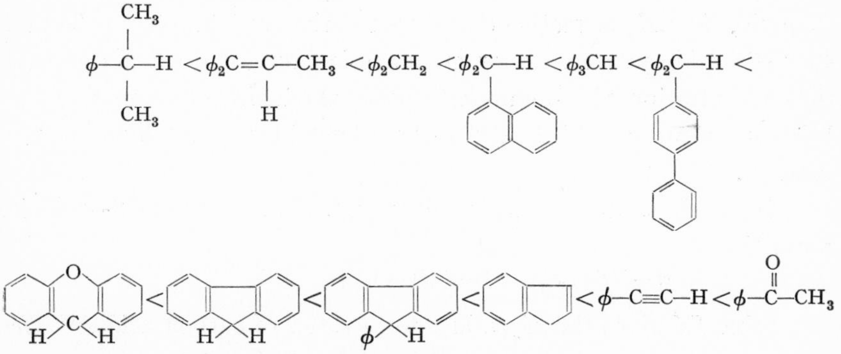

Spectrophotometry has been used in the measurement of the dissociation constants of some weak acids using the color of the ion as an indicator. The dissociation constant of tris-(p-nitrophenyl)-methane in ethanolic sodium ethoxide at 25° is 3.66×10^{-18}.[343] Another method makes use of the difference in optical rotation between menthol and sodium mentholate to find the position of the equilibrium:[344]

$$Menthol + NaR \rightleftharpoons Sodium\ mentholate + RH$$

Quantitative measurements of the strength of an acid are best based on electrometric measurements of the pH of the partly neutralized solution. Conductivity measurements are likely to give ionization constants that are too high due to the presence of conducting impurities. Estimates of acid strength from rate data are also somewhat unreliable

[342] J. B. Conant and G. W. Wheland, *J. Am. Chem. Soc.*, **54**, 1212 (1932).
[343] R. S. Stearns and G. W. Wheland, *J. Am. Chem. Soc.*, **69**, 2025 (1947).
[344] W. K. McEwen, *J. Am. Chem. Soc.*, **58**, 1124 (1936).

since the factors causing deviations from the extrathermodynamic relationships between rate and equilibrium constants are as yet understood only qualitatively. Another limitation is in the range of accessible or even meaningful acid strengths. The basicity of the solvent, usually water, exerts a leveling effect. Acids of a structure very favorable to the stabilization of a negative charge are completely ionized in water and further favorable changes in the structure of the acid have no effect in that solvent. On the other hand, extremely weak acids have "ionization constants" so low as to be outside the range in which such a thing can be given a direct operational definition. As an example, the pK_a of methane has been variously estimated as 34 and 40.[345,346] Taking the former or more acidic figure, it is calculated that the concentration of oxonium ions due to the ionization of methane in 1 M concentration is of the order of one such ion to ten billion liters of solution.

The acids shown below are all strong, that is to say off-scale, in water.[347]

$$H-C(NO_2)_3 \qquad H-C(SO_2CH_3)_3 \qquad H-C(CN)_3$$

Table IX gives the K_a values for a series of carbon acids.[346] The constants have not been corrected for the presence of enols.

TABLE IX

Acid	K_a (water, 25°)
acetone	10^{-20}
chloroacetone	3×10^{-17}
diethyl ethylmalonate	10^{-15}
1,1-dichloroacetone	10^{-15}
CH$_3$—SO$_2$—C(H)(H)—SO$_2$—CH$_3$	1×10^{-14}

$$\begin{array}{c} H \\ | \\ CH_3-SO_2-C-SO_2-CH_3 \\ | \\ H \end{array}$$

(Table continued)

[345] G. Schwarzenbach, *Z. physik. Chem.*, **A176**, 151 (1936).
[346] R. G. Pearson and R. L. Dillon, *J. Am. Chem. Soc.*, **75**, 2439 (1953).
[347] H. J. Backer, *Rec. trav. chim.*, **67**, 894 (1948); L. Birckenbach and K. Huttner, *Ber.*, **62**, 153 (1929).

TABLE IX *(continued)*

Acid	K_a (water, 25°)
EtOOC—CH$_2$—COOEt	5×10^{-14}
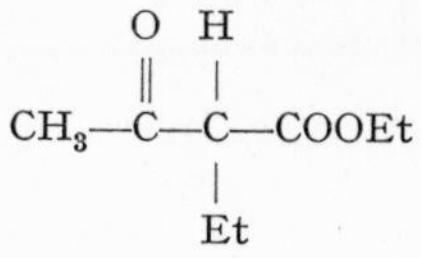 CH$_3$—C(=O)—CH(COOEt)—Et (with structural formula showing O, H, Et)	2×10^{-13}
HPO$_4^=$	4.8×10^{-13}
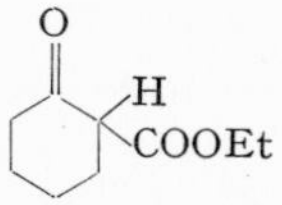 cyclohexanone with H and COOEt	3×10^{-12}
NC—CH$_2$—CN	6.5×10^{-12}
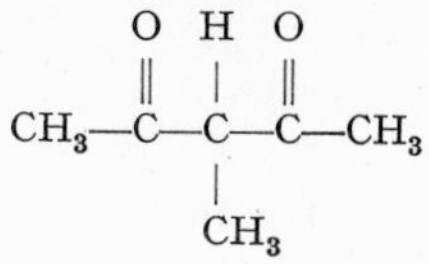 CH$_3$—C(=O)—C(CH$_3$)(H)—C(=O)—CH$_3$	1×10^{-11}
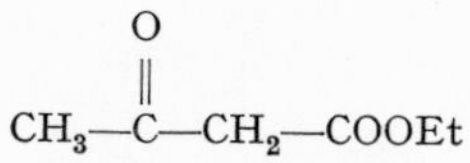 CH$_3$—C(=O)—CH$_2$—COOEt	2.1×10^{-11}
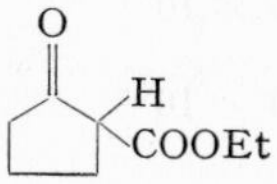 cyclopentanone with H and COOEt	3×10^{-11}
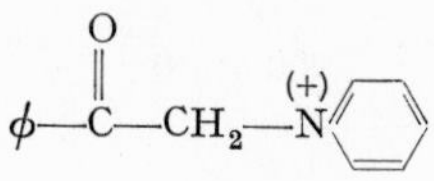 ϕ—C(=O)—CH$_2$—N$^{(+)}$ (pyridinium)	3.1×10^{-11}
HCO$_3^-$	5.6×10^{-11}
CH$_3$NO$_2$	6.1×10^{-11}
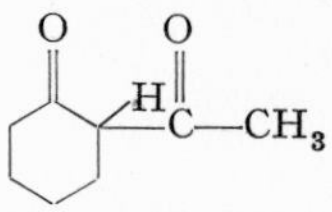 cyclohexanone with H, C(=O)—CH$_3$	8.1×10^{-11}
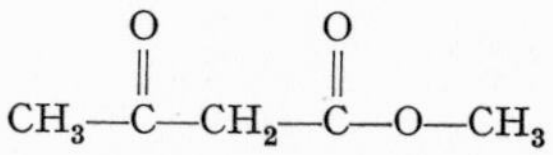 CH$_3$—C(=O)—CH$_2$—C(=O)—O—CH$_3$	1×10^{-10}
phenol	1.3×10^{-10}

(Table continued)

TABLE IX *(continued)*

Acid	K_a (water, 25°)

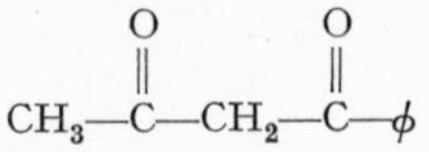

Acid	K_a (water, 25°)
$CH_3—\overset{O}{\overset{\|}{C}}—CH_2—\overset{O}{\overset{\|}{C}}—\phi$	4×10^{-10}
HCN	7.2×10^{-10}
$CH_3—\overset{O}{\overset{\|}{C}}—CH_2—\overset{O}{\overset{\|}{C}}—CH_3$	1×10^{-9}
$CH_3CH_2NO_2$	2.5×10^{-9}
(cyclopentanone ring)—$\overset{H}{\underset{}{}}\overset{O}{\overset{\|}{C}}—CH_3$	1.5×10^{-8}
$CH_3—\overset{O}{\overset{\|}{C}}—\underset{\underset{Br}{\|}}{\overset{H}{\overset{\|}{C}}}—\overset{O}{\overset{\|}{C}}—CH_3$	1×10^{-7}
$\phi—\overset{O}{\overset{\|}{C}}—CH_2—\overset{O}{\overset{\|}{C}}—CF_3$	1.5×10^{-7}
carbonic acid*	4.3×10^{-7}
(thiophene)S—$\overset{O}{\overset{\|}{C}}—CH_2—\overset{O}{\overset{\|}{C}}—CF_3$	8.0×10^{-7}
$CH_3—\overset{O}{\overset{\|}{C}}—CH_2—\overset{O}{\overset{\|}{C}}—H$	1.2×10^{-6}
$\overset{\overset{O}{\overset{\|}{C}—CH_3}}{\underset{\underset{\underset{\underset{CH_3}{\|}}{O=C}}{\|}}{H—C}}\!\!\overset{O}{\underset{\|}{—C—CH_3}}$	1.4×10^{-6}

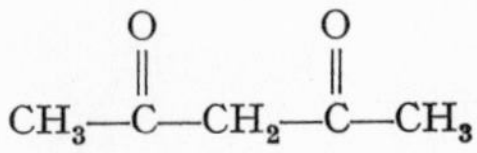

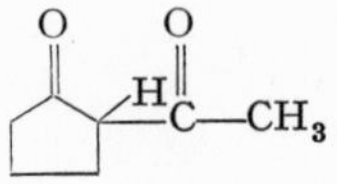

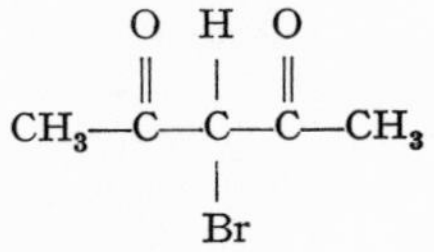

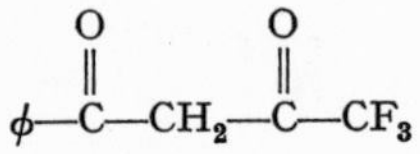

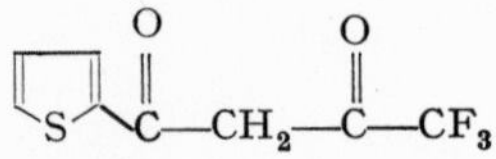

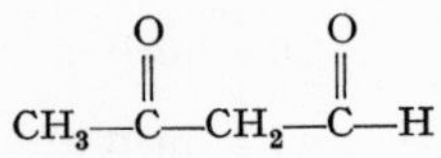

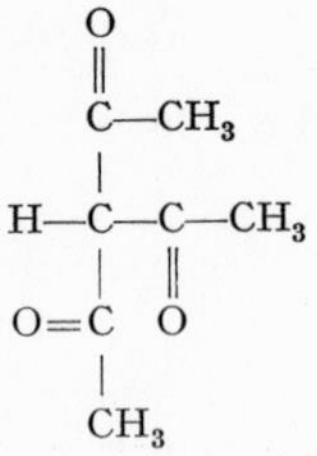

(Table continued)

TABLE IX *(continued)*

Acid	K_a (water 25°)
Et—O—C(=O)—CH$_2$—NO$_2$	1.5×10^{-6}
CH$_3$—C(=O)—CH$_2$—NO$_2$	8.0×10^{-6}
H—C(=O)—CH$_2$—C(=O)—H	1.0×10^{-5}
acetic acid	1.75×10^{-5}
CH$_3$SO$_2$C—H with C—CH$_3$ (=O) groups	2×10^{-5}
CH$_3$—C(=O)—CH$_2$—C(=O)—CF$_3$	2×10^{-5}
benzoic acid	6.3×10^{-5}
O$_2$N—CH$_2$—NO$_2$	2.7×10^{-4}
carbonic acid	1.3×10^{-4}
chloroacetic acid	1.3×10^{-3}

* Certain oxygen acids have been included in the table for orientation. Two values are given for carbonic acid, the lower value being for the overall acidity of a solution of carbon dioxide in water. Carbonic acid, H_2CO_3, is actually a fairly strong acid.[348]

[348] D. Berg and A. Patterson, Jr., *J. Am. Chem. Soc.*, **75**, 5197 (1953).

Structure and Stability of Carbanions

The stability of a carbanion (or ion pair) is increased by certain substituents and decreased by others. It is possible to rank the various structures in an order of increasing stability of the carbanion just as was done for carbonium ions. It will be recalled that our information about carbonium ions does not suffice for a prediction of the effect of temperature changes on the relative stabilities, and that it is unknown to what degree an increase in stability actually reflects a decrease in potential energy. The situation is similar in the case of carbanions; the precise relationship of the stabilities is an unknown function of the temperature. It is also likely that the effects of structural changes are somewhat dependent on the solvent. Nevertheless it is possible to make valuable qualitative comparisions of the various structures and to interpret them in terms of resonance and other potential energy quantities.

An examination of the acidity series on pages 179 and 180 shows two structural effects. Conjugation with a neutral unsaturated group is helpful in stabilizing carbonium ions, carbanions, and free radicals indiscriminately. But other structures can be classified as positive charge stabilizing (electron-releasing) or negative charge stabilizing (electron-withdrawing) and these categories are mutually exclusive. In fact, a structure of the sort that stabilizes a positive charge actually reduces the stability of a carbanion, while structures that stabilize negative charge are not merely indifferent but actually destabilizing in a carbonium ion. Keeping the effect of conjugation with phenyl and similar groups constant, the order of increasing stability of the carbanions is the reverse of the order of increasing stability of the corresponding carbonium ions. Methyl groups, for example, stabilize carbonium ions but have the opposite effect on carbanions, relative to the covalent molecule. Another example is the cyclopentadiene part structure. This makes the carbanions LIX and LX markedly more stable than otherwise similar ions.

(LIX)   (LX)

The ortho-ring junction that converts the triphenylmethyl structure into that of the ion LX increases the stability of the carbanion but decreases that of the carbonium ion. It will be recalled that this structural modification of the triphenylcarbonium ion had about the same effect as the introduction of one to two nitro groups.

The acid strengthening effect of a carbonyl group adjacent to the carbon-hydrogen bond is due in large part to the existence of a low energy resonance structure in which the negative charge is placed on oxygen rather than on carbon. Both the ion and the acidic enolic modification of the carbonyl compound thus have a double bond, and the geometrical requirements of this double bond must be met if either the enol or the enolate ion are to be stable. The lack of acidity of 2,6-diketobicyclo[2.2.2]octane, as contrasted with cyclohexandione-1,3, is evidence for the essentially enolic structure of the ions obtained from ketones.[349] A similar activation of adjacent carbon-hydrogen by the sulfone group is only moderately interfered with by the bridge-head structure.[350] It has been suggested that the reason for this is that there is no such strict angular requirement for d-p atomic orbital overlap as there is for the p-p overlap of a carbon to carbon double bond.[350, 351] Other evidence indicates that a good deal of the effect of the sulfone and sulfonium substituents is a resonance effect and not just a field effect due to the positive charge on sulfur.[352]

Non-acidic

Acidic

Table X shows the qualitative effect of various groups on the acidity of mono and disubstituted carbon acids and oxygen acids. Unfortunately, many of the acidities have been estimated from extra-

[349] P. D. Bartlett and G. F. Woods, *J. Am. Chem. Soc.*, **62**, 2933 (1940).
[350] W. von E. Doering and L. K. Levy, *J. Am. Chem. Soc.*, **77**, 509 (1955).
[351] H. P. Koch and W. E. Moffitt, *Trans. Faraday Soc.*, **47**, 7 (1951).
[352] W. von E. Doering and A. K. Hoffmann, *J. Am. Chem. Soc.*, **77**, 521 (1955); W. von E. Doering and K. C. Schreiber, *ibid.*, **77**, 514 (1955).

thermodynamic relationships between rate and equilibrium constants rather than directly measured. If the estimated acidities are correct, the effect of the substituent depends on the other structural details to a greater degree than might have been anticipated.

TABLE X

Order of Acidities in Water at 25°

$$H{-}CH_2X \quad H{-}CH_2NO_2 > H{-}CH_2{-}\overset{\displaystyle O}{\overset{\|}{C}}{-}CH_3 > H{-}CH_2{-}SO_2CH_3* >$$

$$H{-}CH_2{-}\overset{\displaystyle O}{\overset{\|}{C}}{-}OH* > H{-}CH_2{-}\overset{\displaystyle O}{\overset{\|}{C}}{-}OEt* > H{-}CH_2CN > H{-}CH_2Cl*$$

$$H{-}CHX_2 \quad H{-}CH(NO_2)_2 > H{-}CH(CH)_2 \overset{\displaystyle O}{} > H{-}CH(\overset{\displaystyle O}{\overset{\|}{C}}{-}CH_3)_2 >$$

$$H{-}CH(CN)_2 \qquad > H{-}CH(COOEt)_2 > H{-}CH(SO_2CH_3)_2$$

$$H{-}O{-}X \quad H{-}O{-}NO_2 > H{-}O{-}\overset{\displaystyle O}{\overset{\|}{C}}{-}H \quad > H{-}O{-}\overset{\displaystyle O}{\overset{\|}{C}}{-}OH \quad >$$

$$H{-}O{-}\overset{\displaystyle O}{\overset{\|}{C}}{-}CH_3 > H{-}O{-}Cl$$

* Estimates, reference 346.

The solubility in various bases can give a qualitative idea, but only a qualitative idea, of the relative acidity of organic compounds. The disulfonic ester LXI gives an impression of greater acidity than malonic ester because LXI will dissolve in dilute sodium hydroxide solution and because it will react with diazomethane while malonic ester will do neither.[353] The disulfone LXII will dissolve in dilute sodium hydroxide even though it will not react with diazomethane, a result indicating a somewhat greater acidity than that of malonic ester and contradicting the figures (water, 25°) of Table IX. Solubility in base is a composite effect rather than a simple function of the acidity of the dissolved substance.

[353] F. Arndt and B. Eistert, *Ber.*, **74**, 423 (1941).

$$CH_2(SO_3CH_3)_2 \qquad\qquad CH_2(SO_2CH_3)_2$$
$$\text{(LXI)} \qquad\qquad\qquad \text{(LXII)}$$

Structure and Rate of Formation of Carbanions

Many of the reactions of the weak carbon acids are reactions of the carbanion, the rate being the rate of ionization and independent of the concentration or nature of the reagent that determines what the product will be.

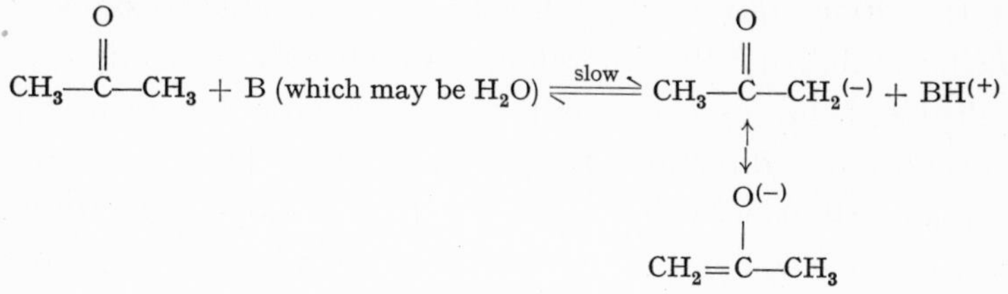

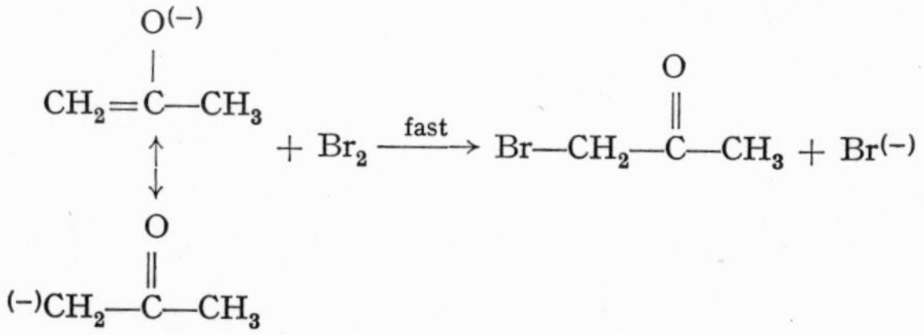

$$\underset{\text{O}}{\overset{\text{O}}{\underset{\parallel}{}}}$$

CH$_3$—C—CH$_3$ + B (which may be H$_2$O) $\underset{}{\overset{\text{slow}}{\rightleftharpoons}}$ CH$_3$—C—CH$_2{}^{(-)}$ + BH$^{(+)}$

O$^{(-)}$
|
CH$_2$=C—CH$_3$

O$^{(-)}$
|
CH$_2$=C—CH$_3$ + Br$_2$ $\xrightarrow{\text{fast}}$ Br—CH$_2$—C—CH$_3$ + Br$^{(-)}$

O
‖
$^{(-)}$CH$_2$—C—CH$_3$

In this respect such reactions are analogous to the S_n1 or limiting reactions of compounds producing carbonium ions, although the intermediate is a solvated carbanion rather than a solvated carbonium ion. In the base-catalyzed halogenation of ketones, for example, the rate is independent of the halogen concentration and is the same for the reaction with bromine as for the reaction with chlorine.[354]

If a sufficiently wide range of structures is considered, there is a definite parallelism between the effect of structural change on the ionization equilibrium constant and the rate constant. This parallelism is conveniently described as a linear relationship between the logs of the equilibrium and rate constants, a relationship which is equivalent to a linear relationship between the free energy and the free energy of

[354] A. Lapworth, *J. Chem. Soc.*, **85**, 30 (1904); P. D. Bartlett, *J. Am. Chem. Soc.*, **56**, 967 (1934).

activation. When the structural variation is in the catalysing base that removes the proton from the ketone, the relationship is an example of the Brønsted catalysis law.[355, 356]

The linear free energy relationship is one that can plausibly be expected, although not rigorously derived, whenever the transition state resembles both the carbon acid and the ion.[357]

$$\underset{\text{Acid and base}}{C\!-\!H\ B^{(-)}} \qquad \underset{\text{Transition state}}{\overset{\delta^{(-)}\qquad\ \delta^{(-)}}{C\cdots H\cdots B}} \qquad \underset{\text{Ion and conjugate acid}}{C^{(-)}\ H\!-\!B}$$

If the transition state is like the ion it is reasonable to suppose that any factor stabilizing the ion will also stabilize the transition state to some degree, hence accelerating the reaction as well as displacing the equilibrium in the direction of greater ionization. Deviations from the linear relationship between the logs of the rate and equilibrium constants are only to be expected when, for some reason, the ion does not resemble the transition state. Nitro compounds deviate from the best compromise straight line for the carbon acids in general by ionizing too slowly for compounds of their acid strength.[346] The ion is stabilized disproportionately more by the nitro substituent than the transition state is. This may be due to the relative unimportance of the enolate resonance structure in the transition state:

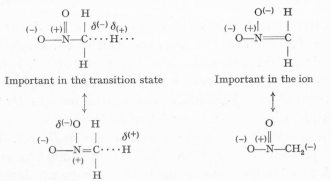

Important in the transition state   Important in the ion

Unimportant in the transition state   Less important in the ion

[355] R. P. Bell, *J. Phys. & Colloid Chem.*, **55**, 885 (1951); L. P. Hammett, *Chem. Revs.*, **17**, 125 (1936).

[356] J. N. Brønsted, *Principles and Problems in Energetics*, Interscience, New York-London, 1955.

[357] J. E. Leffler, *Science*, **117**, 340 (1953).

Any resonance structure for the transition state in which the negative charge is very far removed from the departing proton should contribute less stabilization in the transition state than in the ion. Figure 2 shows the abnormally slow rate of ionization for nitromethane and nitroethane

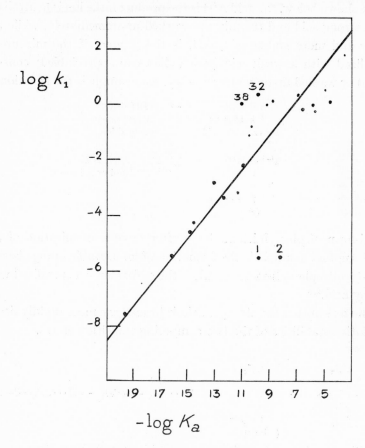

Fig. 2. A plot of log ionization rate constant against log acid dissociation constant for some carbon acids in water at 25°, [346]

(points 1 and 2). Points 32 and 38 which are abnormally fast, but less aberrant than the nitro compounds, are for methyl acetoacetate and malononitrile. Since the extent to which the transition state resembles the ion will depend on the stability of the ion, it is not expected that plots of this sort will be linear over a very large range in K_a.[346,357]

In neutralizing a resonance hybrid ion it is always the stronger, more highly dissociated, of two possible acids that is formed the more rapidly. This accounts for the difference in product of the neutralization under equilibrium as compared with rate-controlled conditions. In the scheme shown below, the acid A'H is the product if the ion is neutralized with a strong acid and the mixture worked up immediately, while the weaker and more stable acid, AH, is the product if the mixture is neutralized with a weak acid (which allows an appreciable $I^{(-)}$ concentration) or worked up only after a delay. An example is the isolation of

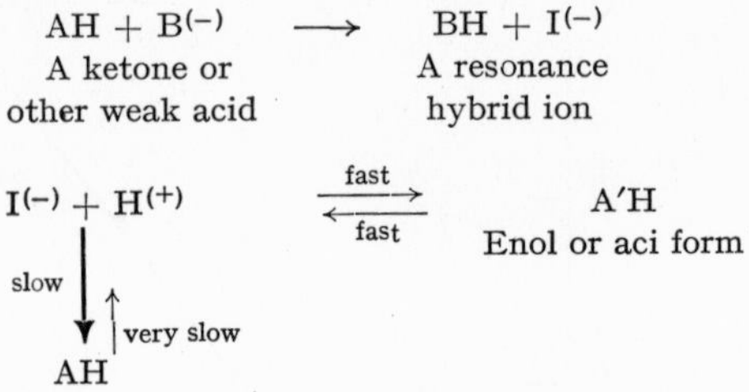

$$AH + B^{(-)} \longrightarrow BH + I^{(-)}$$

A ketone or   A resonance
other weak acid   hybrid ion

$$I^{(-)} + H^{(+)} \underset{fast}{\overset{fast}{\rightleftarrows}} A'H$$

Enol or aci form

slow $\downarrow \uparrow$ very slow

AH

the aci-form of phenylnitromethane after rapid neutralization of the salt.[358] Another example is the formation of an unstable orange isomer of tris-(p-nitrophenyl)-methane when the carbanion is neutralized with a strong acid.[359]

The reason that the stronger acid is formed the more rapidly lies in the relative stabilities of the two competing transition states.

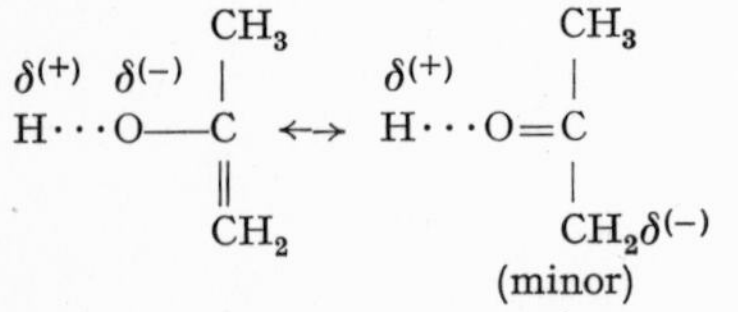

Transition state for enol formation 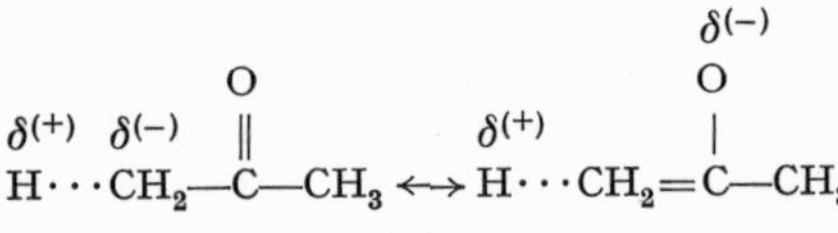   Transition state for ketone formation

In the enol transition state the structure that is the more stable by virtue of having the negative charge on oxygen rather than on carbon also has the least separation of charge. In the ketone transition state the enolate structure that should otherwise be important in stabilizing the

[358] A. G. Catchpole, E. D. Hughes, and C. K. Ingold, *J. Chem. Soc.*, **1948**, 11.
[359] G. N. Lewis and G. T. Seaborg, *J. Am. Chem. Soc.*, **61**, 1894 (1939).

transition state is rendered much less so by the separation of charge that it involves. The transition state for ketone formation is therefore of higher free energy and the corresponding reaction is slower.

A special mechanism is conceivable for proton transfer reactions in view of the small size and mass of the proton: the proton might make a quantum jump through the potential energy barrier rather than surmount it in the classical way. However, the reaction between nitroethane and hydroxide ion in aqueous ethanol, which was investigated with this possibility in mind, obeys the Arrhenius equation accurately over a temperature range from $-32°$ to $+20°$.[360] At low temperatures the proportion of molecules having the requisite energy for surmounting the energy barrier is so low that any tunneling through the barrier should be more conspicuous. The tunnel effect should therefore manifest itself by an unexpectedly high rate at low temperatures. Since the reaction is in fact no faster at low temperatures than is predicted by extrapolation of the data at higher temperatures, the tunneling effect is unimportant.

Although it is tempting to explain the effect of changes in structure on the rate of formation of the carbanion in terms of potential energy considerations alone, it appears that the situation is somewhat more complicated than that, perhaps because of the participation by the solvent and because of the entropy changes associated with steric effects. Thus compound LXIII releases a proton to water at 25° about ten times as fast as compound LXIV, yet the activation energy of the ionization of LXIV is actually lower rather than higher.[361] The accelerating effect of the structural change is manifested as a less negative entropy of activation for compound LXIII.

<pre>
     O H O   O H O
     ‖ | ‖   ‖ | ‖
CH₃—C—C—C—CH₃   CH₃—C—C—C—OEt
        | |
       CH₃   Et

    (LXIII)   (LXIV)
</pre>

[360] R. P. Bell, *Trans. Faraday Soc.*, 34, 229 (1938); R. P. Bell and A. D. Norris, *J. Chem. Soc.*, 1941, 854.
[361] R. G. Pearson and J. M. Mills, *J. Am. Chem. Soc.*, 72, 1692 (1950).

In general either the activation energy or the activation entropy or both may vary in a series of proton transfer reactions.[360] In the absence of more data on the temperature effects it is perhaps best to classify the structures as favorable or unfavorable to the negative charge at a particular temperature and defer analysis in terms of resonance and other effects except in cases where the change in acidity or rate of ionization is a particularly large and striking one. Table XI gives the rates of some proton transfers from carbon acids to water at 25°.[346] Replacing a hydrogen with methyl in nitromethane is seen to have very little effect, while the same substitution in acetoacetone lowers the rate by a factor of about 200. An added ethyl group in acetoacetic ester lowers the rate by a factor of about 160 and has about the same effect in malonic ester. Bromine in nitromethane increases the rate by about a factor of 300, by a factor of five in acetoacetic ester, by a factor of ten in malonic ester, only 40% in acetoacetone, and actually decreases the rate by a factor of two in benzoylacetone. The effect of a substituent is therefore very much a function of the particular type of compound studied, the variety of the effects being exceeded only by the variety of adjustable parameters available for purposes of explanation.

TABLE XI[346]

Rate of transfer of protons to water at 25°

Compound	k (min.$^{-1}$)
CH_3NO_2	2.6×10^{-6}
$EtNO_2$	2.2×10^{-6}
$CH_3CHClNO_2$	3.4×10^{-5}
$\underset{\displaystyle \ \ \ \ \ \ \ \ \ \ \ }{\overset{\displaystyle O}{\overset{\displaystyle \|}{EtOC}}}-CH_2NO_2$	3.8×10^{-1}
$CH_3-\overset{\displaystyle O}{\overset{\displaystyle \|}{C}}-CH_2-NO_2$	2.2
$CH_2(NO_2)_2$	~ 50
CH_2BrNO_2	8×10^{-4}

(Table continued)

TABLE XI *(continued)*

Compound	k (min.$^{-1}$)
$CH_3-\overset{\displaystyle O}{\overset{\|}{C}}-CH_3$	2.8×10^{-8}
$CH_3-\overset{\displaystyle O}{\overset{\|}{C}}-CH_2Cl$	3.3×10^{-6}
$CH_3-\overset{\displaystyle O}{\overset{\|}{C}}-CHCl_2$	4.4×10^{-5}
$CH_3-\overset{\displaystyle O}{\overset{\|}{C}}-CH_2COOEt$	7.2×10^{-2}
$CH_3-\overset{\displaystyle O}{\overset{\|}{C}}-\underset{\underset{\displaystyle Et}{\|}}{CH}COOEt$	4.5×10^{-4}
$CH_3-\overset{\displaystyle O}{\overset{\|}{C}}CHBr-COOEt$	3.6×10^{-1}
$CH_3-\overset{\displaystyle O}{\overset{\|}{C}}-CH_2-\overset{\displaystyle O}{\overset{\|}{C}}-CH_3$	1.0
$CH_3-\overset{\displaystyle O}{\overset{\|}{C}}-\underset{\underset{\displaystyle CH_3}{\|}}{CH}-\overset{\displaystyle O}{\overset{\|}{C}}-CH_3$	5×10^{-3}
$CH_3-\overset{\displaystyle O}{\overset{\|}{C}}-CHBr-\overset{\displaystyle O}{\overset{\|}{C}}-CH_3$	1.4
$CH_3-\overset{\displaystyle O}{\overset{\|}{C}}-CH_2-\overset{\displaystyle O}{\overset{\|}{C}}-\phi$	6.6×10^{-1}
$CH_3-\overset{\displaystyle O}{\overset{\|}{C}}-CHBr-\overset{\displaystyle O}{\overset{\|}{C}}-\phi$	3.3×10^{-1}

(Table continued)

TABLE XI *(continued)*

Compound	k (min^{-1})
$CH_3-\overset{O}{\overset{\|}{C}}-CH_2-\overset{O}{\overset{\|}{C}}-CF_3$	9.0×10^{-1}
$\phi-\overset{O}{\overset{\|}{C}}-CH_2-\overset{O}{\overset{\|}{C}}-CF_3$	5.0×10^{-1}
thienyl $-\overset{O}{\overset{\|}{C}}-CH_2-\overset{O}{\overset{\|}{C}}-CF_3$	6.0×10^{-1}
cyclopentanone-$\overset{O}{\overset{H\|}{C}}-OEt$	1.4×10^{-1}
cyclohexanone-$\overset{O}{\overset{H\|}{C}}-OEt$	5.8×10^{-4}
$CH_3-\overset{O}{\overset{\|}{C}}-CHCH_3SO_2Et$	1.1×10^{-2}
$CH_3-SO_2-CH_3$	$\sim 2 \times 10^{-10}$
CH_3CN	$\sim 4 \times 10^{-12}$
$CH_2(CN)_2$	9.0×10^{-1}
$EtO\overset{O}{\overset{\|}{C}}-CH_2-CN$	7×10^{-2}
$CH_2(COOEt)_2$	1.5×10^{-3}
$CHBr(COOEt)_2$	1.8×10^{-2}
$EtCH(COOEt)_2$	2×10^{-5}
CH_3COOH (methyl hydrogen)	2×10^{-11}
$CH_2(COOH)_2$	$\sim 1.7 \times 10^{-1}$
$CH_3-\overset{O}{\overset{\|}{C}}-CH_2-COOH$	7.8
$CH_3-\overset{O}{\overset{\|}{C}}-NH_2$	$\sim 2 \times 10^{-12}$

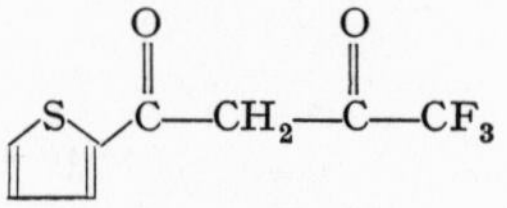

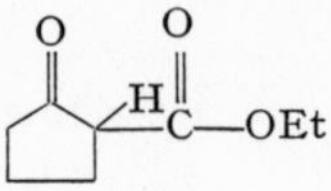

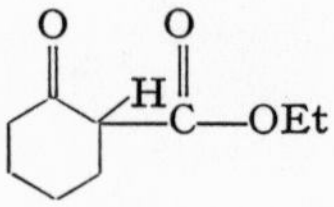

Structural changes in the base that removes a proton from nitroethane in water give changes in rate that do not always parallel the changes in the strength of the base as measured in water. However, if the rates in water are compared with the base strengths measured in *chlorobenzene*, a better Brønsted relationship is obtained. The bases for which this has been tried are the mono, di, and tri-*n*-butylamines. The rate increases as successive hydrogens are replaced by *n*-butyl groups while the base strength in water decreases. It has been suggested that the base-strengthening inductive effect of the alkyl groups is counteracted by a decrease in the solvation of the substituted ammonium ion by water.[362] Since the solvation is less important in chlorobenzene, the solvation anomaly is also less. This explanation of course requires that the solvation of the transition state for proton removal from nitroethane be much less than that of the ammonium ion in water, a reasonable assumption. Tying back the alkyl groups to give the cage-like quinuclidine molecule increases the rate of reaction with nitroethane still further over that of the tertiary amines, presumably because of a decreased steric hindrance in the transition state. When the bases are restricted to variously substituted pyridines or quinolines, a satisfactory Brønsted relationship is observed between the rates and the base strengths in water except for those bases with two substituents ortho to the nitrogen, these being too slow for their base strengths. Apparently the transition state for proton removal from nitroethane is more sensitive to steric hindrance than is the ammonium ion.[363]

The Geometry of Carbanions

Carbanions might have a geometry like that of ammonia and the amines, a pyramidal structure with the non-bonding electron pair occupying an orbital at the top of the pyramid. As is well-known, the potential barrier to the inversion of the amine by pulling the nitrogen through the plane of the attached groups is low enough so that the two asymmetric forms of a suitably substituted amine are not separable. Asymmetric nitrogen exists only in compounds where a rigid cage

[362] R. G. Pearson and F. V. Williams, *J. Am. Chem. Soc.*, **76**, 258 (1954).
[363] R. G. Pearson and F. V. Williams, *J. Am. Chem. Soc.*, **75**, 3073 (1953).

structure prevents the inversion. In ammonia itself the inversion has so small a barrier that the two forms are actually in resonance. The resonance gives rise to an energy level splitting detectable in the microwave spectrum. Sulfonium compounds, on the other hand, have been resolved, so analogy is divided in its prediction of the behavior of carbanions. Since the oximes exist in isolable syn and anti forms, a carbanion of the double bonded type might have a better chance of retaining its structure.

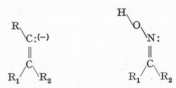

The *stable* carbanions may belong in a special category since their stability is in most cases due to resonance, and the resonance has geometrical requirements that might or might not be the same as those of the bond hybridization of an ordinary carbanion. The central hydrogen of triptycene has none of the acidity of the central hydrogen of triphenylmethane.[364]

All things considered, the best *a priori* guess would be that carbanions of any degree of stability will be incapable of retaining optical asymmetry but capable of retaining a cis or trans configuration at a double bond. Neither expectation is contradicted by the available facts.

Early reports of the persistance of optical activity in nitro-substituted carbanions have since been shown to be erroneous.[365, 366] The treatment of optically active 2-nitrooctane with sodium ethoxide or hydroxide produces an optically inactive salt.[365] Optically active 4-nitropentanoic acid racemizes and enolizes at the same rate in the presence of a base.[366] Optically active phenyl *sec*-butyl ketone racemizes and undergoes deuterium exchange at the same rate in the presence of $DO^{(-)}$[367]. Of course this could conceivably be due to the tendency of the

[364] P. D. Bartlett, M. J. Ryan, and S. G. Cohen, *J. Am. Chem. Soc.*, **64**, 2649 (1942).

[365] N. Kornblum, N. N. Lichtin, J. T. Patton, and D. C. Iffland, *J. Am. Chem. Soc.*, **69**, 307 (1947).

[366] W. Theilacker and G. Wendtland, *Ann.*, **570**, 33 (1950).

[367] S. K. Hsü, C. K. Ingold, and C. L. Wilson, *J. Chem. Soc.*, **1938**, 78.

ion, whether optically active or not, to accept a proton to form the necessarily inactive enol rather than the possibly active ketone. But the planar, and hence inactive, resonance hybrid structure for the ion seems to be a necessary part of the explanation for the more rapid formation of enol than of ketone on reaction with an acid. Other evidence favoring a largely enolate structure for the ion is the fact that the spectra of ethoxycrotonic ester in alcohol and acetoacetic ester in sodium ethoxide are very similar, especially when a large excess of alkali is used with the acetoacetic ester.[368]

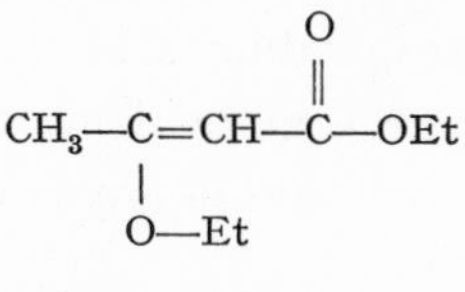

$$CH_3-C=CH-\overset{\overset{\displaystyle O}{\|}}{C}-OEt \qquad\qquad CH_3-C=CH-\overset{\overset{\displaystyle O}{\|}}{C}-OEt$$

$$\underset{\displaystyle O-Et}{|} \qquad\qquad\qquad \underset{\displaystyle \underset{(-)}{O}}{|}$$

Ethoxycrotonic ester 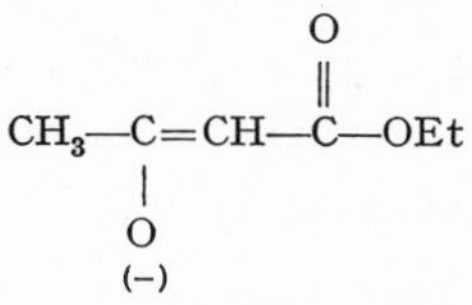   Ion from acetoacetic ester

The only currently unrefuted evidence even suggestive of an optically active carbanion is the report of optically active 2-octyl-lithium.[369] It should be recalled, however, that ordinary alkyl lithium compounds are volatile, soluble in non-polar solvents, and generally more covalent than ionic in their behavior.

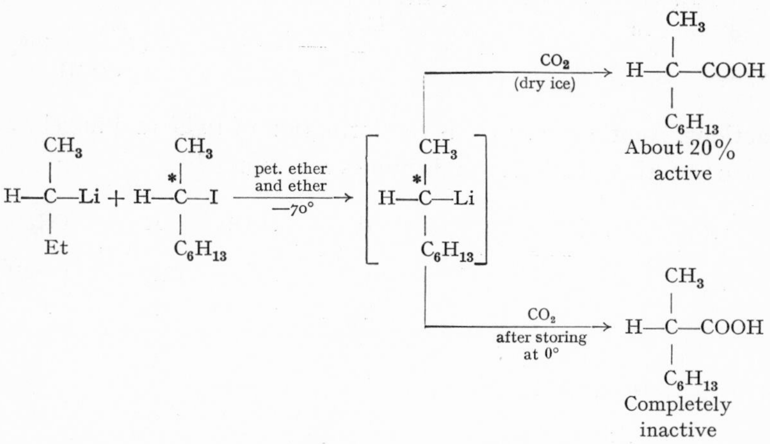

[368] A. Hantzsch, Ber., 43, 3049 (1910).
[369] R. L. Letsinger, J. Am. Chem. Soc., 72, 4842 (1950).

Neither of the two reactions involved in the conversion of the iodide to the acid is definitely known to involve a free carbanion. The racemization of the *sec*-octyl lithium when it is warmed to 0° for twenty minutes before carbonation may be a matter of ionization at the higher temperature, less optical stability of the carbanion at the higher temperature, or both.

The situation with regard to the vinyl lithium compounds is similar.[370] Both *cis* and *trans*-monobromostilbenes undergo the lithium-bromine exchange reaction in benzene-ether below 0°. Both form the corresponding stilbene in 60% yield on subsequent treatment with methyl alcohol and both form the corresponding acid in about the same yield on carbonation. But again there is no evidence for entirely free carbanions or even ion pairs as intermediates in any stage of these

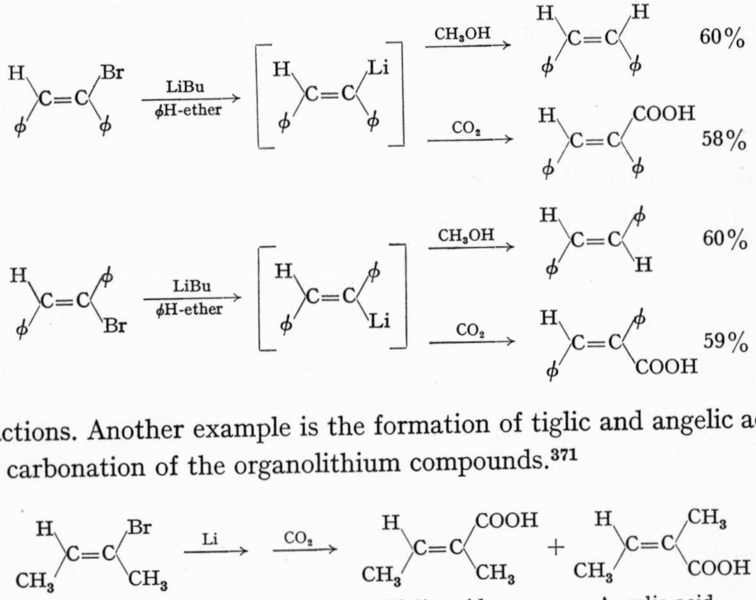

reactions. Another example is the formation of tiglic and angelic acids by carbonation of the organolithium compounds.[371]

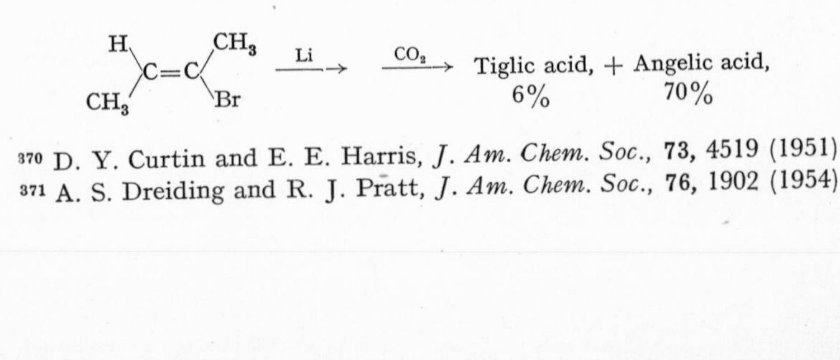

Tiglic acid   Angelic acid,
22%   9%

Tiglic acid, + Angelic acid,
6%   70%

[370] D. Y. Curtin and E. E. Harris, *J. Am. Chem. Soc.*, **73**, 4519 (1951).
[371] A. S. Dreiding and R. J. Pratt, *J. Am. Chem. Soc.*, **76**, 1902 (1954).

Carbanions derived from cyclopropane might be expected to act like those derived from ethylene in view of the similarity of the two systems in other respects. Evidence for at least a certain lack of geometrical stability for the carbanion derived from cyclopropane exists in the base catalyzed cis-trans conversion of the isomers of compound LXV.[372] The carbanion involved may, of course, be stabilized by resonance with the adjacent unsaturated substituent and an experiment truly analogous to those done with the vinyl lithium system might have a different result, planar resonance structures being avoided. Such resonance structures are somewhat disfavored by stereoelectronic factors causing the double bond exocylic to the cyclopropane ring to have a high energy, but this may not be sufficient. Racemization of a cyclopropane derivative having the active hydrogen on an asymmetric carbon of the ring has also been observed in a basic medium.[373] The ineffectiveness of resonance structures having a double bond exoclic to the cyclo-propane ring seems to retard the latter reaction. It is also noteworthy that nitrocyclopropane is relatively stable to bromine addition and oxidation, and will not dissolve in base of a strength sufficient to effect the solution of 2-nitropropane.[374]

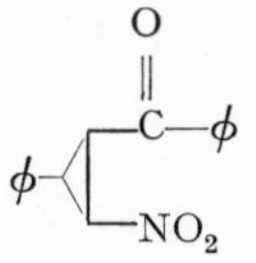

$$\phi-\underset{\substack{\displaystyle | \\ -NO_2}}{\overset{\substack{O \\ \| \\ -C-\phi}}{<}}$$

(LXV)

[372] E. P. Kohler and L. I. Smith, *J. Am. Chem. Soc.*, **44,** 624 (1922).
[373] H. M. Walborsky and F. M. Hornyak, *J. Am. Chem. Soc.*, **77,** 6026 (1955).
[374] H. B. Hass and H. Shechter, *J. Am. Chem. Soc.*, **75,** 1382 (1953).

CHAPTER X

Reactions of Carbanions

Even those organometallic compounds that are essentially covalent accept protons and exhibit other reactions suggestive of carbanions. In such cases it is not known whether the actual basic reagent is the organometallic compound or the carbanion formed by its dissociation. The problem is analogous to the classification of nucleophilic displacement reactions into categories corresponding to the existence or non-existence of a kinetically free carbonium ion intermediate. Although there is no doubt about the existence of carbanions under favorable circumstances, there is usually considerable doubt whether a specified carbanion-like reaction is entirely due to actual carbanions. Kinetic data like those used in resolving the comparable question with regard to carbonium ions are lacking, but would consist of a first order reaction of an organometallic compound with an acid or other reagent other than the solvent.

Reactions as Bases

In the preceding chapter the formation of the less stable of two isomeric acids on rapid neutralization of an organometallic compound was explained in terms of a free ion or ion pair as the reagent. The compounds involved were the salts of comparatively strong acids, however, and the media were highly polar. The ion or ion pair would be less likely to be the reagent in the case of the salt of a very weak acid, such as an alkyl lithium compound, in a non-polar solvent. Salts of unsaturated but weak acids might exist in either of two partly covalent forms; this possibility provides an alternative explanation for the formation of the less stable of the two isomeric acids on neutralization. Presumably the bulk of the covalent or partly covalent salt will have a structure like that of the more stable of the two acids:

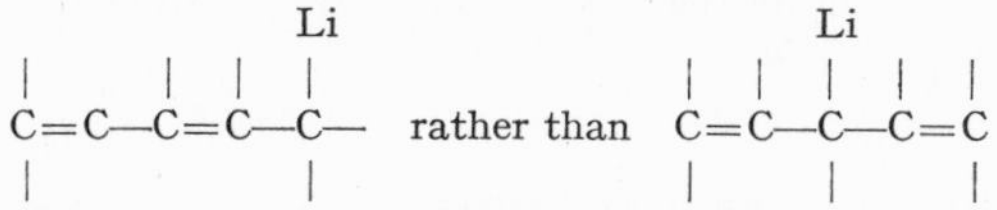

A decisive factor in making one salt and one acid the more stable might be the conjugation of the double bonds in the favored structures. A concerted, and sometimes cyclic, reaction of the predominant salt would give the less stable acid:

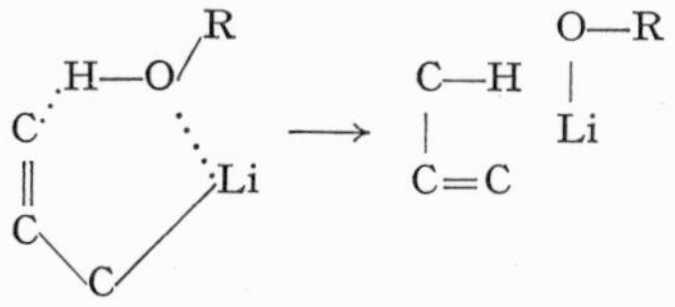

Whatever the best explanation may be, an indication that allylic alkali metal compounds or allylic carbanions do in fact form the less stable of the two possible acids on neutralization is found in the results of the reduction of aromatic compounds by dissolving metals.[375] The detection of a paramagnetic intermediate in a similar system and polarographic evidence indicate a one electron transfer in the rate and potential determining step.[375, 376] The mechanism therefore involves ions (or organometallic intermediates) like the following:

$$Ar \rightleftharpoons Ar(\underline{\cdot}) \rightleftharpoons Ar^{(=)} \rightleftharpoons ArH^{(-)} \rightleftharpoons ArH_2$$

When anisole is reduced by an alkali metal in liquid ammonia either a stable, conjugated diolefin or a less stable, unconjugated diolefin can be isolated, the latter being the product when the reaction mixture is neutralized with a strong acid such as ammonium chloride. The free ions, whether they are present to any great extent or not, are the resonance hybrid LXVI.

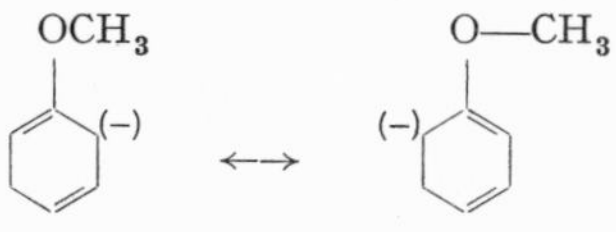

(LXVI)

[375] A. J. Birch, *J. Chem. Soc.*, **1950**, 1551.
[376] T. L. Chu and S. C. Yu, *J. Am. Chem. Soc.*, **76**, 3367 (1954).

The transition states for reaction of the ion with a proton are mainly represented by the structures **LXVII** and **LXVIII**.

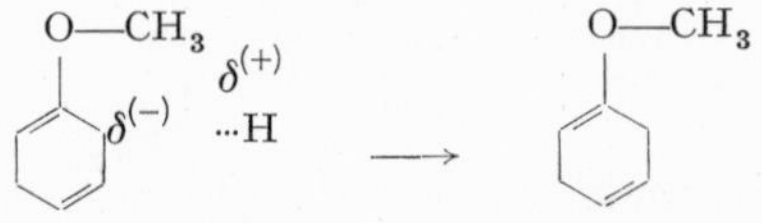

O—CH$_3$

$\delta^{(+)}$

$\delta^{(-)}$ ...H $\longrightarrow$ O—CH$_3$

(LXVII)   (LXIX)

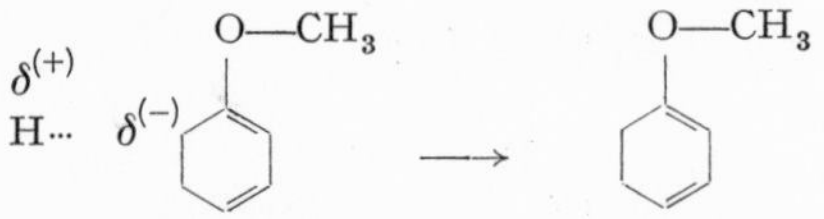

$\delta^{(+)}$

H... $\delta^{(-)}$ O—CH$_3$ $\longrightarrow$ O—CH$_3$

(LXVIII)   (LXX)

There seems to be no reason why the transition state **LXVIII** should not be more stable than the transition state **LXVI**, just as the corresponding diene is more stable than the other diene. Hence it would be expected that the faster reaction would produce the stable product, **LXX**, while in fact **LXX** is formed only under conditions where an equilibrium ensures that the product will be the more stable isomer. The alternative explanation in terms of a covalent, or at most an intimate ion pair, intermediate thus seems more likely for this particular case.

O—CH$_3$

—Na $\rightleftharpoons$ OCH$_3$ Na—

Less stable   More stable

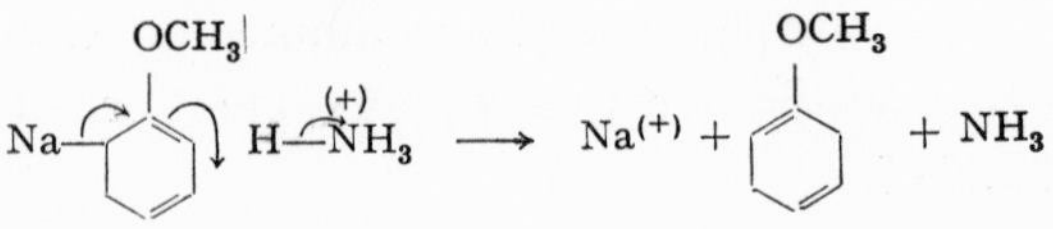

OCH$_3$

Na— H—$\overset{(+)}{N}$H$_3$ $\longrightarrow$ Na$^{(+)}$ + OCH$_3$ + NH$_3$

When a weak acid is used to neutralize the salt, enough is left unneutralized to give small amounts of the less stable salt via the ion and eventually lead to the irreversible conversion of almost all of the material to the more stable diene. Possibly the more stable diene is formed from the ion directly.

Direction of Reaction With Aromatic Compounds

In some reactions of carbanions or organometallic compounds with very weak acids the base has a choice of protons and can give more than one salt. An example is the nuclear metallation of a substituted benzene in which the product may be oriented ortho, meta, or para. The actual results of a few such reactions are shown in Table XII.

TABLE XII

No.	Ref.	Reaction
1	377	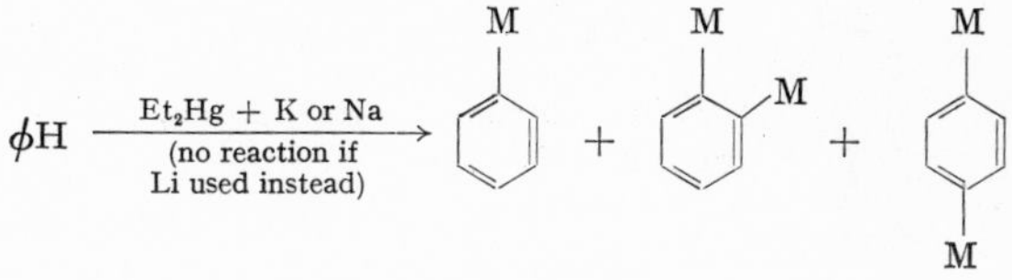
2	377	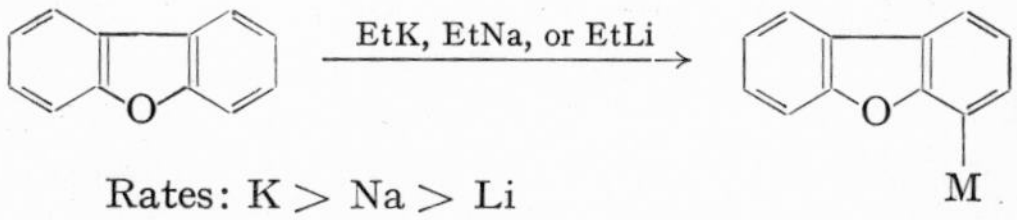 Rates: K > Na > Li
3	378	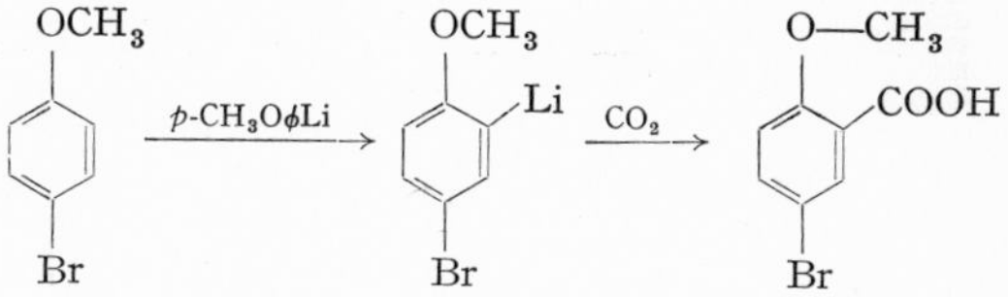
4	379	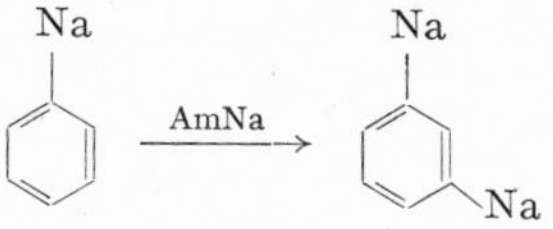
5	379	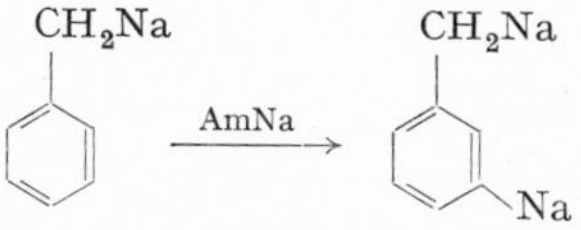

(*Table continued*)

TABLE XII *(continued)*

No.	Ref.	Reaction

6   380

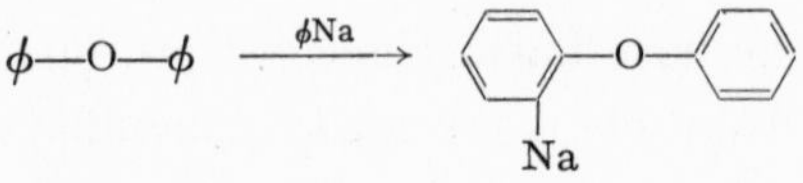

7   380

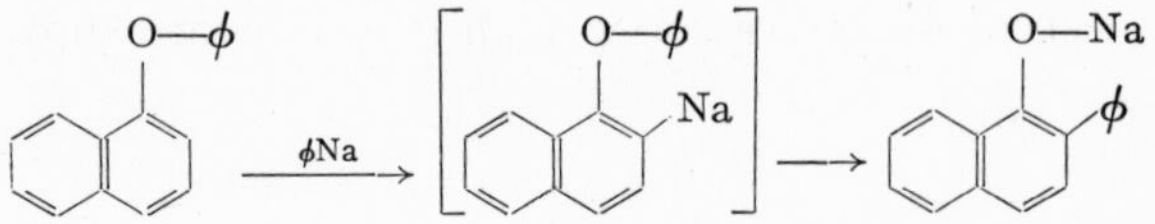

8   381

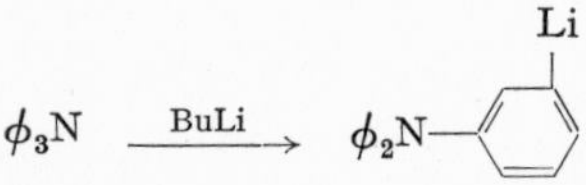

(but other tertiary amines, ethers, and thio-ethers are metallated ortho by this reagent.)

9   382

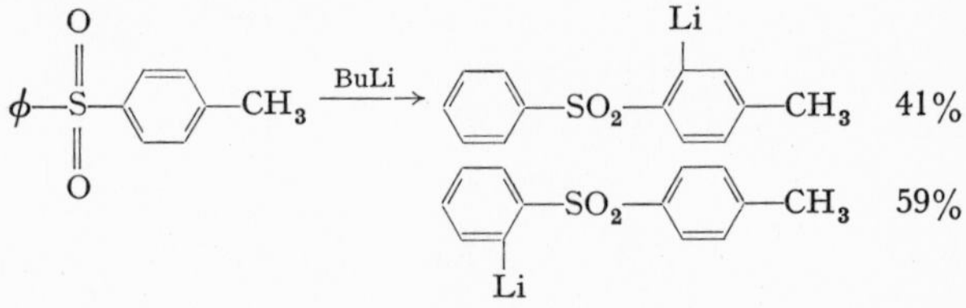

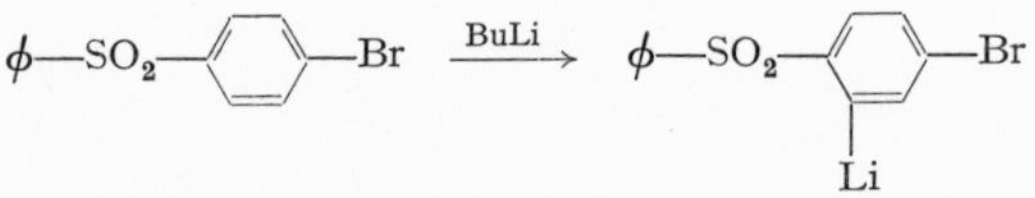

10   383

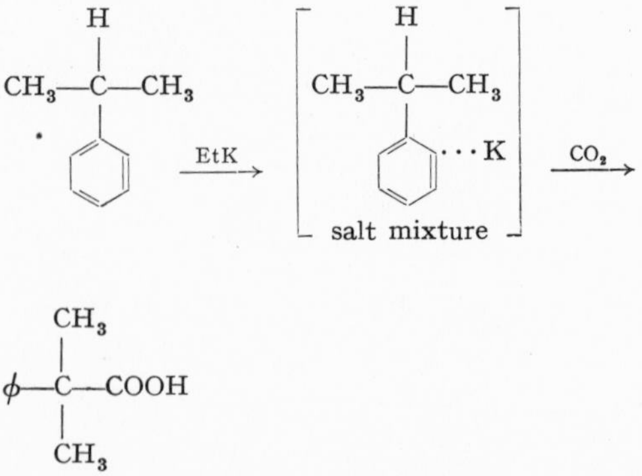

(Table continued)

TABLE XII *(continued)*

No.	Ref.	Reaction

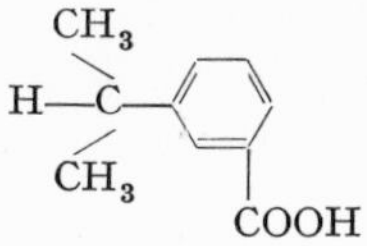

+ H—C(CH₃)(CH₃)—C₆H₄—COOH (mostly)

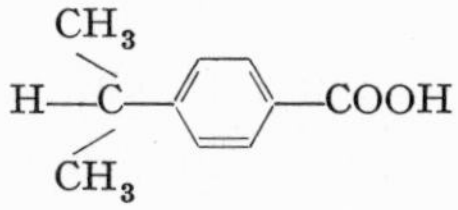

+ H—C(CH₃)(CH₃)—C₆H₄—COOH (considerable)

+ H—C(CH₃)(CH₃)—C₆H₄(COOH) (relatively little)

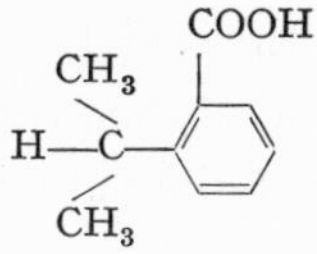

11   384   φ—CF₃ $\xrightarrow{\text{BuLi}}$ [o-CF₃-C₆H₄-Li] (mostly) + [m-CF₃-C₆H₄-Li] (some)

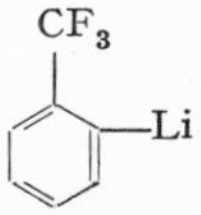

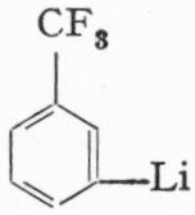

The nature of the groups activating or deactivating the benzene ring towards metallation suggests that an electron-withdrawing inductive effect is of primary importance. Reaction 10 of Table XII, in which an electron-releasing inductive effect of the isopropyl group deactivates the ring positions in accord with their distance from the isopropyl group, gives more than half as much metallation at the para position as at the two meta positions combined and very little attack at the two ortho positions. This sort of behavior seems appropriate to a

---

[377] H. Gilman and R. V. Young, *J. Org. Chem.*, **1**, 315 (1936).

[378] H. Gilman, W. Langham, and F. W. Moore, *J. Am. Chem. Soc.*, **62**, 2327 (1940).

[379] A. A. Morton, *Chem. Revs.*, **35**, 1 (1944).

[380] A. Lüttringhaus and G. Wagner-von Sääf, *Ann.*, **557**, 25 (1947).

[381] G. E. Coates, *Quart. Revs. (London)*, **4**, 217 (1950).

[382] W. E. Truce and O. L. Norman, *J. Am. Chem. Soc.*, **75**, 6023 (1953).

[383] D. Bryce-Smith, *J. Chem. Soc.*, **1954**, 1079.

[384] J. D. Roberts and D. Y. Curtin, *J. Am. Chem. Soc.*, **68**, 1658 (1946).

transition state like LXXI. In reaction 11 the activating effect of the inductive withdrawal of electrons by the trifluoromethyl group is felt most strongly at the ortho positions, less so at the meta positions,

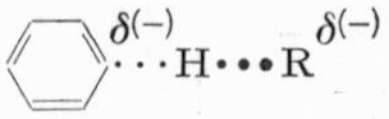

(LXXI)

and at the para position not enough to compete. The almost exclusive ortho metallation of most ethers, amines, and other compounds in which the substituent has a reactive unshared electron pair is very likely due to the coordination of the cation at the hetero atom to give a cyclic transition state for removal of the proton, the cation increasing the electron-withdrawing power of the substituent.[384] A quantitative study of the products and rates of these reactions under variation of

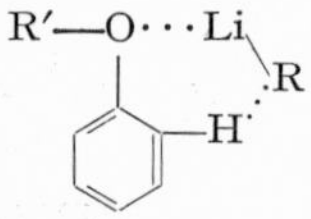

Cyclic transition state

the metal from lithium to potassium might afford a test of the cyclic mechanism. Potassium would probably coordinate less with the ether oxygen, yet the increased ionic character of the alkyl potassium should increase the rate of hydrogen abstraction by any mechanism. Less coordination with the ether oxygen should lead to a greater proportion of reaction at the meta and para positions.

Some apparent anomalies in Table XII are the divergent results of reactions 1 and 4. In reaction 1 the alkyl sodium was generated *in situ* and the difference in the result may be due to the reaction of something other than the alkyl sodium. The exclusively meta dimetallation reported for reaction 4 is also anomalous since a purely inductive deactivation of the ring should give at least some of the para isomer. Another anomaly is the meta orientation in reaction 8. The nitrogen of triphenylamine is not very basic, however, and might not participate in the special mechanism proposed for reaction at the ortho position.

Displacement and Addition Reactions of
Organometallic Compounds

Organometallic compounds or carbanions undergo a number of reactions in which the carbanion or carbanion-like moiety of the organometallic compound acts as a nucleophilic displacing agent. Examples are the formation of hydrocarbons from alkyl halides, alkyl halides from halogens, and ketones from acid chlorides or esters. The latter two reactions are closely related to the base-catalyzed condensations and are perhaps additions as well as displacement reactions. Related addition reactions are the carbonation of organometallic compounds and the addition to ketones or aldehydes.

$$\phi_3CNa + CH_3I \longrightarrow \phi_3CCH_3 + NaI$$

$$(p\text{-}O_2N\phi)_3CNa + Br_2 \longrightarrow (p\text{-}O_2N\phi)_3C\text{---}Br + NaBr$$

$$\phi_3CNa + \phi\text{---}\overset{\overset{\text{O}}{\|}}{C}\text{---}Cl \longrightarrow \phi_3C\text{---}\overset{\overset{\text{O}}{\|}}{C}\text{---}\phi + NaCl$$

$$\phi_3CNa + CO_2 \longrightarrow \phi_3CCOOH$$

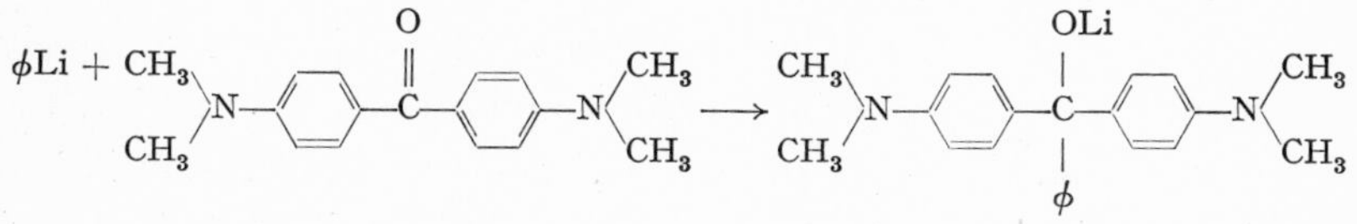

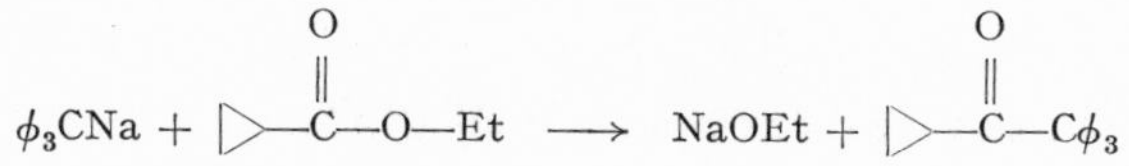

$$\phi_3CNa + \triangleright\text{---}\overset{\overset{\text{O}}{\|}}{C}\text{---}O\text{---}Et \longrightarrow NaOEt + \triangleright\text{---}\overset{\overset{\text{O}}{\|}}{C}\text{---}C\phi_3$$

$$RMgX + H\text{---}C(OEt)_3 \longrightarrow R\text{---}\overset{\overset{\text{OEt}}{|}}{\underset{\underset{\text{OEt}}{|}}{C}}\text{---}H + EtOMgX$$

The nucleophilic displacement reactions of organolithium compounds with alkyl halides are second order insofar as the rates have been measured, but there are unexplained examples of autocatalysis and non-reproducable rate constants. The product of the reaction in the case of the methylallyl chlorides is the same mixture regardless of which of the isomeric methylallyl chlorides is used. This suggests that the transition state of the product determining step involves a single resonance hybrid carbonium ion in both cases.[385] The behavior with Grignard reagents is similar.[385]

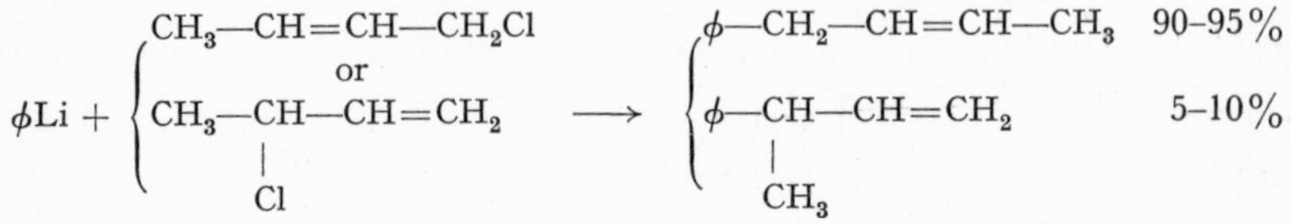

$$\phi Li + \begin{cases} CH_3-CH=CH-CH_2Cl \\ \quad\quad or \\ CH_3-\underset{\underset{Cl}{|}}{CH}-CH=CH_2 \end{cases} \longrightarrow \begin{cases} \phi-CH_2-CH=CH-CH_3 \quad 90\text{-}95\% \\ \phi-\underset{\underset{CH_3}{|}}{CH}-CH=CH_2 \quad\quad 5\text{-}10\% \end{cases}$$

Similarly 1-butyl lithium reacts with optically active sec-butyl bromide to give an extensively racemized product.[386] On the other hand, benzyl sodium couples with sec-butyl bromide to give only 26% racemization. The factors favoring racemization or rearrangement of the alkyl halide in reactions of this sort are a metal cation coordinating with the departing halogen and a relatively undissociated organometallic compound which waits for the ionization of the alkyl halide rather than attacking it directly.[387] The reaction of phenyl lithium with unsymmetrically substituted epoxides opens the ring at the less substituted carbon atom, suggesting a concerted, rather than a carbonium ion, mechanism for that reaction.[388]

The reactions of Grignard reagents with ketones, aldehydes, esters, etc. have been much used but have been the object of relatively little quantitative study owing to the complications presented by the Grignard reagent. The Grignard reagent, it will be recalled, is a colloidal mixture of alkylmagnesium halide, magnesium halide, and dialkyl magnesium and on top of all that reacts at an inconveniently high rate. It is clear from the frequent dependence of the course of the Grignard and related reactions on the nature of the metal that the metallic ion plays an important and intimate role in such reactions. The two mechanisms shown below have been proposed for the reduction and addition reactions of ketones.[389]

[385] S. J. Cristol, W. C. Overhults, and J. S. Meek, *J. Am. Chem. Soc.*, **73**, 813 (1951).

[386] H. D. Zook and R. N. Goldey, *J. Am. Chem. Soc.*, **75**, 3975 (1953).

[387] J. F. Lane and S. E. Ulrich, *J. Am. Chem. Soc.*, **72**, 5132 (1950).

[388] S. J. Cristol, J. R. Douglass, and J. S. Meek, *J. Am. Chem. Soc.*, **73**, 816 (1951).

[389] C. G. Swain and H. B. Boyles, *J. Am. Chem. Soc.*, **73**, 870 (1951).

In the addition reaction the second molecule of Grignard reagent may be replaced by a molecule of magnesium bromide, and for this reason it is possible, by increasing the magnesium bromide concentration, to double the amount of addition at the expense of the

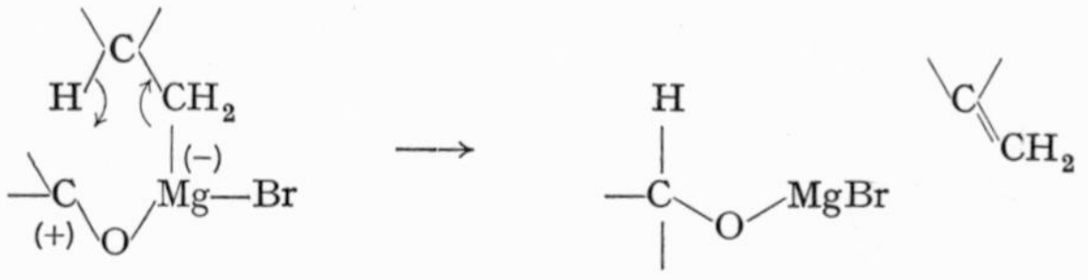

Reduction

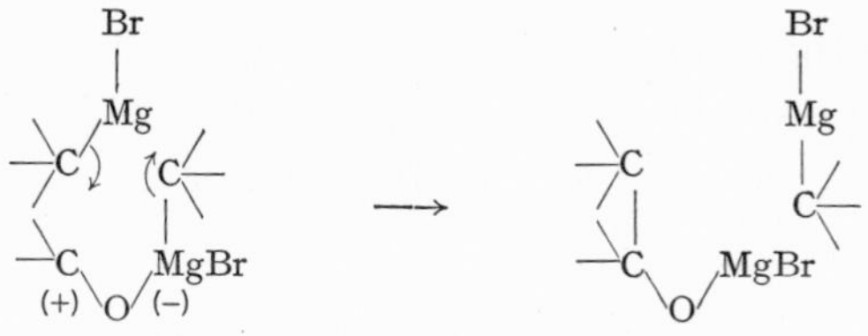

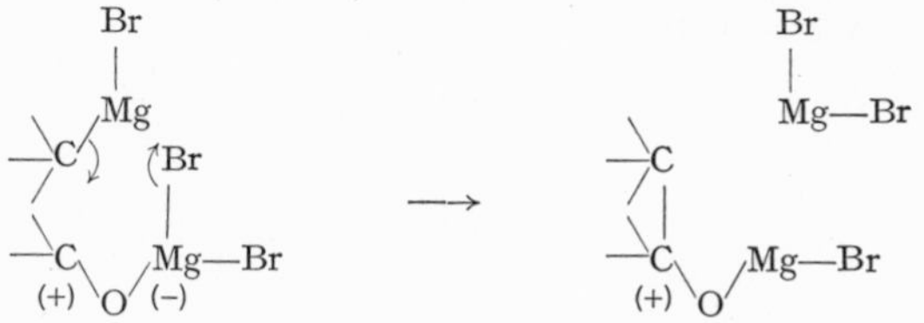

Addition

competing reduction reaction. It will be recalled that reduction takes place extensively only when the ketone is hindered; it evidently has less severe steric requirements than the competing addition reaction. Reduction of ketones by Grignard reagents, if this mechanism is correct in detail, is essentially the same sort of reaction as the aluminum alkoxide catalyzed reduction by alcohols. The evidence for this transition state in the Meerwein-Ponndorf reduction is the predictability of the steric course of the reaction when the reduction leads to the introduction of a new center of asymmetry.[390] The bulky group R tends to be next to the methyl group rather than next to the other bulky group R. The alternative transition state with adjacent R's

[390] W. von E. Doering and R. W. Young, *J. Am. Chem. Soc.*, **72**, 631 (1950).

would lead to the formation of the other diastereoisomer. Another test for the mechanism proposed for the Grignard reduction would be a similar stereochemical prediction for that reaction. Asymmetic reduction by a Grignard reagent has indeed been observed.[390a]

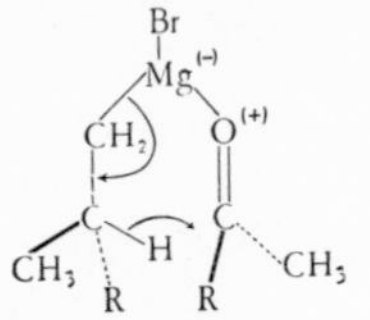

Grignard reduction 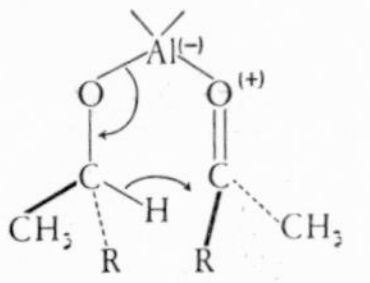   Meerwein-Ponndorf reduction

Even the Cannizzaro reaction might have a similar transition state. Although the coordinating tendency of alkali metals is less than that of aluminum or magnesium, it is not negligible. An alternative structure is possible in this case in which a proton occupies the bridging position.

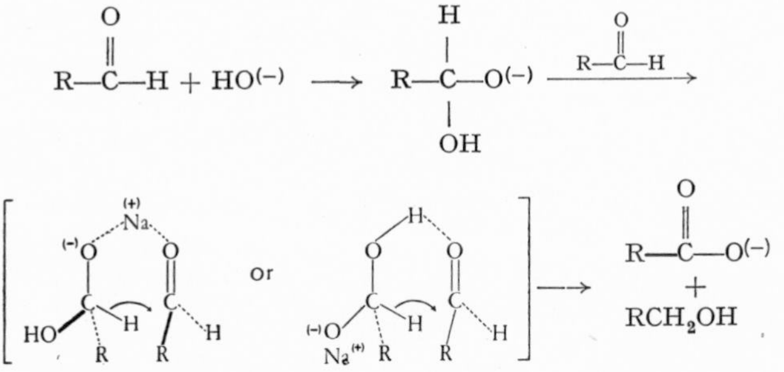

The reactions of alkyl lithium compounds, although closely related to those of the Grignard reagents, are somewhat easier to study because of the greater simplicity of the organometallic reagent. They are very fast reactions but some rates have been successfully measured by resort to the flow method. The reaction is second order and a transition state like LXXII has been suggested.[391]

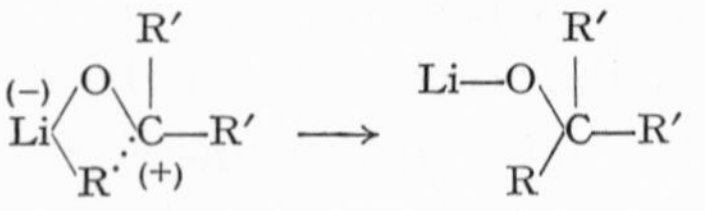

(LXXII)

[390a] H. S. Mosher and E. LaCombe, *J. Am. Chem. Soc.*, **72**, 3994 (1950).
[391] C. G. Swain and L. Kent, *J. Am. Chem. Soc.*, **72**, 518 (1950).

The relative rates for various organolithium compounds are para-tolyl > phenyl > ethyl > isopropyl. As for the ketone, the rate is enhanced by electron-withdrawing substituents which increase the coordinating power of the carbonyl carbon. It therefore appears that the crucial step is the electrophilic attack by the carbonyl on the group R of the organolithium compound.

The addition of Grignard or other organometallic reagents is not limited to carbonyl compounds, but is a reaction that can be expected of any system in which the negative charge can be placed largely on an electronegative atom. In this respect the addition reaction is closely related to the displacement reaction and both might be regarded as displacements of electrons by an electron-rich reagent. The associated metallic cation has been left out of the equations in this section only for considerations of simplicity and ignorance of the details of its part in the reaction: the indicated negative charges will rarely be completely unneutralized.

$$C^{(-)} + \overset{|}{\underset{|}{C}}{=}O \longrightarrow \overset{|}{\underset{|}{C}}{-}C{-}O^{(-)}$$

$$C^{(-)} + C{=}C{-}C{=}O \longrightarrow C{-}C{-}C{=}C{-}O^{(-)}$$

$$C^{(-)} + C{-}Cl \longrightarrow C{-}C + Cl^{(-)}$$

Given a sufficiently electronegative carbon atom, no carbonyl or conjugated carbonyl group is needed for addition to take place. For example, a carbon atom that is part of the cyclopentadiene system is able to stabilize the negative charge quite well. The cyclopentadienyl anion is comparatively stable.[392]

[392] D. Taber, E. I. Becker, and P. E. Speorri, *J. Am. Chem. Soc.*, **76**, 776 (1954).

Even the symmetrical central double bond of dibiphenylenethylene gives a similar reaction.[393] Clearly this sort of reactivity is not a matter of the initial polarization of the unsaturated compound, but rather the energy of the charged transition state. It would be incorrect, for example, to ascribe the electrophilic reactivity of the carbonyl group to the positive charge on carbon. The partial positive charge on carbon and its electrophilicity both belong in the category of consequences rather than causes, consequences of the electronegativity of the oxygen.

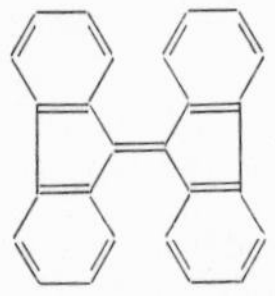

Dibiphenylenethylene

Triphenylsilyl potassium adds like triphenylmethyl sodium to formaldehyde, giving the expected alcohol.

$$\phi_3\text{SiK} + \text{CH}_2\text{O} \longrightarrow \phi_3\text{SiCH}_2\text{OK}$$

$$\phi_3\text{CNa} + \text{CH}_2\text{O} \longrightarrow \phi_3\text{CCH}_2\text{ONa}$$

But with benzophenone the silicon is attached to the oxygen rather than to carbon:[394]

$$\phi_3\text{SiK} + \phi_2\text{C}{=}\text{O} \longrightarrow \phi_3\text{Si}-\text{O}-\overset{\displaystyle \phi}{\underset{\displaystyle \phi}{\overset{|}{\underset{|}{\text{C}}}}}-\text{H}$$

No corresponding reaction of anionic carbon is known, the electro-negativity of oxygen being of more importance than the resonance of the phenyl groups or steric hindrance of the carbonyl carbon. Tetra-valent carbon can not readily expand its octet as can tetravalent silicon; this may be a factor increasing the strength of a silicon-oxygen bond over that of a carbon-oxygen bond. The compound that might be produced by the addition of a carbanion to the oxygen of the carbonyl group is unstable. When synthesized by another route it isomerizes into the usual addition product.[395]

[393] E. D. Bergmann, *J. Am. Chem. Soc.*, **75**, 2761 (1953).
[394] H. Gilman and T. C. Wu, *J. Am. Chem. Soc.*, **76**, 2502 (1954).
[395] G. Wittig and W. Happe, *Ann.*, **557**, 205 (1947).

$$\phi - \underset{\underset{OCH_3}{|}}{\overset{\overset{OCH_3}{|}}{C}} - \phi \quad \xrightarrow{NaK} \quad \phi - \underset{\underset{K}{|}}{\overset{\overset{OCH_3}{|}}{C}} - \phi \quad \xrightarrow{CO_2} \quad \phi - \underset{\underset{COOH}{|}}{\overset{\overset{OCH_3}{|}}{C}} - \phi$$

$$\downarrow$$

$$\phi - \underset{\underset{CH_3}{|}}{\overset{\overset{OK}{|}}{C}} - \phi$$

The lithium derivative isomerizes faster than the corresponding sodium or potassium compound.

The addition of a carbanion to a double bond conjugated with a carbonyl, nitrile, or sulfonyl group can give the usual simple addition product or it can give an intermediate carbanion which continues the reaction as a chain polymerization.

$$R^{(-)} + CH_2 = CH - CN \longrightarrow [R - CH_2 - \overset{(-)}{CH} - CN \longleftrightarrow R - CH_2 - CH = C = N^{(-)}]$$

$$R - CH_2 - CH^{(-)} + CH_2 = CH - CN \longrightarrow \left[R - CH_2 - \underset{\underset{CN}{|}}{CH} - CH_2 - CH^{(-)} \right] \text{ etc.}$$

The initiating anion need not be a carbanion but is always a strong base in any case, $NH_2^{(-)}$ being a example.[396] A thing to be guarded against in all the reactions of organometallic compounds is the possibility of confusing a free radical reaction with a carbanion reaction.[397] This might be the source of some of the anomalies in the metallation reaction, for example. In the case of polymerization, however, a powerful diagnostic tool is available in the nature of the product formed from a mixture of monomers. Sodium in liquid ammonia, for example, forms a copolymer rich in methyl methacrylate, even from a monomer mixture rich in styrene: that particular polymerization reaction is therefore an anionic chain rather than a radical or cationic chain.[398, 399] An example of initiation by organometallic compounds is the polymeriza-

[396] F. C. Foster, *J. Am. Chem. Soc.*, **74**, 2299 (1952).
[397] A. A. Morton and A. E. Brachman, *J. Am. Chem. Soc.*, **76**, 2973 (1954).
[398] Y. Landler, *Compt. rend.*, **230**, 539 (1950).
[399] D. C. Pepper, *Quart. Revs. (London)*, **8**, 88 (1954).

tion of methyl methacrylate by Grignard reagents and by triphenylmethyl sodium.[400] The reaction does not take place with butadiene
under the same conditions. The anionic chain is believed to be
terminated by proton transfer since the molecular weight of the polymer
initiated by triphenylmethyl sodium is lowered if triphenylmethane is
present as a source of protons.

$$\phi_3C^{(-)}+CH_2=\overset{\overset{\displaystyle CH_3}{|}}{C}-CN\longrightarrow \left[\phi_3C-CH_2-\overset{\overset{\displaystyle CH_3}{|}}{\underset{(-)}{C}}-CN\right]\longrightarrow \left[\phi_3C-CH_2-\overset{\overset{\displaystyle CH_3}{|}}{\underset{\underset{\displaystyle CN}{|}}{C}}-CH_2-\overset{\overset{\displaystyle CH_3}{|}}{\underset{\underset{\displaystyle CN}{|}}{C^{(-)}}}\right]\ \text{etc.}$$

$$\phi_3C-\left(CH_2-\overset{\overset{\displaystyle CH_3}{|}}{\underset{\underset{\displaystyle CN}{|}}{C}}-\right)_n-CH_2-\overset{\overset{\displaystyle CH_3}{|}}{\underset{\underset{\displaystyle CN}{|}}{C^{(-)}}}+RH\longrightarrow \phi_3C-\left(CH_2-\overset{\overset{\displaystyle CH_3}{|}}{\underset{\underset{\displaystyle CN}{|}}{C}}-\right)_n-CH_2-\overset{\overset{\displaystyle CH_3}{|}}{\underset{\underset{\displaystyle CN}{|}}{C}}-H+R^{(-)}$$

Note that methacrylonitrile lacks an acidic hydrogen for self-termina-
tion of chains.

The site of reaction on an unsaturated organometallic molecule is
not restricted to the most probable position of the metallic atom or
cation or to a position corresponding to any one resonance structure
of the anion. This has been discussed in a previous section with
reference to the special case of reaction with a proton. Although the
multiple reactivity is particularly noticeable in the case of derivatives
of carbonyl compounds, it is not entirely lacking even in the case of
the derivatives of unsaturated hydrocarbons. Triphenylmethyl sodium
reacts with triphenylsilyl chloride to give not only the substance
related to hexaphenylethane but also a substance related to Chichibabin's hydrocarbon.[401] It will be recalled that both the triphenylcarbonium ion and triphenylmethyl radical did the same sort of thing.

$$\phi_3CNa + \phi_3SiCl \longrightarrow \begin{cases} \phi_3C-Si\phi_3 \\[2em] \phi_3Si-\!\!\!\!\overset{\displaystyle \phi}{\underset{\displaystyle \phi}{\bigcirc}}\!\!\!\!-C-H \end{cases}$$

[400] R. G. Beaman, *J. Am. Chem. Soc.*, **70**, 3115 (1948).

Apparently all three types of tricovalent triphenylcarbon compound, the radical and both ions, are able to manifest their unsaturation at a para-ring position as well as at the central carbon atom. A less exotic example of reaction at a ring position is afforded by benzyl magnesium chloride. This Grignard reagent reacts with formaldehyde to give o-tolylcarbinol, with ethyl sulfate to give both p-ethyltoluene and n-propylbenzene, but with carbon dioxide to give only the expected and malodorous phenylacetic acid. In general organometallic compounds of the benzyl or allyl types can react at either position. Furthermore, the site of reaction depends not only on the nature of the electrophilic reagent but also on the metal:[402]

$$
\begin{array}{ccc}
CH_2=CH\!\!\diagdown & & CH_2=CH\!\!\diagdown \\
& \!\!\!\!\!\!\!\!\!\!CHMgBr \xrightarrow{\ CO_2\ } & \!\!\!\!\!\!\!\!\!\!CHCOOH \\
CH_2=CH\!\!\diagup & & CH_2=CH\!\!\diagup
\end{array}
$$

$$
\begin{array}{ccc}
CH_2=CH\!\!\diagdown & & CH_2=CH\!\!\diagdown \\
& \!\!\!\!\!\!\!\!\!\!CHNa & \!\!\!\!\!\!\!\!\!\!CH \\
CH_2=CH\!\!\diagup & \xrightarrow{\ CO_2\ } & CH_2-CH\!\!\diagup \\
& & \quad\ | \\
& & \ COOH
\end{array}
$$

These differences in the course of the reaction of Grignard and sodium compounds are not limited to carbonations but are also observed in carbonyl addition reactions. Whereas cinnamylmagnesium bromide always reacts at the secondary carbon atom next to the benzene ring, the sodium compound may react at either the secondary or the primary position, depending on the electrophilic reagent.[403]

$$
\phi CH=CHCH_2MgBr + CO_2 \longrightarrow \phi\!-\!CH\!-\!CH=CH_2 \\
| \\
COOH
$$

$$
\phi CH=CH\!-\!CH_2Na + CO_2 \longrightarrow \phi\!-\!CH\!-\!CH=CH_2 + \phi CH=CH\!-\!CH_2COOH \\
| \\
COOH
$$

$$
\quad\quad\quad\quad\quad\quad\quad\quad 90\% \quad\quad\quad\quad\quad\quad\quad 10\%
$$

[401] A. G. Brook, H. Gilman, and L. S. Miller, *J. Am. Chem. Soc.*, **75**, 4759 (1953).

[402] R. Paul and S. Tchelitcheff, *Compt. rend.*, **224**, 1118 (1947).

[403] T. W. Campbell and W. G. Young, *J. Am. Chem. Soc.*, **69**, 3066 (1947).

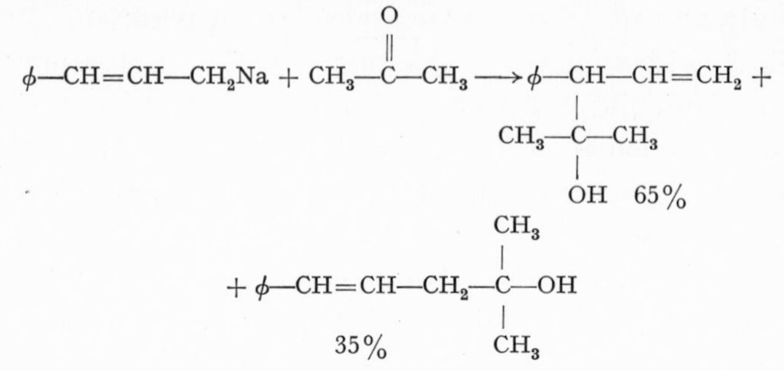

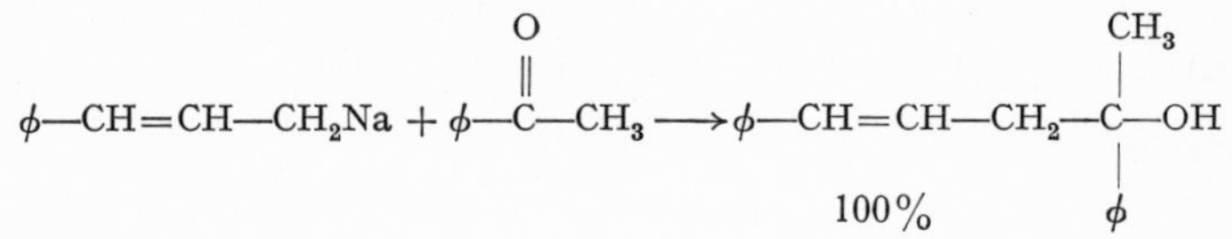

$$\phi—CH=CH—CH_2Na + CH_3—\overset{\overset{\displaystyle O}{\|}}{C}—CH_3 \longrightarrow \phi—\underset{\underset{\displaystyle CH_3—\underset{\underset{\displaystyle OH \quad 65\%}{|}}{C}—CH_3}{|}}{CH}—CH=CH_2 +$$

$$+ \phi—CH=CH—CH_2—\underset{\underset{\displaystyle CH_3}{|}}{\overset{\overset{\displaystyle CH_3}{|}}{C}}—OH$$

$$35\%$$

$$\phi—CH=CH—CH_2Na + \phi—\overset{\overset{\displaystyle O}{\|}}{C}—CH_3 \longrightarrow \phi—CH=CH—CH_2—\underset{\underset{\displaystyle \phi}{|}}{\overset{\overset{\displaystyle CH_3}{|}}{C}}—OH$$

$$100\%$$

It can be concluded from these results that at least one, if not both, of the two organometallic compounds reacts as such rather than as the free carbanion, because the behavior of the free ion should be independent of the nature of the metal. It seems plausible that reaction at the secondary position goes by way of a cyclic transition state involving the metal.

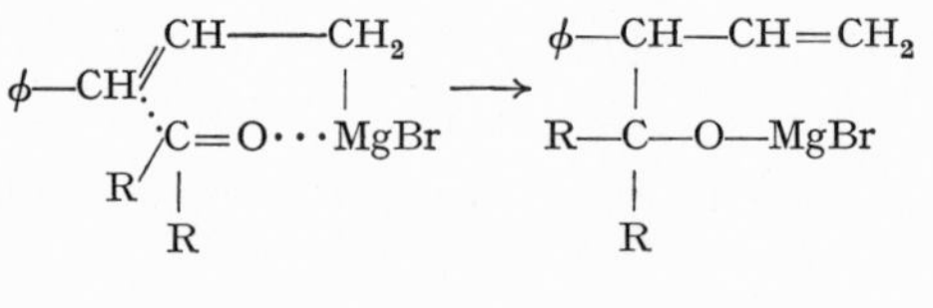

The sodium of the organosodium compound is less effective as a Lewis acid than is the magnesium of the Grignard reagent, which may account for some of the differences. With sodium as the metal, the direction of reaction seems to be decided by steric effects, the bulkier reagents avoiding the secondary position.

A similar inference about the importance of the metal can be drawn from the differences in behavior with carbon-nitrogen multiple bond systems:[404]

[404] H. Gilman and R. H. Kirby, *J. Am. Chem. Soc.*, **55**, 1265 (1933).

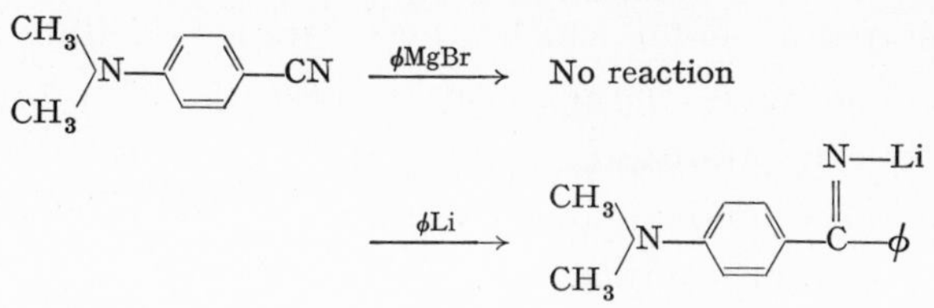

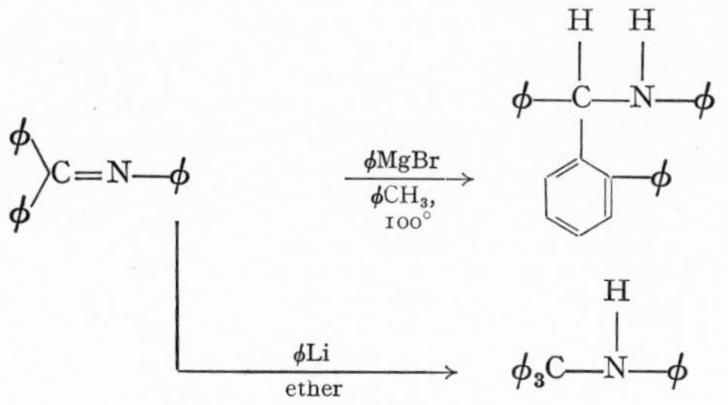

Decarboxylation

One of the several mechanisms for decarboxylation is the reverse of the familiar carboxylation reaction of organometallic compounds or carbanions. Many of the acids RCOOH that are readily decarboxylated in basic media are compounds for which the corresponding $R^{(-)}$ is a comparatively stable carbanion.[405] The postulated intermediate has actually been trapped or diverted in a few cases as the product of an aldol condensation.[406]

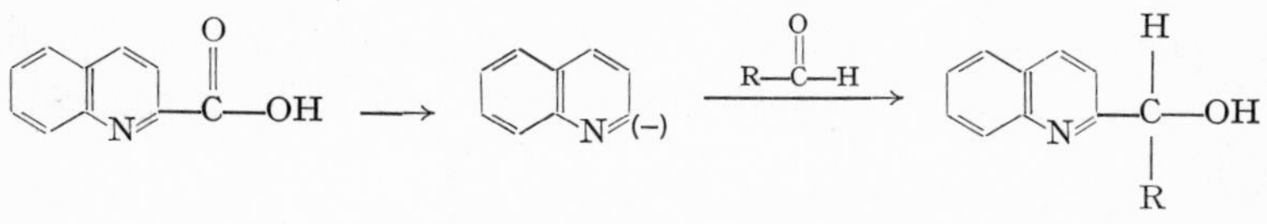

In the case of sodium tris-(p-nitrophenyl)-methide the carboxylation reaction with carbon dioxide to give the acid fails to take place, although less stable carbanions are readily carbonated.[410]

Since the nature of the metal is of importance in the carbonation reaction, it should also have some effect on the rate and perhaps the product of the decarboxylation reaction, especially in the case of

[405] H. Schenkel and M. Schenkel-Rudin, *Helv. Chim. Acta*, **31**, 514 (1948).
[406] P. Dyson and D. L. Hammick, *J. Chem. Soc.*, **1937**, 1724.

β,γ-unsaturated acids for which a cyclic transition state is plausible. Under acid conditions the reaction has been shown to take the route indicated by the transition state LXXIII.[407] The transition state LXXIV would be similar and, of course, identical to the transition state for a carboxylation reaction.

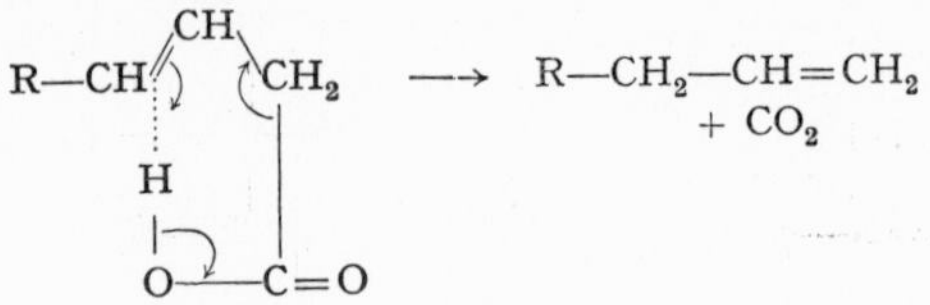

$$R-CH\overset{\displaystyle CH}{\underset{\displaystyle H}{\diagup}}\ CH_2 \quad \longrightarrow \quad R-CH_2-CH=CH_2 \\ + CO_2$$

$$O \overset{}{\longrightarrow} C=O$$

(LXXIII)

$$R-CH\overset{\displaystyle CH}{\diagup}\ CH_2 \quad \longrightarrow \quad \left[\begin{array}{c} R-CH-CH=CH_2 \\ | \\ Mg\ +CO_2 \\ | \\ X \end{array} \right] \longrightarrow RCH_2-CH=CH_2$$

$$\underset{X}{Mg-O-C}{\diagdown}O$$

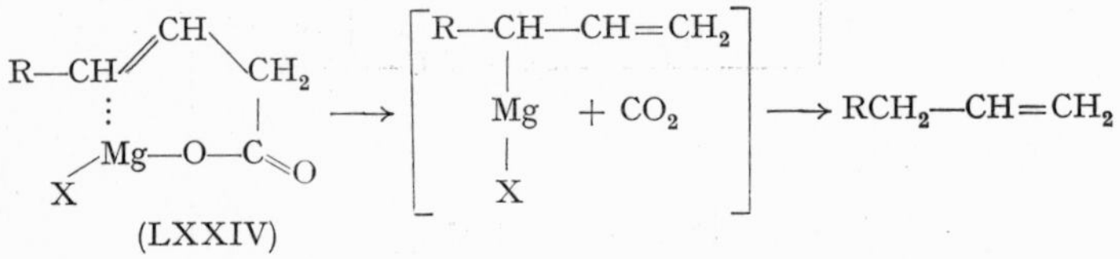

(LXXIV)

The decarboxylation of acids of this type should be catalyzed by magnesium.

The Oxidation of Carbanions

The removal of an electron from a carbanion oxidizes it to a free radical and sometimes, in the presence of oxygen, to a peroxide. Organometallic compounds give many radical-like reactions of course, and a possible oxidation mechanism for such compounds is a preliminary dissociation into radicals followed by oxidation of the radicals and the metal.

$$R^{(-)} \longrightarrow R\cdot \xrightarrow{\ O_2\ } R-O-O-R$$

However, the indubitably ionic quaternary ammonium compounds LXXV and LXXVI also react with oxygen, although the products have not been investigated.[408, 409]
The highly colored and presumably highly ionic alkali salts of tris-

[407] R. T. Arnold, O. C. Elmer, and R. M. Dodson, *J. Am. Chem. Soc.*, **72**, 4359 (1950).
[408] W. Schlenk and J. Holtz, *Ber.*, **49**, 603 (1916).
[409] L. A. Pinck and G. E. Hilbert, *J. Am. Chem. Soc.*, **68**, 2011 (1946).

$$\phi_3C^{(-)}\overset{(+)}{N}(CH_3)_4$$

(LXXV)

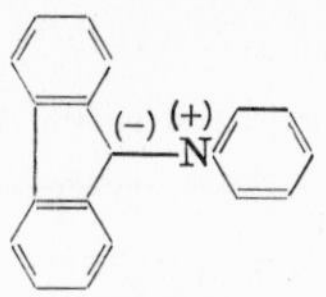

(LXXVI)

(p-nitrophenyl)-methane are also sensitive to air, being oxidized to the carbinol.[410] A similar reaction of Grignard reagents with the air is the reason for its exclusion in Grignard syntheses. The autoxidation of the Grignard reagent produces the corresponding alcohols in yields of 60-80%. Tritylmagnesium bromide is an exception, giving the peroxide instead of the alcohol.[411] Phenols are produced in much lower yield from the aromatic Grignard reagents unless an aliphatic Grignard reagent is also present.[412] The autoxidation of Grignard reagents is chemiluminescent, except that in the case of the aliphatic compounds it is first neccessary to remove the ether to get luminescence.[413] Phenylmagnesium bromide also gives off light in the reaction with trichloronitromethane.[413] The epoxide LXXVII reacts with methylmagnesium bromide to give an intermediate of unknown structure which, on treatment with water, regenerates the olefin from which the epoxide was prepared.[414]

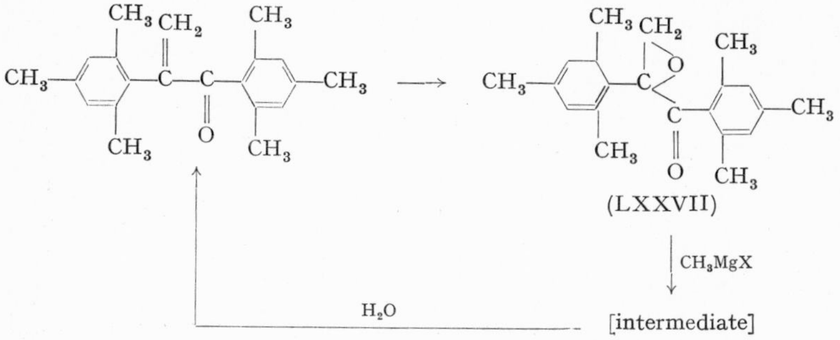

(LXXVII)

The autoxidation of Grignard reagents can be diverted from its usual production of alcohols and be made to give hydroperoxides if the

[410] K. Ziegler and E. Boye, *Ann.*, **458**, 248 (1927).

[411] J. Schmidlin, *Ber.*, **39**, 628, 4183 (1906).

[412] M. S. Kharasch and W. B. Reynolds, *J. Am. Chem. Soc.*, **65**, 501 (1943).

[413] J. Lifschitz and O. E. Kalberer, *Z. physik. Chem.*, **102**, 393 (1922).

[414] R. C. Fuson, D. J. Byers, C. H. Sperati, R. E. Foster, and P. F. Warfield, *J. Org. Chem.*, **10**, 69 (1945).

Grignard solution is slowly added to oxygen-saturated ether.[415]
Phenylmagnesium bromide on autoxidation in ether gives the usual
complicated mixture associated with most radical reactions; one of
these products is α-phenylethanol, indicating attack on the sovent.[416]
The kinetics of the autoxidation of 2-nitropropane in basic solution
together with the catalysis by ferric ion and inhibition by arsenic
trioxide suggested the mechanism of page 31. Similar mechanisms are
highly probable for the autoxidation of organometallic compounds.
Sodium persulfate oxidizes the sodium derivative of nitrocyclohexane
to products indicating an oxidation of the carbanion to the radical.[417]

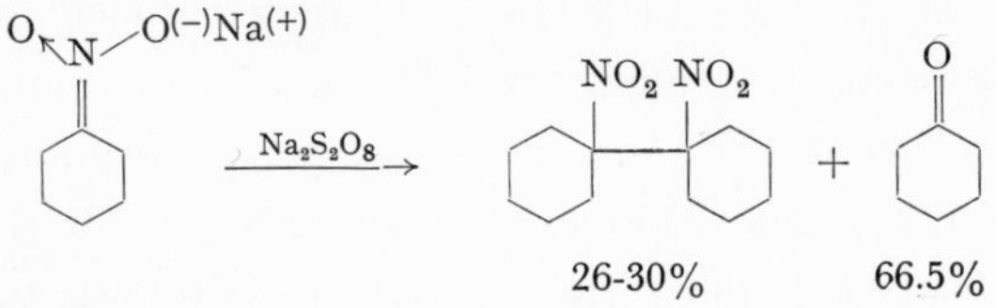

26-30%   66.5%

[415] C. Walling and S. A. Buckler, *J. Am. Chem. Soc.*, **75,** 4372 (1953).
[416] H. Gilman and A. Wood, *J. Am. Chem. Soc.*, **48,** 806 (1926).
[417] H. Shechter and R. B. Kaplan, *J. Am. Chem. Soc.*, **75,** 3980 (1953).

CHAPTER XI

Base-Catalyzed Reactions
of Carbon Acids

Direction of the Reaction

Most aliphatic ketones can lose a proton from either of two carbon atoms adjacent to the carbonyl. The question of which of the possible carbanions or salts is the effective reagent in a given base-catalyzed reaction depends on the nature of the electrophilic reagent with which the ion subsequently reacts. Thus alkyl methyl ketones lose a primary proton in their reactions with alkali and iodine, alkali and an aldehyde, or alkali and carbon dioxide, but lose a secondary proton in certain other reactions.

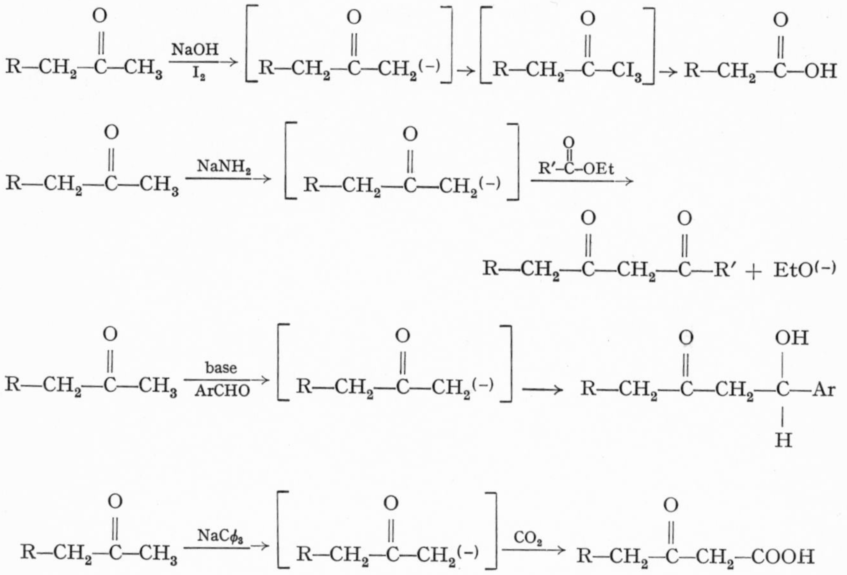

$$R-CH_2-\overset{O}{\overset{\|}{C}}-CH_3 \xrightarrow[I_2]{NaOH} \left[R-CH_2-\overset{O}{\overset{\|}{C}}-CH_2^{(-)} \right] \rightarrow \left[R-CH_2-\overset{O}{\overset{\|}{C}}-CI_3 \right] \rightarrow R-CH_2-\overset{O}{\overset{\|}{C}}-OH$$

$$R-CH_2-\overset{O}{\overset{\|}{C}}-CH_3 \xrightarrow{NaNH_2} \left[R-CH_2-\overset{O}{\overset{\|}{C}}-CH_2^{(-)} \right] \xrightarrow{R'-\overset{O}{\overset{\|}{C}}-OEt}$$
$$R-CH_2-\overset{O}{\overset{\|}{C}}-CH_2-\overset{O}{\overset{\|}{C}}-R' + EtO^{(-)}$$

$$R-CH_2-\overset{O}{\overset{\|}{C}}-CH_3 \xrightarrow[ArCHO]{base} \left[R-CH_2-\overset{O}{\overset{\|}{C}}-CH_2^{(-)} \right] \longrightarrow R-CH_2-\overset{O}{\overset{\|}{C}}-CH_2-\overset{OH}{\underset{H}{\overset{|}{\underset{|}{C}}}}-Ar$$

$$R-CH_2-\overset{O}{\overset{\|}{C}}-CH_3 \xrightarrow{NaC\phi_3} \left[R-CH_2-\overset{O}{\overset{\|}{C}}-CH_2^{(-)} \right] \xrightarrow{CO_2} R-CH_2-\overset{O}{\overset{\|}{C}}-CH_2-COOH$$

The reactions in which the methyl ketone loses a primary proton are all fast reactions, and the direction of the reaction is determined by the fact that an electron-releasing alkyl group slows down the removal of the secondary proton from the methylene group. On the other hand a slow reaction, like the base-catalyzed reaction of ketones with dimethyl sulfate in ether, gives a product corresponding to the removal of a proton from the more alkylated carbon.[418]

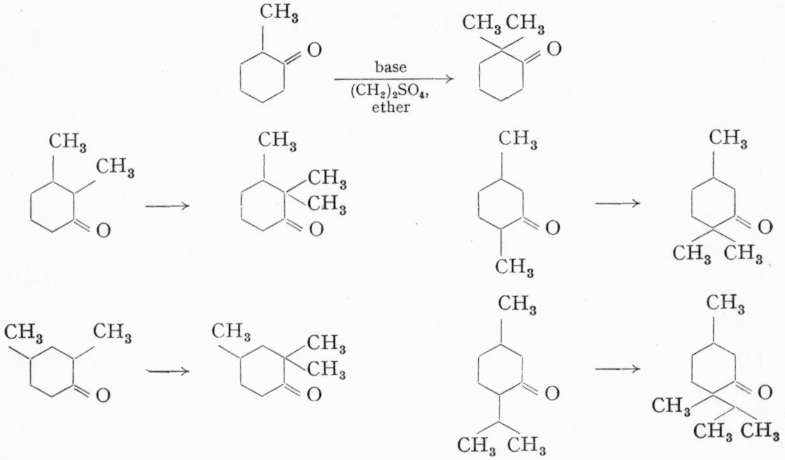

The direction of these slower reactions is determined not by the more rapid removal of a particular proton, but by the greater stability of a particular salt. Although methyl groups retard the removal of the proton they stabilize the ion or enolate once formed. The reason for this is that the transition state for proton removal has the negative charge largely on the carbon atom where it is subject to interaction with the electron-releasing alkyl group. In the fully formed ion on the other hand, the charge is largely on oxygen and the ion is stabilized by the interaction of the alkyl group with the double bond.

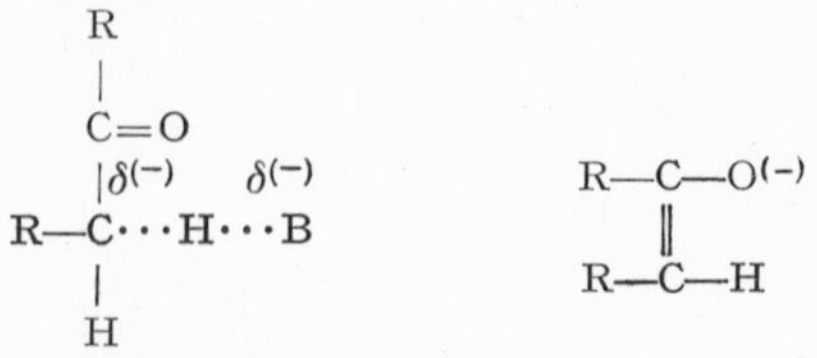

Transition state   Ion

[418] H. M. E. Cardwell, *J. Chem. Soc.*, **1951**, 2442.

Under different conditions, where presumably the reaction with dimethyl sulfate is made fast enough to compete with the back reaction to regenerate the ketone, the product is partly that characteristic of the first mentioned group of reactions in which the rate of proton removal, rather than the amount of salt, controlled the product.

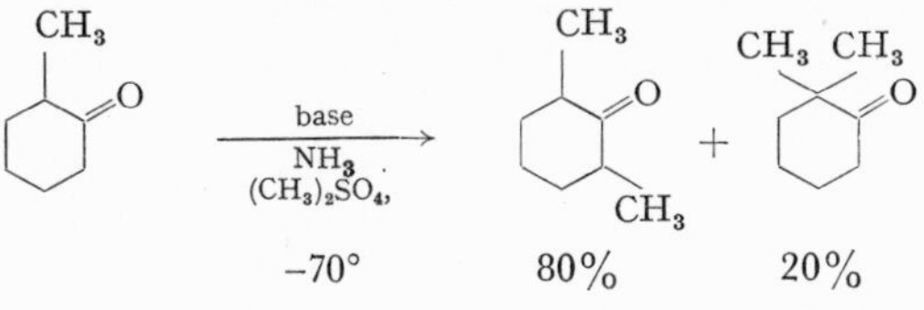

Base catalyzed condensation reactions of esters and ketones have an additional factor of importance in determining the product, and this is the fact that the overall reaction, as well as the intermediate steps, is highly reversible. The final product may be rate or equilibrium determined, and in the latter case the result may depend on the relative acidity of the various possible products. In a highly basic medium the product will be partly in the form of a salt and the stability of the salt is then a product-determining factor. Failure of a condensation to take place may be due either to an insufficiently high concentration of carbanions or to the instability of the product. The reactions of ethyl isobutyrate will illustrate both points.[419]

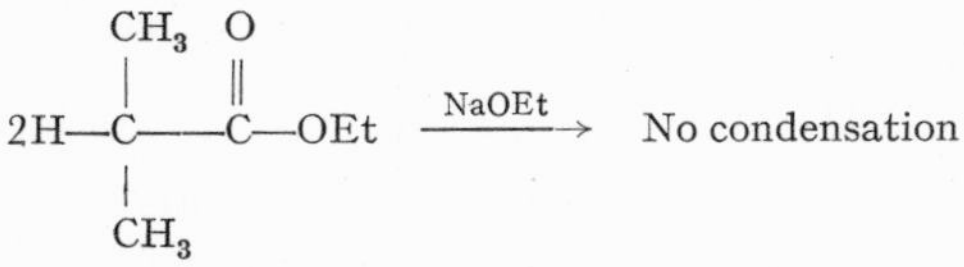

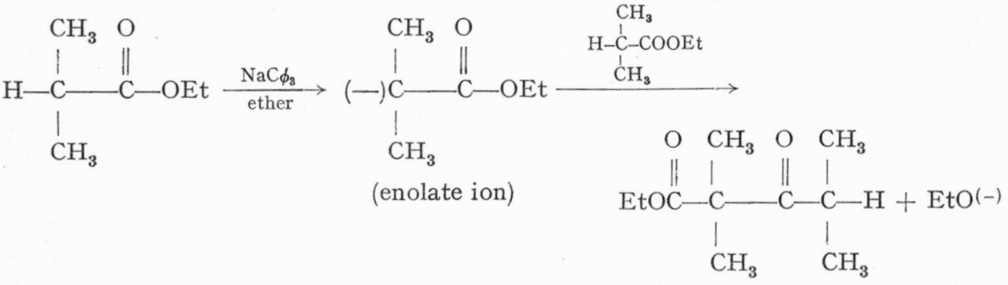

The success of the reaction with sodium triphenylmethide as a catalyst might have been due to the conversion of the keto ester into a sodio

[419] W. B. Renfrow, Jr., and C. R. Hauser, *J. Am. Chem. Soc.*, **60**, 463 (1938).

derivative, thus displacing an unfavorable equilibrium. But it appears rather to be the result of a faster reaction with the higher concentration of intermediate enolate ion produced by the stronger base. Thus the ester will also condense under these conditions with ethyl benzoate, giving a product that has no active hydrogen at all and hence can not be stabilized as a salt. The reaction of the ethyl benzoate-ethyl isobutyrate mixture can in fact give two products, one rate controlled, the other equilibrium controlled.

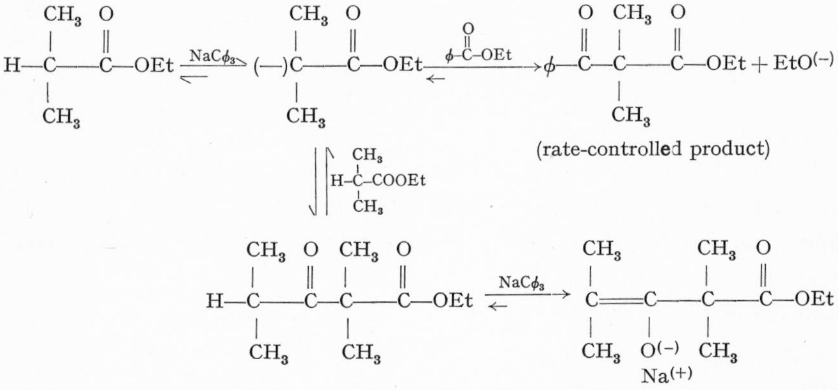

(rate-controlled product)

(equilibrium-controlled product)

The benzoyl derivative is the more rapidly formed, but on standing it is slowly and irreversibly converted into the salt of the isobutyryl derivative.

The esters **LXXVIII** and **LXXIX** also fail to undergo the Claisen condensation with sodium ethoxide as the catalyst, but do give the reaction if mesitylmagnesium bromide is used.[420]

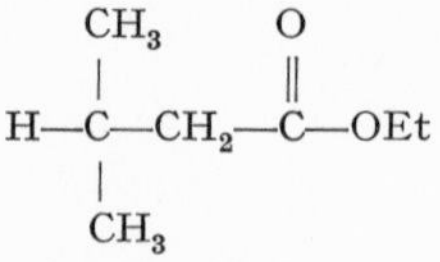

(LXXVIII) 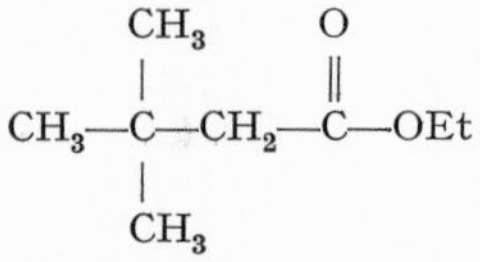   (LXXIX)

In some condensation reactions the product is attained only by way of rather implausible looking intermediates of high energy. The stable product represents a free energy sink that drains off the high energy

[420] M. A. Spielman and M. T. Schmidt, *J. Am. Chem. Soc.*, **59**, 2009 (1937)·

intermediate as fast as it is formed, driving an otherwise impossible reaction to completion. The Michael rearrangement seems to be an example of this:[421]

$$\phi-CH=CH-\overset{\overset{\displaystyle O}{\|}}{C}-O-Et + H-\overset{\overset{\displaystyle COOEt}{|}}{\underset{\underset{\displaystyle CH_3}{|}}{C}}-COOEt \quad \underset{\longleftarrow}{\overset{NaOEt}{\longrightarrow}} \quad \left[\begin{array}{c} \phi-CH-CH_2-\overset{\overset{\displaystyle O}{\|}}{C}-OEt \\ | \\ CH_3-\overset{}{\underset{}{C}}-COOEt \\ | \\ COOEt \end{array} \right]$$

$$\underset{\substack{\displaystyle \text{Stable product} \\ \text{(as enolate)}}}{\left[\begin{array}{c} \overset{\displaystyle COOEt}{\underset{}{|}} \\ \phi-CH-\overset{}{\underset{}{C}}-H \\ | \quad\quad | \\ CH_3-C-H \quad COOEt \\ | \\ COOEt \end{array} \right]} \quad \overset{\longrightarrow}{\longleftarrow} \quad \overset{\displaystyle \uparrow NaOEt}{\left[\begin{array}{c} \phi-CH-CH-\overset{\overset{\displaystyle O}{\|}}{C}-OEt \\ | \quad\quad | \\ CH_3-C-\quad-C-O^{(-)} \\ | \quad\quad | \\ COOEt \quad OEt \end{array} \right]}$$

The product of simple addition across the double bond is only weakly acidic whereas the final product has a hydrogen activated by two carbethoxy groups and is removed from the equilibrium by conversion to the enolate salt. The stability of the final salt serves to drag the reaction over the barrier that the cyclobutane intermediate must represent.

In the condensation of alkyl methyl ketones with esters, the primary hydrogen is the one lost as in the reactions previously discussed with carbon dioxide, aldehydes, etc. The reaction is with the more rapidly formed and less hindered ion rather than with the ion that would be present in higher concentration at equilibrium.

Condensation reactions are conveniently written as carbanion reactions, and yet it is clear that the metallic cation is important too. For example, sodium and lithium give quite different results in the condensation of acetophenone and *tert*-butyl acetate.[422] The various rate and equilibrium constants depend on the nature of the associated metal. Lithium, zinc, and magnesium, which give the aldol condens-

[421] A. Michael and J. Ross, *J. Am. Chem. Soc.*, **52**, 4598 (1930).
[422] C. R. Hauser and W. H. Puterbaugh, *J. Am. Chem. Soc.*, **75**, 4756 (1953).

ation with the above system, have greater coordinating power than sodium, which does not give the aldol condensation. Acetophenone

$$\phi-\overset{O}{\overset{\|}{C}}-CH_3+CH_2=\overset{O^{(-)}Na^{(+)}}{\overset{|}{C}}-O-\overset{CH_3}{\underset{|}{\overset{|}{C}}}-CH_3 \underset{\longleftarrow}{\overset{ether}{\longrightarrow}} \left[\phi-\overset{O^{(-)}Na^{(+)}}{\overset{|}{C}}=CH_2+CH_3-\overset{O}{\overset{\|}{C}}-O-\overset{CH_3}{\underset{|}{\overset{|}{C}}}-CH_3 \right]$$

$$\downarrow ether$$

$$\phi-\overset{O}{\overset{\|}{C}}-CH_2-\overset{O}{\overset{\|}{C}}-CH_3+CH_3-\overset{CH_3}{\underset{|}{\overset{|}{C}}}-ONa$$

(after two hours)

$$\phi-\overset{O^{(-)}Na^{(+)}}{\underset{|}{\overset{|}{C}}}-CH_2-\overset{O}{\overset{\|}{C}}-O-\overset{CH_3}{\underset{|}{\overset{|}{C}}}-CH_3$$

$$CH_3 \qquad\qquad CH_3$$

(after 15 minutes)
30% yield

but $\phi-\overset{O}{\overset{\|}{C}}-CH_3+CH_2=\overset{O^{(-)}Li^{(+)}}{\underset{|}{\overset{|}{C}}}-O-\overset{CH_3}{\underset{|}{\overset{|}{C}}}-CH_3 \xrightarrow{ether} \phi-\overset{O^{(-)}Li^{(+)}}{\underset{|}{\overset{|}{C}}}-CH_2-\overset{O}{\overset{\|}{C}}-O-\overset{CH_3}{\underset{|}{\overset{|}{C}}}-CH_3$

reacts with phenyl lithium primarily to give the carbinol but with phenyl sodium to give benzene and sodium enolate.

Still another possibility in the base-catalyzed reactions of carbonyl compounds is alkylation or similar reaction at the oxygen atom. This is the predominant reaction of phenoxide ion, of course, but for enolates with less resonance stabilization it is exceptional and requires special conditions. Even phenolates react at carbon when the reagent is carbon dioxide, but this may be due merely to the instability of the alternative carbonic half ester. The association of enolate ions with a proton is evidently not very different from the association with metallic cations. Although the equilibrium mixture is about 92% ketone, the sodium derivative of acetoacetic ester reacts with acetic acid in cold petroleum ether to give the enol. The Perkin ring closure reaction, which depends on C-alkylation, gives the alternative O-alkylation only when it is applied to the synthesis of a four membered ring:

[423] K. von Auwers, *Ber.*, **71**, 2082 (1938).

$$
\underset{\text{CH}_2}{\diagup}\!\!\begin{array}{c}\overset{\text{COCH}_3}{|}\\\text{CH}_2\text{—C—H}\\|\\\text{CH}_2\text{Br}\quad\text{C—OEt}\\\|\\\text{O}\end{array}
\quad\xrightarrow{\text{NaOEt}}\quad
\underset{\text{CH}_2}{\diagup}\!\!\begin{array}{c}\overset{\text{COCH}_3}{|}\\\text{CH}_2\text{—C}^{(-)}\\|\\\text{CH}_2\text{Br}\quad\text{C—OEt}\\\|\\\text{O}\end{array}
\quad\xrightarrow{\;\;/\!\!/\;\;}\quad
\begin{array}{c}\overset{\text{COCH}_3}{|}\\\text{CH}_2\text{—C—COOEt}\\|\qquad|\\\text{CH}_2\text{—CH}_2+\text{Br}^{(-)}\end{array}
$$

$$
\downarrow
$$

$$
\underset{\text{CH}_2}{\diagup}\!\!\begin{array}{c}\overset{\text{COCH}_3}{|}\\\text{CH}_2\text{—C}\diagdown\\\qquad\quad\text{C—OEt} + \text{Br}^{(-)}\\\text{CH}_2\text{—O}\diagup\end{array}
$$

Hydroxymethylene compounds are O-alkylated by potassium carbonate and an alkyl halide in acetone, but these conditions produce only the usual C-alkylation with β-diketones or keto esters.[423] Nitro-compounds have also been reported to give either O- or C-alkylation.[424] While acylation of the sodium derivative of acetoacetic ester normally takes place on carbon, O-acylation is the result in pyridine.

Base-Catalyzed Rearrangement Reactions

The carbonium ion rearrangement is essentially an internal displacement reaction in which a carbonium ion becomes bonded to some other portion of the same molecule. Certain base-catalyzed rearrangements have been discussed in the section on carbonium ion rearrangements because they have the distinguishing characteristic of being *internal electrophilic displacements* by an atom bearing at least a partial positive charge.

A certain dualism is observable in carbonium ion-carbanion chemistry, a dualism rather like that of lines and points in projective geometry. The reader may recall that interchanging the words "line" and "point" in a theorem of projective geometry converts it into a statement that is also a theorem, sometimes the same one. For most carbonium ion reactions a corresponding carbanion reaction is known. The dualism can be used as a method for the invention of new, or at least unobserved, carbanion reactions. The carbanionic reaction corresponding to the carbonium ion rearrangement is of course the *internal nucleophilic*

[424] J. T. Thurston and R. L. Shriner, *J. Org. Chem.*, **2**, 183 (1937).

displacement. The carbanion rearrangements have not been studied in the same detail as carbonium ion rearrangements, and the ideas corresponding to migration aptitude and the neighboring group effect, for example, have not yet been so fully developed.

$$
\begin{array}{c}
\text{O--CH}_3 \\
| \\
\phi\text{--C--K} \\
| \\
\phi
\end{array}
\longrightarrow
\left[
\begin{array}{c}
\text{O--CH}_3 \\
| \\
\phi\text{--C}^{(-)} \\
| \\
\phi
\end{array}
\right]
\longrightarrow
\left[
\begin{array}{c}
\text{O.} \\
| \;\; \text{:CH}_3 \\
\phi\text{--C} \cdot \\
| \\
\phi
\end{array}
\right]^{(-)}
\begin{array}{c}
\text{OK} \\
| \\
\phi\text{--C--CH}_3 \\
| \\
\phi
\end{array}
\qquad 425
$$

Since the lithium salt rearranges faster than the potassium salt in this rearrangement from oxygen to carbon, it is likely that the lithium ion is coordinated to oxygen during the rearrangement.

$$
\begin{array}{c}
\text{O--}\phi \\
| \\
\phi\text{--C--Na} \\
| \\
\phi
\end{array}
\longrightarrow
\left[
\begin{array}{c}
\text{O--}\phi \\
| \\
\phi\text{--C}^{(-)} \\
| \\
\phi
\end{array}
\right]
\longrightarrow
\left[
\begin{array}{c}
\overset{(+)}{\text{Na}}\cdots\text{O} \\
| \\
\phi\text{--C} \\
| \\
\phi
\end{array}
\right]
\begin{array}{c}
\text{ONa} \\
| \\
\phi\text{--C--}\phi \\
| \\
\phi
\end{array}
\qquad 425
$$

$$
\phi_3\text{C--CH}_2\text{Cl} \xrightarrow[\text{NH}_3]{\text{Na}}
\left[
\phi_3\text{C--CH}_2\text{Na}
\right]
\longrightarrow
\left[
\phi_2\text{C--CH}_2
\right]
\begin{array}{c}
\text{Na} \\
| \\
\phi_2\text{C--CH}_2\phi
\end{array}
\qquad 426
$$

$$
\begin{array}{c}
\text{CH}_3 \\
| \\
\phi\text{--CH}_2\text{--N--CH}_3 \\
|^{(+)} \\
\text{CH}_3
\end{array}
\xrightarrow{\phi\text{Li}}
\left[
\begin{array}{c}
\text{CH}_3 \\
| \\
\phi\text{--CH--N--CH}_3 \\
{}_{(-)}\;\;{}^{(+)}| \\
\text{CH}_3
\end{array}
\right]
\longrightarrow
\left[
\begin{array}{c}
\text{H}\;\;\text{CH}_3 \\
|\;\;\;\; | \\
\phi\text{--C--N--CH}_3 \\
\cdots\cdots \\
\text{CH}_3
\end{array}
\right]
\begin{array}{c}
\text{H}\;\;\text{CH}_3 \\
|\;\;\;\; | \\
\phi\text{--C--N} \\
|\;\;\;\; | \\
\text{CH}_3\;\text{CH}_3
\end{array}
\;427
$$

$$
\begin{array}{c}
\text{CH}_3 \\
{}^{(+)}| \\
\phi\text{CH}_2\text{--N--CH}_3 \\
| \\
\text{CH}_2 \\
| \\
\phi
\end{array}
\xrightarrow{\phi\text{Li}}
\left[
\begin{array}{c}
\text{H}\;\;\text{CH}_3 \\
|\;\;\;\; | \\
\phi\text{--C--N--CH}_3 \\
\cdots\cdots \\
\text{CH}_2 \\
| \\
\phi
\end{array}
\right]
\longrightarrow
\begin{array}{c}
\text{H}\;\;\text{CH}_3 \\
|\;\;\;\; | \\
\phi\text{--C--N--CH}_3 \\
| \\
\text{CH}_2 \\
| \\
\phi
\end{array}
\qquad 427
$$

The last reaction shows that the benzyl group has a superior migration aptitude in the Stevens rearrangement. It is more reactive in nucleophilic

425 G. Wittig and W. Happe, *Ann.*, **557**, 205 (1947).
426 G. W. Watt, *Chem. Revs.*, **46**, 317 (1950).
427 S. W. Kantor and C. R. Hauser, *J. Am. Chem. Soc.*, **73**, 4122 (1951).

displacements, just as the better migrating groups of the carbonium ion rearrangement are more reactive in electrophilic displacements (aromatic substitution).

With sodamide in liquid ammonia the Stevens reaction takes a different course.[427] Alternative mechanisms are given for the first example shown below, one showing the proton removed from a methyl group, the other from a benzyl group. In the second example the product allows one of the corresponding mechanisms to be eliminated.

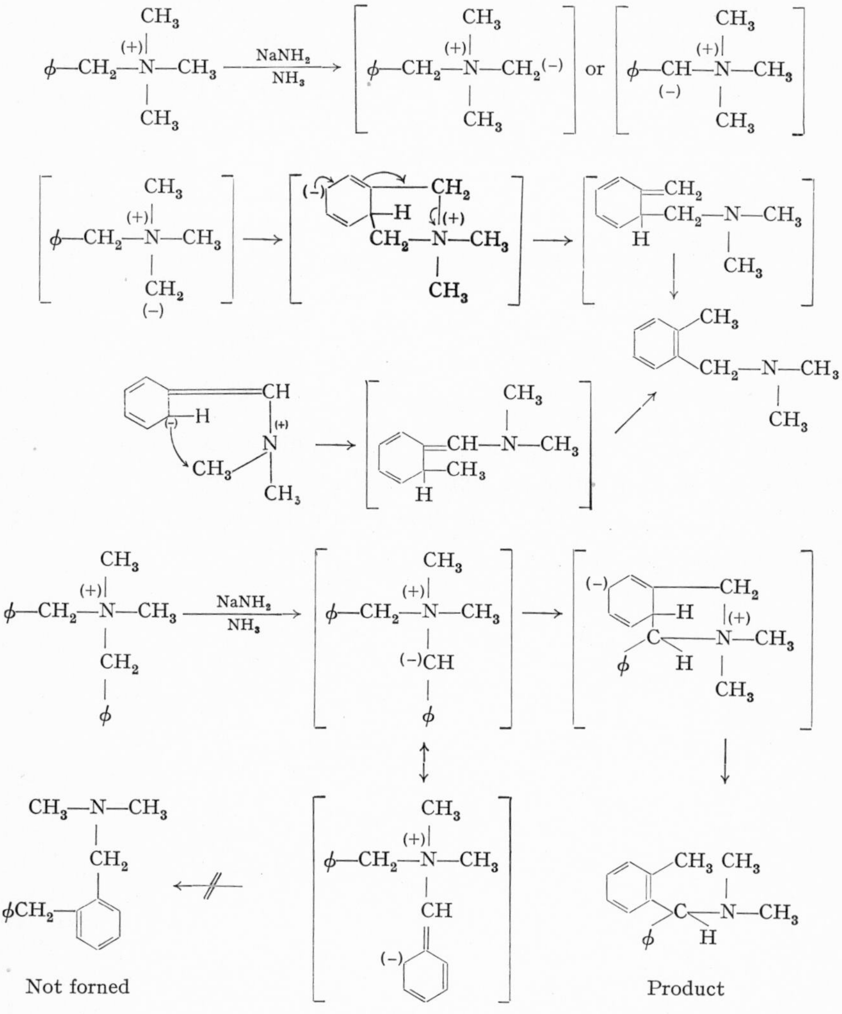

$$
\phi-CH_2-\overset{\overset{CH_3}{\overset{(+)|}{}}}{N}-CH_3 \xrightarrow[NH_3]{NaNH_2} \left[\phi-CH_2-\overset{\overset{CH_3}{\overset{(+)|}{}}}{N}-CH_2{}^{(-)}\right] \text{ or } \left[\phi-\overset{\overset{CH_3}{\overset{(+)|}{}}}{\underset{(-)}{CH}}-\overset{\overset{}{}}{N}-CH_3\right]
$$

Not forned

Product

The cyclic stage of the reaction with sodamide in liquid ammonia corresponds to a Friedel-Crafts ring closure reaction in the carbonium ion series, a reaction that is often an alternative to the carbonium ion rearrangement.

Just as in its carbonium ion twin, the carbanion rearrangement takes place with retention of configuration of the migrating group. This proves at once that the reaction is intramolecular and that the displacement takes place at the front side.[428]

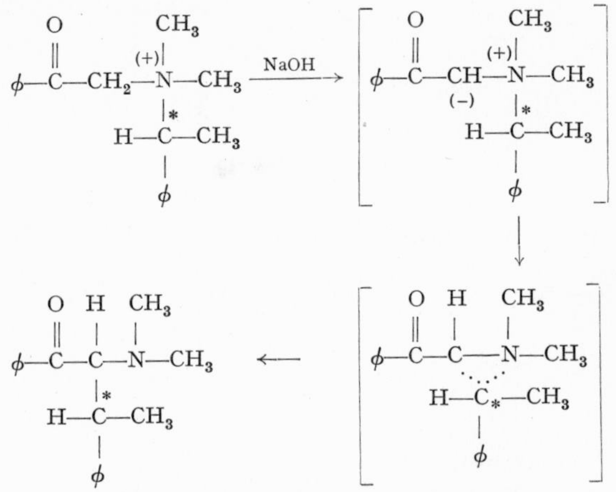

A reaction related to the pure carbanion rearrangement, but one that eventually involves an external displacing agent as well, is the Favorskii reaction. It has been shown with the aid of isotopic tracers that the mechanism is:[429]

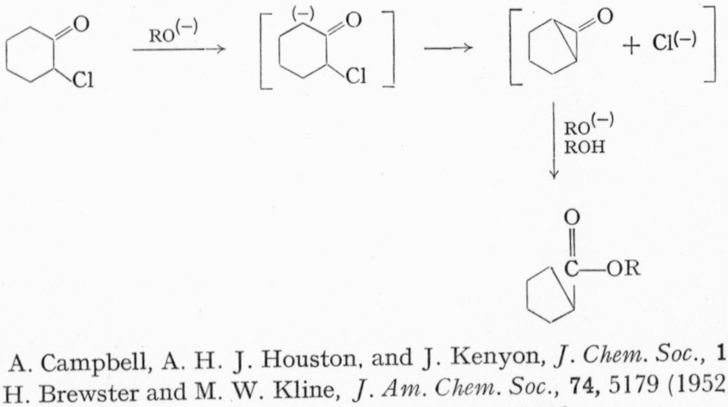

[428] A. Campbell, A. H. J. Houston, and J. Kenyon, *J. Chem. Soc.*, 1947, 93: J. H. Brewster and M. W. Kline, *J. Am. Chem. Soc.*, **74**, 5179 (1952).
[429] R. B. Loftfield, *J. Am. Chem. Soc.*, **72**, 632 (1950).

In the discussion of carbonium ions it was shown that the important feature was not the charge but the deficiency of electrons, so that various hetero intermediates of other than unit positive charge could be regarded as carbonium ion analogs. Similarly, any atom with an unshared pair of electrons can be regarded as a carbanion analog. Thus the familiar neighboring group effect of carbonium ion chemistry is also an example of the reaction of a carbanion analog. That particular reaction can be considered from either point of view and is reminiscent of those theorems of projective geometry which merely regenerate themselves when "points" and "lines" are interchanged.

$$
\begin{array}{c}
\overset{\text{Cl}}{\underset{|}{\zeta}} \\
\text{CH}_2 \\
\text{Cl—CH}_2\text{—CH}_2\text{—}\overset{..}{\underset{..}{\text{S}}}\overset{\uparrow}{\cdots}\diagup^{\text{CH}_2}
\end{array}
$$

A carbanion chemist's view of mustard solvolysis

$$
\begin{array}{c}
\text{CH}_2\Big\langle\!\!\begin{array}{l}\overset{..}{\text{S}}\text{—CH}_2\text{CH}_2\text{Cl} \\ \overset{\searrow}{}\\ \text{CH}_2\end{array} \\
\underset{|}{\overset{|}{\zeta}}\text{Cl}
\end{array}
$$

A carbonium ion chemist's view of mustard solvoysis

A reaction that offers a closer parallel to the neighboring group effect of carbonium ion chemistry is a possible concerted mechanism for the Michael rearrangement:

$$
\begin{array}{c}
\text{CH}_2\text{—CH}_2\text{—COOEt} \\
\underset{|}{|} \\
\text{CH}_3\text{—C—COOEt} \xrightarrow{\text{B}^{(-)}} \\
\underset{|}{|} \\
\text{EtO—C} \\
\underset{\parallel}{} \\
\text{O}
\end{array}
\left[
\begin{array}{c}
\overset{\text{B}^{(-)}}{\vdots} \\
\text{H} \\
\text{H}\diagdown\!\vdots \\
\text{CH}_2\text{——C—COOEt} \\
\underset{|}{\vdots} \\
\text{CH}_3\text{—C———C—OEt} \\
\underset{|}{}\ \ \overset{\parallel}{} \\
\text{COOEt O}
\end{array}
\right]
\rightarrow
\left[
\begin{array}{c}
\text{H} \\
| \\
\text{CH}_2\text{——C—COOEt} \\
\underset{|}{|}\ \ \underset{|}{} \\
\text{CH}_3\text{—C———C—OEt} \\
\underset{|}{|}\ \ \underset{|}{} \\
\text{COOEt O} \\
\text{(-)}
\end{array}
\right]
$$

The Role of Cations

The organic chemist is well aware that the reactions of organo-metallic compounds and base-catalyzed reactions are very much influenced by the nature of the metal or the cation associated with the base. He does not expect exactly the same results from the use of sodium and potassium hydroxides, and regards the latter as the more drastic catalyst even though both are strong bases in water. The different effects of the cations can be ascribed to chemical differences on the one hand and to differences in salt effect on the other. If the metal is believed to coordinate with some electronegative atom in the transition state its specific properties are considered as chemical, if not they are classified as specific salt effects. The boundary between the two effects is not clear and, if anything, is usually drawn in such a way as to include too many phenomena in the question-begging category of specific salt effects. More and more specific salt effects are yielding to explanation in microscopic terms or in terms of chemical equilibria. Examples of the chemical approach to certain salt effects are to be found both in the fields of reaction kinetics and of solubility.[430-432] It is very likely that many reactions will go with or without the intimate participation of the cation, the path taken depending on the concentration. Many reactions are independent of the nature of the cation (of a single charge type) in solutions less than 1 N in fairly good ionizing solvents, but give different products with different cations in the more concentrated solutions often used in preparative organic work.[432] Numerous examples of the dependence of carbanion reactions on the nature of the metal have already been cited in various parts of this and the preceding chapter. A few additional ones are noted below:

$$\phi\text{---}O^{(-)} + CO_2 \quad \xrightarrow[\substack{\text{pressure}\\ \text{NaOH}}]{\text{heat}} \quad \begin{array}{c} O^{(-)}Na^{(+)} \\ \\ COO^{(-)}Na^{(+)} \end{array}$$
$$Na^{(+)}$$

[430] M. M. Jones and E. Griswold, *J. Am. Chem. Soc.*, **76**, 3247 (1954).
[431] A. R. Olson and T. R. Simonson, *J. Chem. Phys.*, **17**, 1167 (1949).
[432] O. L. Brady and J. Jakobovits, *J. Chem. Soc.*, **1950**, 767.

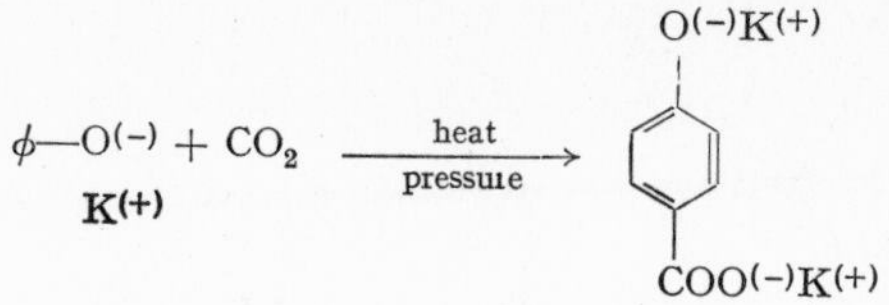

$$\phi\text{—}O^{(-)} + CO_2 \xrightarrow[\text{pressure}]{\text{heat}}$$

433

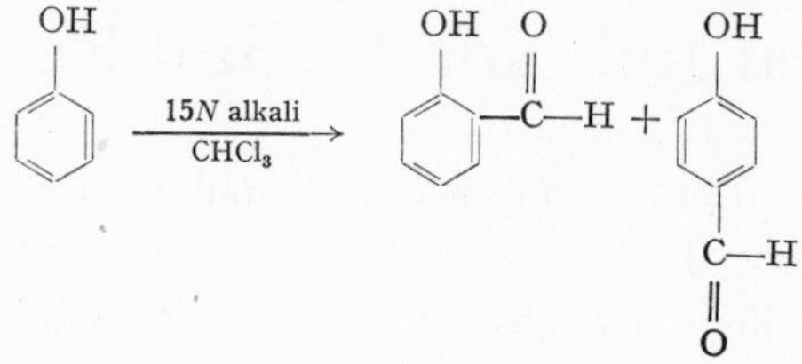

$$\phi\text{—}CH=CH\text{—}CH_2^{(-)}Na^{(+)} + \phi\text{—}\overset{O}{\overset{\|}{C}}\text{—}CH_3 \longrightarrow \phi\text{—}CH=CH\text{—}CH_2\text{—}\overset{\phi}{\underset{CH_3}{\overset{|}{C}}}\text{—}OH$$

434

Cation   ortho/para ratio

Cation	ortho/para ratio
Na	2.08
K	1.24
Cs	0.98
Et$_3$NCH$_3^{(+)}$	0.52

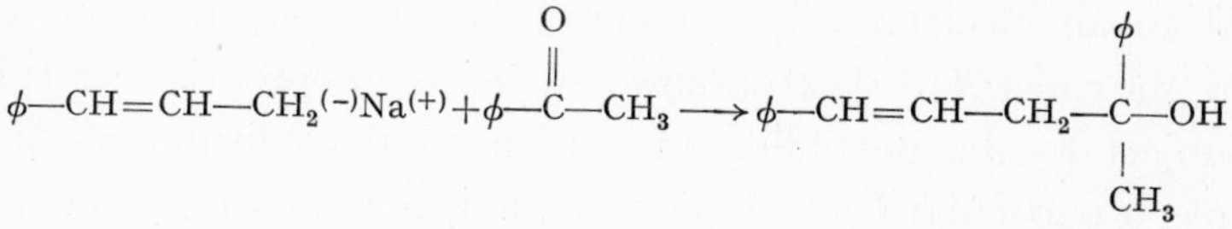

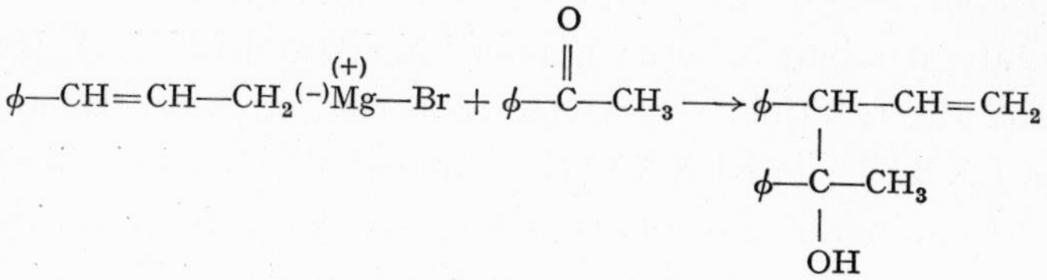

[433] H. Kolbe, *J. prakt. Chem.*, **10** (ii), 95 (1874).

[434] T. W. Campbell and W. G. Young, *J. Am. Chem. Soc.*, **69**, 3066 (1947).

CHAPTER XII

Radical and Non-Radical Reactions

Polar reactions form no clearly definable category. There is no minimum amount of change in charge separation that must occur before we are willing to call a reaction polar. The ambiguity arises in its most acute form in the case of reactions that can be written as the movement of one pair of electrons out of a given region concerted with the entry of another pair. There is, of course, no guarantee that electrons move in pairs even for reactions that pass exclusively through singlet (non-radical) states. Thus a reaction that fails to show the usual response of polar reactions to solvent or structural changes might involve a perfectly concerted flow of electron pairs or, alternatively, a transition from an electronically symmetrical ground state molecular orbital to an electronically symmetrical transition state molecular orbital, the concept of electron-flow here being inappropriate or at least not subject to the possibility of experimental confirmation. If, for example, a particular Diels-Alder reaction is not concerted, and shows the proper structural and medium effects, and gives evidence of an intermediate, it might be written as in LXXX and LXXXI. If on the other hand the reaction is perfectly concerted, a choice between the diagrams LXXXII and LXXXIII is impossible, and it is likely that they are meaningless except as devices to keep from accidentally changing the number of electrons in the formula, aids to electronic bookkeeping.

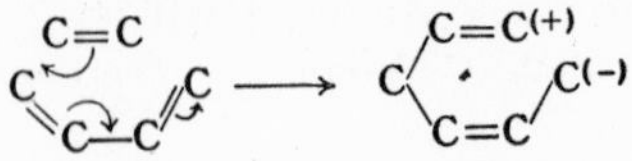

(LXXX)   (LXXXI)

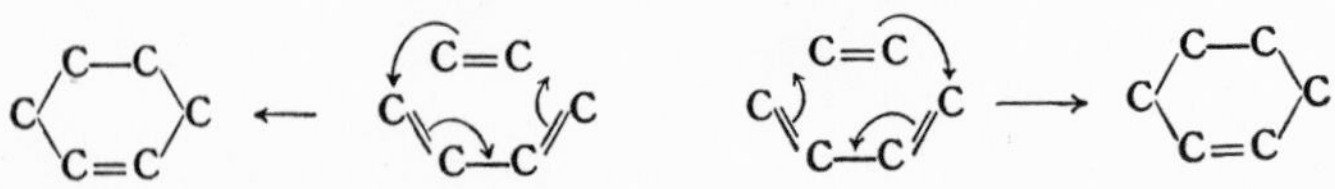

(LXXXII)   (LXXXIII)

While polar reactions are polar only to various degrees, the situation is somewhat better with regard to radical reactions. A free radical has, and a non-radical has not, an uncompensated magnetic moment which shows up experimentally as paramagnetism or as paramagnetic resonance absorption. Of course the concentration of free radicals in a radical reaction might be too low to demonstrate by these methods, yet the concept itself is a sharp one. Radical reactions can involve a considerable shifting of dipoles and hence exhibit some of the polar traits of indubitably polar and non-radical reactions. The experimental problem of distinguishing a free radical reaction from a non-radical one is therefore sometimes difficult.

The clear-cut theoretical distinction between radicals and non-radicals, and hence between radical and non-radical reactions, is possible only because of the virtual prohibition of resonance between states of different multiplicity. Diradical (triplet) resonance structures need not be considered in describing the singlet state of an olefin, nor do singlet state olefin structures need to be considered in describing the diradical to which an olefin might be converted.[435] While it is true that a small amount of resonance between singlet and diradical states can be induced by a powerful and non-uniform magnetic field, this small amount of resonance merely facilitates transitions to the diradical state. That is, even in the presence of a paramagnetic catalyst an olefin is not yet itself a diradical although it is more easily excited to the diradical state. We are therefore not troubled with theoretical as well as experimental uncertainties in deciding what is a radical reaction and what is not. This is in contrast to the continuous variation in ionic bond character that prevents a precise definition of a polar reaction.

When the experimental difficulties prevent the use of the defining property of uncompensated magnetic moment in assigning a radical mechanism, the decision is usually still possible on other grounds. But it is worth noting that perhaps no other single criterion is entirely reliable. Decision may be reached by the cumulative consideration of several pieces of evidence, each one of which is known to have exceptions, and no one of which would be convincing alone. We are on particularly sure ground in a few fortunate cases where both the polar and the radical reactions are known and can be compared.

[435] P. Yuster and S. I. Weissman, *J. Chem. Phys.*, **17**, 1182 (1949).

The Characteristics of Polar and Radical Reactions

A typical polar (and non-radical) reaction contrasts with a typical radical (and not very polar) reaction in the ways listed in Table XIII. Each statement of Table XIII has known or easily foreseeable exceptions, and some of the statements may not be true even for a majority of radical or non-radical reactions. Perhaps Stefansson would call these propositions "Standard Errors."[436] The Typical Radical Reaction is a *useful* concept whose status is something like that of the Literary Ostrich[436] and other fauna of strictly metaphorical habitat but very well-known behavior. Real ostriches are useless for metaphorical purposes and no one expects them to behave like literary ostriches.

Substituent Effects

The stabilization of a carbonium ion, carbanion, or related transition state by a substituent reflects the electrostatic nature of the substituent and its ability to accept the type of charge being stabilized. On the other hand, the electrostatic nature of the substituent and its ability to accept charges should be matters of relative indifference to the stability of the free radical. Thus when an intermediate or transition state is stabilized by a substituent like the methoxy group and destabilized by a substituent like the nitro group, the intermediate or transition state might reasonably be expected to bear a positive charge. A reverse effect by the same substituents would indicate a negative charge. A radical on the other hand might be expected to be stabilized by substituents of both types, particularly by those with conjugated unsaturation. The effect of polar but saturated substituents should be less with uncharged radicals than with charged intermediates.

There are two difficulties in the application of the substituent effect criterion:

(*a*) The magnitude of the effect is often dependent on the temperature. [437]A small substituent effect might be an accident of the temperature chosen rather than an indication of a non-polar reaction.

[436] V. Stefansson, *The Standardization of Error*, Norton, New York, 1927.

TABLE XIII

Typical Polar (Non-radical) and Typical Radical Behavior

	Polar	Radical
Substituent effects	A specific type of substituent accelerates the reaction, another specific type slows it down.	Both types of substituent have the same effect and it is usually a small one.
Solvent effects	A "polar" solvent has a large accelerative or decelerative effect.	Very little difference between solvents unless they are involved in chain transfer.
Catalysts	Catalyzed by ions, especially acids and bases, also Lewis acids. Indifferent to traces of radical.	Indifferent to ions, acids, Lewis acids, bases. Large response to traces of added radical.
Products	Small number of products in high yield.	Large number of products in low yield and not readily purified.
Inhibitors	Not usually inhibited by trace amounts, not usually a chain reaction.	Often inhibited by traces, often a chain reaction.
Light	Not effective except in raising the temperature.	Often fail to take place in the dark.
Diagnostic reactions	A carbonium ion is trapped by a nucleophilic reagent, a carbanion by an electrophilic reagent. Usually doesn't initiate polymerization or remove atoms from the solvent. Predictable directive effects in aromatic substitution. Predictable migration aptitudes.	A radical is trapped by metals and other radicals, quinones, and nitro-compounds. Will polymerize olefins and attack the solvent. Directive effects and migration aptitudes are predictable but different.

(b) Although some radical reactions show the small and non-specific substituent effects expected of them, others imitate polar, non-radical reactions quite well. The Hammett rho-sigma relationship is known to correlate several types of radical reaction. The parameter ρ is not neccessarily very small and may be either positive or negative, i.e., the radical or its transition state may behave either like a carbanion or a carbonium ion. Some examples are shown in Table XIV.[437]

[437] H. H. Jaffé, *Chem. Revs.*, **53**, 191 (1953).

TABLE XIV
Substituent Effects in Some Reactions of Probable Radical Mechanism

Reaction	Temperature, °C.	ρ	Correlation coefficient
1. ϕ—C(=O)—O—O—C(=O)—ϕ + Xϕ—N(CH$_3$)(CH$_3$) in CHCl$_3$	20	—2.334	0.954
2. X—ϕ—C(=O)—O—O—C(=O)—ϕX Decomposition in ϕ—C(=O)—CH$_3$	80	—0.201	0.687
3. X—ϕ—C(=O)—O—O—C(=O)—ϕX Decomposition in dioxane with an inhibitor of chains present	80	—0.374	0.932
4. Xϕ—C(=O)—O—O—C(=O)—ϕX Initiation of styrene polymerization	60	—.550	0.884
5. X—ϕ—C(=O)—O—O—C(CH$_3$)(CH$_3$)—CH$_3$ Decomposition in ϕ_2O	100	—.903	0.996
	110.1	—.678	0.994
	120.2	—.568	0.999
	130.9	—.525	0.990

(Table continued)

TABLE XIV *(continued)*

Reaction	Temperature, °C.	ρ	Correlation coefficient
6. $X-\phi-\overset{\overset{O}{\|}}{C}-H + \phi-\overset{\overset{O}{\|}}{C}-O \cdot$ In acetic anhydride	30	$-.488$	0.922
7. $X-\phi-\overset{\overset{O}{\|}}{C}-H + p-Cl\phi-\overset{\overset{O}{\|}}{C}-O \cdot$ In acetic anhydride	30	-1.668	0.986
8. 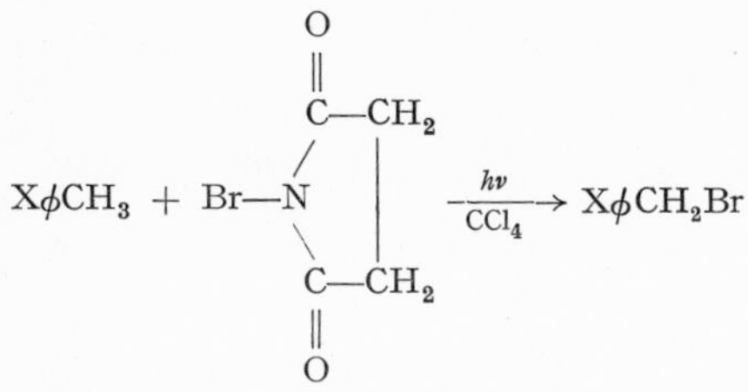 $X\phi CH_3 + Br-N\begin{smallmatrix} \overset{O}{\|} \\ C-CH_2 \\ \\ C-CH_2 \\ \| \\ O \end{smallmatrix} \xrightarrow[CCl_4]{h\nu} X\phi CH_2Br$	80	-1.806	0.977
9. $X\phi CH_3 + Br_2 \xrightarrow[CCl_4]{h\nu} X\phi CH_2Br$	80	-1.369	0.964
10. $X\phi NH-N=CH\phi$ Autoxidation	16–21	-1.7	0.96
11. $\phi NH-N=CH\phi X$ Autoxidation	17–20	-0.35	0.54
12. $X-\phi-\overset{\overset{H}{\|}}{\underset{OH}{C}}-\overset{\overset{O}{\|}}{C}-\phi X$ Autoxidation	10 20	$+1.429$ $+1.335$	0.963 0.975
13. Copolymerization of $X\phi CH=CH_2$ with $\phi-CH=CH_2$	60	$+0.531$	0.989
14. Copolymerization of $X\phi CH=CH_2$ with $CH_2=C-\overset{\overset{O}{\|}}{\underset{CH_3}{C}}-O-CH_3$	60	$+0.038$	0.091
15. Copolymerization of $X\phi CH=CH_2$ with $p\text{-}Cl\phi CH=CH_2.$	60	$+0.103$	0.767

(Table continued

TABLE XIV *(continued)*

Reaction	Temperature, °C.	ρ	Correlation coefficient
16. Copolymerization of $X\phi C{=}CH_2$ with $\underset{CH_3}{\mid}$ maleic anhydride	60	—0.612	0.512
17. $(X\phi)_2C{-}C(\phi X)_2 \xrightarrow[\substack{CH_3COOH \\ (cyclic\ mechanism)}]{Pb(OAc)_4} (X\phi)_2C{=}O$ $\ \ \ \underset{OH\ \ OH}{\mid\ \ \ \ \ \mid}$	18 25 35	—0.426 —0.406 —0.391	0.973 0.983 0.971
18. $X{-}\phi{-}I$ with acetate groups $\xrightarrow[\substack{\phi_2C{-}C\phi_2 \\ \mid\ \ \ \mid \\ OH\ OH}]{CH_3COOH} X\phi I$	34.7	+ 1.438	0.996
19. $Ar_1Ar_2N{-}N{-}N{-}NAr_1Ar_2$ $\ \ \ \ \ \ \underset{\phi}{\overset{C=O}{\mid}}\ \ \underset{\phi}{\overset{C=O}{\mid}}$ Dissociation	—18	—1.302	0.985
20. $ArH + \phi \cdot \longrightarrow Ar\phi$	80	+ 0.675	0.880

Many radical reactions do show the expected small and non-specific response to substituents. Reaction 14 of Table XIV is an example; it has a value of ρ not significantly different from zero and shows almost a random response to the polar nature of the substituent.[438] The dissociation of hexaphenylethanes is obscured by experimental uncertainties but seems to be increased by *both* electron-releasing and electron-withdrawing substituents.

When the reaction is well-established as a radical one it is still possible to find explanations of polar substituent effects, usually in terms of ion-radical intermediates, dipole-dipole repulsion, solvation, or charge-transfer structures like those postulated for π-complexes.[438] Reac-

[438] C. Walling, E. R. Briggs, K. B. Wolfstirn, and F. R. Mayo, *J. Am. Chem. Soc.*, **70**, 1537 (1948).

tion 1 of Table XIV, for example, may involve transfer of an electron from the dimethyl aniline to give a positively charged ion-radical which would account for the favorable effect of electron-releasing substituents in the dimethyl aniline.[439] A dipole-dipole repulsion has been proposed to explain the substituent effect in reaction 4, although it can not be the explanation for polar effects in radical decomposition reactions generally.[440] Reaction 12 is base-catalyzed and its favorable response to electron-withdrawing substituents is merely a matter of stabilizing the negative ion intermediate.[441]

Even leaving aside the reactions in which ionic precursors or ion-radicals rather than neutral radicals are involved, it is clear that a polar response to polar substituents can easily be as great in some radical reactions as in many non-radical "polar" reactions. For example, the ρ value of reaction 13 is comparable to that for the ionization of substituted phenylacetic acids.[438] Although the existence of a ρ-σ relationship can not per se be accepted as evidence of a polar, non-radical mechanism, a sign of ρ opposite to that of a known related ionic reaction may be confirming evidence for a radical mechanism. Thus the nitro group directs ortho-para and facilitates radical substitution reactions in the benzene ring but has the opposite effect in the well-known related reactions in which the attacking reagent is a positive ion. The remaining possibility that the reagent is a negative ion can usually be eliminated on other grounds. As can be seen from some of the examples in Table XIV, the value of ρ depends on the temperature and if ρ is not very large to begin with, a feasible change in temperature might change its sign. It is therefore inadvisable to conclude too much from the sign of ρ unless ρ is large; the sign of a small value of ρ may be an accident of the temperature and not particularly significant as regards the mechanism.

[439] L. Horner and K. Scherf, *Ann.*, **573**, 35 (1951).

[440] C. G. Swain, W. H. Stockmayer, and J. T. Clarke, *J. Am. Chem. Soc.*, **72**, 5426 (1950).

[441] A. Weissberger, *Ber.*, **65**, 1815 (1932).

Diagnostic Reactions

The further reaction subsequent to the formation of the intermediate is often capable of revealing the nature of the intermediate. The aromatic substitution reaction discussed in the previous section is an example of the trapping of an intermediate, the directive effect distinguishing between radicals and cations. Sheer complexity of the product mixture is also indicative of a radical reaction. Mercaptans, which will add to methyl acrylate both by a sulfur anion mechanism and by a sulfur radical mechanism, give considerable polymer as by-product when the radical conditions are used. Suspected carbanions can often be trapped as the product of aldol and similar condensation reactions, the corresponding radical reactions being uncommon. A carbanion can be trapped by the donation of a proton from an acid whereas the acidity of the hydrogen is not very well correlated with the formation of a similar product from a radical. Free radicals themselves are traps for radical intermediates. An example is the reaction of radicals with nitrogen dioxide, α, α-diphenyl-β-picrylhydrazyl, or oxygen. The latter reaction gives a peroxide, but since carbanions are sometimes oxidized to radicals and thence to peroxides the formation of such a product is not in itself complete proof of a free radical mechanism. Another diagnostic reaction is the formation of symmetrical coupling products such as the succinic acid from radical decompositions run in acetic acid or the hexachloroethane from a radical decomposition in carbon tetrachloride. The effect of electrical symmetry can also appear in the form of the kinetic equation; when a radical chain reaction is terminated by the coupling of the radicals, square root reaction orders are sometimes observed. In carbon tetrachloride the isolation of alkyl or acyl chlorides is usually easy and probably constitutes good evidence for a radical mechanism by itself. Of course proof that a reaction has a radical mechanism in one solvent, especially one not very favorable to polar reactions, does not mean that the reaction has a radical mechanism in all solvents. The reaction with metals is also significant and indicative of radicals, but less useful on account of its heterogeneity. And of course an alkali metal can produce radicals by reactions with alkyl halides, with carbonium ions, or with aromatic hydrocarbons.

Another useful test of mechanism is the study of migration aptitudes within the intermediate in case it rearranges. This is analogous to the comparison of aromatic substitution by various mechanisms. It has been used in assigning mechanisms to peroxide decompositions, for example. Migration aptitudes in the oxygen cation are conspicuously different from those in the corresponding neutral oxygen radical. In most cases the mechanism assigned on the basis of migration aptitudes is confirmed by the response to catalyst and solvent. An opportunity for mistakes in the assignment of mechanism on the basis of migration aptitudes alone exists, of course, in the case of rearrangements whose course is sterically determined.

Except for the slight limitation that it puts on the reaction medium, polymerization is the best of the diagnostic reactions. The susceptibility of various monomers to polymerization initiators of various types depends on the structure of the monomer somewhat as follows:[442]

Y in $CH_2=CHY$	Susceptibility
—CN —COOCH$_3$ $-O-\overset{\overset{\text{O}}{\|}}{C}-CH_3$	Anions (strong bases) and radicals
—CH=CH$_2$ —ϕCl-p —ϕ	Anions, radicals, and cations
—CH$_3$ —OR —ϕOCH$_3$	Cations

There is considerable overlap in the effective range of the initiators, but this is less troublesome than it might seem since the various mechanisms can be expected to differ in their response to inhibitors. And if the alternatives are free radical and ion-pair with one of the possible ions not very reactive, decision is easy. For example, the polar decomposition of p-methoxy-p'-nitro benzoyl peroxide in acrylonitrile initiates

[442] D. C. Pepper, *Quart. Revs.*, (*London*), **8**, 88 (1954).

very little polymerization, whereas benzoyl peroxide is very effective.[443] Acrylonitrile is at the radical and strong base end of the monomer list. Benzoyl peroxide undoubtedly intitiates the polymerization by decomposing into radicals. Any non-concerted polar decomposition of the substituted peroxide would give an oxygen cation, not effective with this monomer, and a benzoate anion which is too weak a base.

Another differential reaction is copolymerization. An equi-molar mixture of styrene and methyl methacrylate gives copolymers of different composition depending on the initiator. The radical chains started by benzoyl peroxide are 51% polystyrene, the cationic chains from stannic chloride or boron trifluoride etherate are 100% polystyrene, and the anionic chains from sodium or potassium are more than 99% polymethyl methacrylate.[444] The radicals attack either monomer indiscriminately, the carbanions prefer methyl methacrylate and the carbonium ions prefer styrene. As can be seen from the data of Table XIV, the reactivity of a radical varies considerably with its structure, and it is worth considering whether this variability would be enough to make a radical derived from sodium or potassium give 99% polymethyl methacrylate.[445] If so, the alkali metal intitiated polymerization would not need to be a carbanionic chain reaction. However, the polymer initiated by triphenylmethyl sodium is also about 99% polymethyl methacrylate, whereas tert-butyl peroxide and p-chlorobenzoyl peroxide give 49 to 51% styrene in the initial polymer.[445]

The Effects of Light

Most photochemical reactions are not very polar and often involve free radical intermediates. But initiation of a reaction by light is no infallible indication of a radical mechanism, as is clear from the example of the photo-ionization of certain triarylmethyl cyanides.[446]

[443] J. E. Leffler, J. Am. Chem. Soc., 72, 67 (1950).
[444] C. Walling, E. R. Briggs, W. Cummings, and F. R. Mayo, J. Am. Chem. Soc., 72, 48 (1950).
[445] R. L. Dannley and E. L. Kay, J. Am. Chem. Soc., 77, 1046 (1955).
[446] I. Lifschitz and G. Girbes, Ber., 61, 1463 (1928); L. Harris, J. Kaminsky, and R. G. Simard, J. Am. Chem. Soc., 57, 1151 (1935); G. N. Lewis, T. T. Magel, and D. Lipkin, ibid., 64, 1774 (1942).

Evidently the positive charge is more readily accepted by the dimethyl-amino group in the excited state, or the resonance description of the excited state of the molecule weights the charge-separated form LXXXIV more heavily.

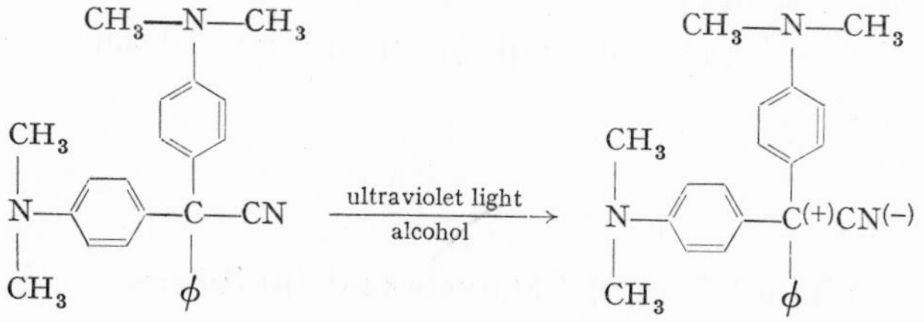

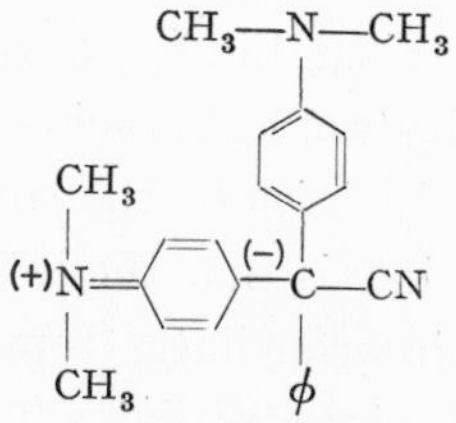

$$CH_3-N-CH_3$$

(LXXXIV)

In spite of such exceptions ionic reactions initiated by light are rare. The reason is probably to be found in the important part played by the solvent in ionization. An ordinary ionization reaction produces solvated rather than free ions and its free energy is very much lowered by the solvation of the ions. It is the solvation energy that usually makes it possible for ionic reactions to compete with related radical reactions. In an ionization reaction in which the energy needed is supplied directly by a photon, the solvent molecules must be arranged *in advance* in the positions they will need to occupy about the solvated ions. This is highly unlikely.

The reason that the solvent molecules need to be pre-oriented is a special case of the Franck-Condon principle. The excited state molecule initially produced by the absorption of radiation has the same geometry possessed by that particular molecule in the ground state. This freezing of the geometry during the excitation process includes the position of the solvent molecules as well. Unless the molecule can store the excitation energy long enough for the solvent molecules to rearrange to their ionization-facilitating positions, no ionization takes place.

It might be objected that all that is needed is a more energetic photon capable of producing unsolvated ions. But the "hot" ions made by such a process can not be expected to have the stability of the less energetic solvated ones, and will probably give different and less clean-cut reactions.

The Effect of Catalysts and Inhibitors

The type of catalyst or inhibitor effective in a reaction tells something about the mechanism, but not always unambiguously. Non-paramagnetic charged catalysts or Lewis acids capable of producing ions from a co-catalyst probably initiate the appropriate ionic or polar reaction. The guiding principle is that the intermediates produced will resemble the catalyst, ionic intermediates from ions or substances known to ionize readily, and radical intermediates from radicals or substances known to dissociate into radicals. Thus catalytic activity on the part of a mineral acid, or even a weak acid, a Lewis acid, or a carbonium ion indicates a polar reaction mechanism in which the crucial intermediates are positively charged or at least ion pairs in which the positive end is the substrate. The initiation of polymerization by triphenylcarbonium ions has already been mentioned and the same ion appears to catalyze the disproportionation of nitromethane into ammonia and carbon dioxide, as does dry hydrogen chloride.[447] Similarly the action of strong bases initiates reactions in which the crucial intermediate is, or resembles, a carbanion or other negative ion.

Neither the catalysis by acids nor by bases is conclusive evidence of a non-radical mechanism however. For example, the semiquinone radical is more stable in basic solution where it exists as a negative ion-radical, and the related nitrogen radicals are more stable in acid solution where they exist as positive ion-radicals. In both cases the ion-radicals have symmetrical resonance not possessed by the neutral radical. Thus acid or base catalysis of certain oxidation reactions need not mean

---

[447] B. B. Smith and J. E. Leffler, *J. Am. Chem. Soc.*, **77**, 1700 (1955).

that they are non-radical in nature, but may merely mean that an ion-radical is more stable than a neutral radical.

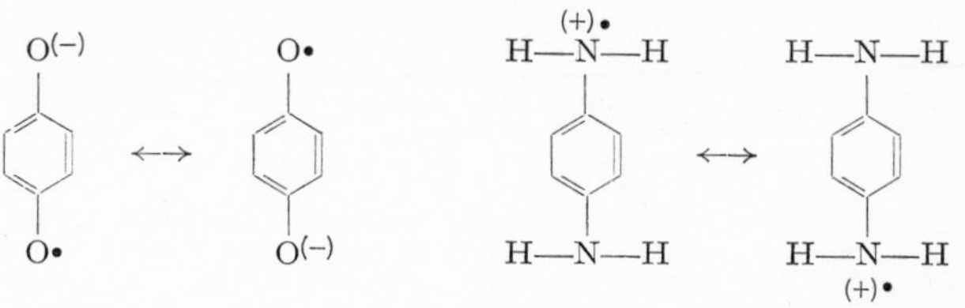

The discovery of diradicals in sulfuric acid or Lewis acid solutions of bianthrone and thianthrene raises the possibility of acid-catalyzed radical reactions for any unsaturated compound.[448] Anything that increases the equilibrium concentration of the diradical should promote radical reactions. These results are important because previous to their discovery few chemists would have hesitated to say that a reaction catalyzed by sulfuric acid or aluminum trichloride, for example, was an entirely ionic one. Now we would not want to venture such an opinion without other reasons.

Catalysis (initiation) by a free radical, on the other hand, is fairly conclusive evidence of a radical reaction, provided it is known that the catalyst is indeed a free radical and that it does not have pronounced polar properties as well. Many classes of compound once thought to decompose exclusively into ions or exclusively into radicals are now known to do both. Peroxides are one well-known example, N-halo-amides are another. Catalysis by benzoyl peroxide probably does indicate a radical reaction since there is no evidence that this particular peroxide tends to give ions even under the most favorable conditions. But many other peroxides are known to decompose into ions, or at least ion pairs, as well as into radicals. The decomposition of azo compounds can also be either radical or ionic, the dialkyl azo compounds tending to give radicals, the diazonium compounds either radicals or ions. Catalysis by a borderline example of an azo compound would therefore be dubious evidence of either kind of mechanism. The initiation of the polymerization of octyl vinyl ether by triphenylmethyl chloride in polar

[448] J. M. Hirshon, D. M. Gardner, and G. K. Fraenkel, *J. Am. Chem. Soc.*, **75**, 4115 (1953).

solvents is probably a polar reaction, but catalysis by triphenylmethyl iodide would be more ambiguous since trityl iodide gives trityl ions and trityl radicals with approximately equal facility.

Catalysis by radicals will usually be due to a radical addition or displacement reaction, hydrogen and halogen being the atoms on which the displacement most often occurs. It is usually a chain reaction: once the substrate is converted into a radical it carries the reaction to many molecules of substrate. Examples are polymerization and autoxidation.

$$R\cdot + \overset{|}{\underset{|}{C}}{=}\overset{|}{\underset{|}{C} \longrightarrow R{-}\overset{|}{\underset{|}{C}}{-}\overset{|}{\underset{|}{C}}\cdot \xrightarrow{\;C=C\;} R{-}\overset{|}{\underset{|}{C}}{-}\overset{|}{\underset{|}{C}}{-}\overset{|}{\underset{|}{C}}{-}\overset{|}{\underset{|}{C}}\cdot \text{ etc.}$$

$$R\cdot + H{-}\overset{|}{\underset{|}{C}}{-} \longrightarrow RH + \cdot \overset{|}{\underset{|}{C}}{-}$$

$$\cdot\overset{|}{\underset{|}{C}}{-} + O_2 \longrightarrow \cdot OO\overset{|}{\underset{|}{C}}{-}$$

$$-\overset{|}{\underset{|}{C}}{-}H + \cdot OOC{-} \longrightarrow -\overset{|}{\underset{|}{C}}\cdot + HOO{-}\overset{|}{\underset{|}{C}}{-} \text{ etc.}$$

Anything that breaks the chain by converting the active chain-carrying species into an ordinary uncreactive molecule *inhibits* the reaction, and since the chains are often long an inhibitor may be effective in very small traces. The chain-starting catalysts may also be effective in very small amounts provided that no inhibitor is also present. The fact that a reaction is a chain reaction sensitive to small amounts of catalysts and inhibitors does not necesssarily mean that it is a radical chain, but the nature of the substances effective as catalysts or inhibitors will usually differentiate a radical chain from an ionic one. An example of an ionic chain reaction is the polymerization of an olefin-Lewis acid system when water is added as a co-catalyst. Water is so very effective that it is suspected that the polymerization observed in some cases with the driest obtainable reaction mixtures is due to the presence of minute and unavoidable amounts of water.

The Magnetic Field Effects

A transition between states of different multiplicity, as for example the singlet (non-radical) and triplet (diradical) states, is an improbable or "forbidden" one under ordinary circumstances. A circumstance that should lift the quantum mechanical interdiction on such a transition is the presence of an intense non-homogeneous magnetic field; hence such a field should accelerate any reaction involving a change in multiplicity just as it increases the intensity of absorption bands corresponding to such transitions.[449] A possible example of this is the catalysis of the cis-trans isomerization of olefins by paramagnetic substances.[450,456] However, in the case of the isomerization of dimethyl maleate into the fumarate, ferric chloride (paramagnetic) is less effective as a catalyst than aluminum chloride (diamagnetic). Either the transition states and intermediates of this reaction are not diradicals, the ferric chloride functioning as a Lewis acid rather than as a source of magnetic field, or the polar effects outweigh the magnetic effects even in the generation of a diradical.[451] The latter is quite possible in view of the results of Hirshon, Gardner, and Fraenkel on the stabilization of diradicals by acids.[448] The much weaker and more homogeneous fields obtainable by an external magnet have been shown experimentally to be without effect both on radical polymerization and on the decomposition of benzoyl peroxide. It is perhaps worth pointing out that magnetic fields are expected to orient electron spins in free radicals but not the radical itself. Experiments with paramagnetic ions have not yet been tried

$$
R\cdot + \phi-\!\!\overset{O}{\underset{\|}{C}}\!\!-O-O-\!\!\overset{O}{\underset{\|}{C}}\!\!-\phi \longrightarrow
\begin{cases}
R\cdot + 2\phi CO\cdot \longrightarrow R-O-\overset{O}{\underset{\|}{C}}-\phi + \phi-\overset{O}{\underset{\|}{C}}-O\cdot \\[2mm]
\text{or} \\[2mm]
R-O-\overset{O}{\underset{\|}{C}}-\phi + \phi-\overset{O}{\underset{\|}{C}}-O\cdot
\end{cases}
$$

[449] P. Yuster and S. I. Weissman, *J. Chem. Phys.*, **17**, 1182 (1949).

[450] J. L. Magee, W. Shand, Jr., and H. Eyring, *J. Am. Chem. Soc.*, **63**, 677 (1941).

[451] W. I. Gilbert, J. Turkevich, and E. S. Wallis, *J. Org. Chem.*, **3**, 611 (1939).

with benzoyl peroxide. Pending such experiments, part of the induced decomposition of benzoyl peroxide by free radicals might be due to the field effect of the radical rather than to concerted decomposition and bond formation.

On the other hand, the formation of radicals from hydroperoxides and ferrous ion is a reduction reaction apparently uncomplicated by any catalytic effect of the ferric ion produced.[452]

$$ROOH + Fe^{(++)} \longrightarrow R{-}O\bullet + HO^{(-)} + Fe^{(+++)}$$

Also, ferric ion promotes nuclear (ionic) bromination of benzene derivatives at the expense of the radical reaction at the side chain.

An effect somewhat like that anticipated for paramagnetic substances is also expected of atoms of high atomic number, whether paramagnetic or not. Close to such a nucleus there is an intense electric field and consequently an intense magnetic field in the reference system of a moving electron. This results, for example, in the production of color when ethyl iodide is added to α-chloronaphthalene, a band corresponding to a forbidden transition of the α-chloronaphthalene being strengthened to the point where it becomes visible.[453] However, the rate of the unimolecular decomposition of benzoyl peroxide in benzene is not increased by added iodine, at least in moderate concentrations.[454] Either the peroxide decomposition goes by way of a singlet transition state or the proportion of the benzoyl peroxide in intimate association with the iodine is negligible at the concentrations used.

There are other possible examples of a magnetic field effect. Ferromagnetic Fe_2O_3 is a better catalyst for the decomposition of potassium chlorate and for the oxidation of benzidine by hydrogen peroxide than is the ordinary variety of Fe_2O_3.[455] Organometallic compounds and the Grignard reagent in particular are well-known to give both polar (carbanion-like) and radical reactions. The latter are pro-

[452] I. M. Kolthoff and A. I. Medalia, *J. Am. Chem. Soc.*, **71**, 3789 (1949).

[453] M. Kasha, *J. Chem. Phys.*, **20**, 71 (1952).

[454] G. S. Hammond, *J. Am. Chem. Soc.*, **72**, 3737 (1950).

[455] S. S. Bhatnagar, P. L. Kapur, A. S. Bhatnagar, and M. A. Quayyum, *J. Indian Chem. Soc.*, **18**, 391 (1941).

[456] B. Tamamushi and H. Akiyama, *Bull. Chem. Soc. Japan*, **12**, 382 (1937); E. Gelles and K. S. Pitzer, *J. Am. Chem. Soc.*, **77**, 1974 (1954).

moted by catalysts like Co^{++} or Fe^{++}, which must be rigidly excluded from the reaction mixture if a good yield of the products of the polar reaction is to be obtained.[457] Color changes in the reaction mixture with cobalt suggest a reaction with the Grignard reagent to give the corresponding cobalt compound. The cobalt compound is unstable and is the source of the radicals; its instability may be due to its paramagnetism.

$$CH_3MgCl + CoCl_2 \longrightarrow [CH_3—Co—Cl] \longrightarrow CH_3\cdot + \cdot CoCl$$

The present status of the field effects may be summarized as follows: both the high nuclear charge and paramagnetic effects seem to be well-established for spectroscopic transitions,[449,453] but neither of them has been demonstrated unambiguously for radical reaction rates.

Solvent Effects

While it is usually true that the most polar reactions exhibit the strongest dependence of rate or equilibrium on the nature of the solvent, it is not true that radical reactions in general are *completely* indifferent to the solvent. Not only do many radical reactions have considerable polar character, but dipole-dipole and other purely electrostatic effects are by no means the sole source of intermolecular forces. The problem of solvent effects on radical reactions is a complex one because it must be established in discussing the solvent effect that any radical chain transfer to the solvent has been eliminated or corrected for. A radical derived from the solvent will naturally differ from those produced directly by the reagent. The solvent problem is related to that of catalysis, a hydrogen bonding solvent not being very different in effect from an acid catalyst, and a nucleophilic solvent resembling a basic catalyst. The establishment of polar catalytic and structural effects in itself renders polar solvent effects on radical reactions more likely.

A phenomenon that in some cases might tend to conceal the role of the solvent is the tendency for a better solvating medium to change both the activation energy and the activation entropy in such directions as to cancel and give only a minimum effect on the actual rate of the

[457] M. S. Kharasch and W. H. Urry, *J. Org. Chem.*, **13**, 101 (1948).
[458] M. G. Alder and J. E. Leffler, *J. Am. Chem. Soc.*, **76**, 1425 (1954).
[459] J. E. Leffler and R. A. Hubbard, II, *J. Org. Chem.*, **19**, 1089 (1954).

reaction.[458, 459] A survey of solvent effects in non-chain radical reactions, where the rates often do not change much from one solvent to another, reveals that some radical reactions are genuinely indifferent to the nature of the solvent and have a constant activation energy and entropy, while others merely have about the same rate in a series of solvents at some temperature because the change in $\Delta H^{\ddagger}$ almost cancels T times the change in $\Delta S^{\ddagger}$. Aliphatic radicals and radicals in which steric hindrance prevents solvation in both the ground and transition states of the reaction can be expected to belong to the solvent-indifferent group. But more frequently both the reagent molecules and the transition state leading to the formation of radicals are likely to be solvated, and it is unlikely that precisely the same kind and degree of solvation will be most effective in stabilizing both states in spite of their both being without a formal charge. In the section on the effect of substituents we have seen that a polar substituent can have a profound effect on the rate of a radical dissociation reaction; the charge transfer structures contributing to a molecular complex should have a slighter but similar effect on the radical reactivity of a solvated or complexed molecule.

An example of probable solvation effects on the rate of a radical dissociation reaction is the order of increasing rate of the unimolecular part of the decomposition of benzoyl peroxide in various solvents. The inhibited first order rates at 80° fall in the sequence acetic anhydride > dioxane > benzene > cyclohexane > carbon tetrachloride, the range being a factor of 1.6.[440] Note that the sequence resembles that to be expected for a reaction developing charge in the transition state, although the range in rate is the small one rather typical of radical reactions and much less than might be expected of a polar reaction. It will be recalled that electron-repelling substituents accelerated the decomposition of benzoyl peroxide, and it may be significant that such substituents would decrease the interaction with nucleophilic solvents in which the reaction is faster than in more nearly inert solvents. Perfluoromethylcyclohexane is reported to be slower than benzene.[454] Benzoyl peroxide reacts rapidly at room temperature with aromatic amines, including tertiary ones, but this extremely fast reaction could be regarded as a direct oxidation of the amine rather than as a facile decomposition of the peroxide in an ordinary amine-peroxide complex.[460] A drastic increase in rate is also observed in the decomposition of azodibenzoyl when the solvent is changed from benzene to alcohol.[461]

The first order decomposition of acetyl peroxide at 85.2° has the following sequence of increasing rates[462]: carbon tetrachloride < cyclohexane < isooctane < toluene < benzene < gas phase. Acetic acid is about like cyclohexane and propionic acid is intermediate between benzene and the gas phase. The difference in rate between the fastest solvent and the gas phase is about like the difference between the slowest and the fastest solvents, a factor of 1.4. The change in activation energy on passing from toluene to the gas phase corresponds to a rate ratio of about 30, so there must be a compensating change in the pre-exponential factor or entropy of activation. The acids were omitted from the series of solvents first mentioned because the product composition is rather different, a result that has been interpreted in terms of hydrogen bonding of the acetoxy radicals by the solvent acid.[463] Szwarc has interpeted the difference between the rates in solvents and in the gas phase in terms of an enhanced probability for radical recombination within a solvent cage. The differences in activation energy from one solvent to the next do not seem to be correlated with the cohesiveness of the solvent. If there is primary recombination of radicals within the solvent cage, the apparent dissociation rate will depend both on the toughness of the cage wall and on the tendency of the wall to solvate or otherwise react with the radicals within the cage. It is extremely difficult to distinguish between the latter type of solvent effect and solvation of the transition state for radical formation. However, a good radical trap should not only prevent chain reactions but also increase the rate of the dissociation by preventing some of the recombination. Inhibited rate constants, however, are generally less rather than greater than the rate constants obtained by extrapolation to zero concentration.

[460] L. Horner and K. Scherf, *Ann.*, **573**, 35 (1951); Matsuji Takebayashi, private communication.

[461] J. E. Leffler and W. B. Bond, *J. Am. Chem. Soc.*, **78**, 335 (1956).

[462] M. Levy, M. Steinberg, and M. Szwarc, *J. Am. Chem. Soc.*, **76**, 5978 (1954).

[463] M. Levy and M. Szwarc, *J. Am. Chem. Soc.*, **76**, 5981 (1954).

We have seen that there are exceptions, explainable perhaps, but still exceptions, to the statement that radical reactions will not undergo much of a change in rate with change in solvent. Another weakness of

TABLE XV

Some Isokinetic Temperatures Falling within the Usual Experimental Range

Reaction	Approximate isokinetic temperature, °C
Dissociation of 1,1,4,4-tetraphenyl-2,3-dibenzoyl-tetrazane into radicals in chloroform, acetone, ether, and toluene.[464]	90[a]
Decomposition of phenylazotriphenylmethane in cyclohexane, diethyl malonate, and a series of aromatic solvents.[458]	40
Decomposition of triethylsulfonium bromide in a series of alcohols.[465]	60
Saponification of methyl acetate in water, acetone-water, and ethanol-water.[466]	90
Reaction of methyl iodide with pyridine in alcohol-benzene mixtures.[467]	70
Reaction of pyridine or dimethylaniline with allyl bromide in chloroform, acetone, nitrobenzene, and methanol.[468]	30
Decarboxylation of acetonedicarboxylic acid in water and a series of alcohols.[469]	70
Elimination of HCl from the β-isomer of benzene hexachloride in a series of water-alcohol mixtures.[470]	30

[a] This is an iso-equilibrium rather than an isokinetic temperature.

[464] A. Wassermann, *J. Chem. Soc.*, **1942**, 621, 623.

[465] E. A. Moelwyn-Hughes, *The Kinetics of Reactions in Solution*, 2nd edition, Oxford, 1947, p. 78.

[466] R. A. Fairclough and C. N. Hinshelwood, *J. Chem. Soc.*, **1937**, 538.

[467] R. A. Fairclough and C. N. Hinshelwood, *J. Chem. Soc.*, **1937**, 1573.

[468] V. A. Hol'tsshmidt and N. K. Vorab'ev, *Zhur. Fiz. Khim.*, 15, 1087 (1941).

[469] E. O. Wiig, *J. Phys. Chem.*, 32, 961 (1928); 34, 596 (1930).

[470] S. J. Cristol and W. Barasch, *J. Am. Chem. Soc.*, 74, 1658 (1952); S. J. Cristol, N. L. Hause, and J. S. Meek, *ibid.*, 73, 674 (1951).

the response to solvent changes as a criterion of mechanism is the existence of polar reactions insensitive to solvent changes. Because the solvent changes often affect both the energy and entropy of activation, the range in rate constants in a series of solvents is a function of the temperature, just as is the range in rate constants as structural changes are made. If, as is quite often the case, the changes in activation energy tend to parallel the changes in activation entropy, it can be shown that there is a temperature at which the solvent changes produce only a small change or no change in reaction rate. That temperature is known as the *isokinetic temperature*. A range of reaction rate through a factor of two will be considered a small one. The thing that makes it dangerous to use the lack of change in rate with solvent at a single temperature as evidence for a radical mechanism is the possibility that the temperature chosen may be at or near an isokinetic temperature. Like the other criteria for distinguishing radical from polar reactions, the solvent effect should be used in conjunction with other lines of evidence and never by itself.

Table XV lists the isokinetic temperatures of several reactions representing a wide variety of mechanisms, these examples having been chosen because the isokinetic temperature happened to fall in the popular experimental range between 0 and 100°. There are many other polar reactions that have isokinetic temperatures well outside of the accessible temperature range; there are many whose variations in activation energy and entropy are not parallel and these, of course, do not have an isokinetic temperature even approximately. When one of a series of reactions deviates markedly from a parallel trend in activation energy and entropy established by the others, it is probable that it differs in mechanism from the others. This is a better indication of a change in mechanism than either marked differences in rate or in activation energy.

AUTHOR INDEX

SUBJECT INDEX

A

Acetic anhydride, ionization of, 101.
Acetic anhydride solvent system, 101–102.
    acids and bases in, 102.
Acetoacetic ester, acid strength of, 181.
    spectrum of sodio derivative, 197.
Acetone, acid strength of, 180.
    base catalyzed reactions of, 187.
    carbonium compounds in, 97–99.
    photolysis of, 25.
    rate of proton transfer from, 193.
Acetophenone, acidity of, 179.
    condensation of, 226.
Acetylacetone, acid strength of, 182.
    rate of proton transfer from, 193.
Acetylium ions, 101–102.
Acetyl peroxide, decomposition in presence of mercury, 60.
Acid anhydrides, ionization of, 101–102.
Acid catalysis,
    and hydrogen bonding, 144.
    and ion-catalysis, 144–145.
    and the Brønsted relationship, 188, 195.
    as criterion of mechanism, 43–44, 69, 237, 246–247.
    in Beckmann rearrangement, 160.
    in Curtius reaction, 162.
    in peroxide decomposition, 167–170.
    in polymerization, 152–153.
    in radical reactions, 43–44, 69, 237, 246–247.
Acids, correlation of ionization rates and equilibria, 180, 188–189.
    cross-terms in dependence of strength on structure, 186.
    dependence of strength on structure, 180.
    ionization rates, 192.
    meaningful or accessible range of strengths, 180.
    solubility in base, and strength, 186.
    tunneling effect in proton transfer, 191.
Acrylonitrile, polymerization of, 169, 244.
Activation energy (or enthalpy), and solvation, 111, 112.

effect of solvent changes, 129.
effect of structural changes, 111.
for dissociation of hexaphenylethane, 7.
for radical recombination, 7.
isotope effect on 112–113.
parallelism with bond energy, 28.
parallelism with activation entropy, 50, 87, 112, 113, 236, 251, 252, 255.
Activation entropy, and change in multiplicity, 50.
    and energy, see Activation energy.
    and solvation, 111–112.
    and solvent, 79, 129.
    and structural changes, 111.
    and temperature dependence of relative reactivities, 78, 111.
    isotope effects on, 112–113.
    prediction from continuous dielectric solvent model, 129.
Acylium ions, 99, 131–135.
    decarbonylation of, 133.
    reaction with ethers, 134–135.
    structure and stability of, 100–101.
Acyl radicals, decarbonylation of, 33.
Addition, of carbanions, 209–214.
    of carbonium ions, 152–154.
    of diradicals, 47.
    of halogens, 118, 147.
    of hydrogen cyanide, 144–145.
    of protons, 136–144.
    of radicals, 16, 27, 30, 35, 36.
    of triphenylsilyl potassium, 212.
Alcohols, oxidation of, 172–173.
Aldehydes, see Addition.
Aldehydes, radicals from, 33–34.
Alkali metals in liquid ammonia, 71.
Alkoxy radicals, non-rearrangement to α-hydroxyalkyl radicals, 59.
O-Alkylation, 226–227.
p-Alkyl benzhydryl chlorides, solvolysis of, 111.
N-Alkylhydroxylamines, decomposition of, 162, 164.
    migration aptitudes in, 162, 164.
Allylic organometallic compounds, direction of reaction of, 202, 215–216.

E

F

G

H

L

Lead tetraethyl, antiknock function of, 25.
Lead tetramethyl, decomposition of, 24, 27–28.
Lewis acids, as ionization promotors, 94.
  effect of inert solvent components with, 95.
  stabilization of diradicals by, 44, 249.
Lobry de Bruyn rearrangement, 126.
Lossen rearrangement, 165.

M

Magnetic catalysis, 249–251, see also pp. 49–50.
  by heavy nuclei, 250.
  by paramagnetic substances, 250.
Malachite green, geometry of, 90.
Malachite green azide, color in solvents, 98–99.
Malachite green chloride, dissociation of, 98.
Malononitrile, acidity of, 181.
  deviation from rate-equilibrium relationship, 189.
Mass law effect, 107.
Maxwell Demon, 37.
Mechanical production of radicals, 37–38.
Mechanism, dual, 65, 164, 167, 168–169, 171, 247.
Meerwein-Ponndorf reduction, 210.
Menthol, use as indicator, 179.
Mercaptans, addition to methyl acrylate, 65.
Mesitoic acid, esterification of, 86.
Mesityl magnesium bromide, as condensation catalyst, 224.
Metal or metal ion, in condensation reactions, 225–226.
  role of, 145, 215–218, 232.
Meta substituents, effect in radicals, 13.
Methacrylonitrile, polymerization by triphenylmethyl sodium, 214.
Methanesulfonic acid, cryoscopy in, 84.
p-Methoxy-p'-nitrobenzoyl peroxide, polar and radical reactions of, 61, 169.
Methyl acetoacetate, acidity of, 181.
  deviation from rate-equilibrium relationship, 189.

Methyl acrylate, polymerization of, 243.
Methylallyl chlorides, reaction with organometalic compounds, 208.
Methyl bromide, solvolysis of, 110
Methylene diradical, 45.
Methylethylacetyl peroxide, optically active, 27.
Methyl lithium, 175.
Methyl methacrylate polymerization, by Grignard reagents, 214.
  by radicals, 244.
  by sodium or potassium, 244.
  by triphenylmethyl sodium, 214.
Methyl methacrylate-styrene copolymerization, as diagnostic reaction, 244.
Methyl radical, half-life of, 25.
Methyl sodium, 175.
Michael rearrangement, 225.
Migrating group, retention of configuration by, 170, 230.
Migration aptitudes, as criterion of mechanism, 243.
  electronic determination of, 122.
  in nitrogen diradicals, 47, 162–163.
  in oxidation of ketones by peracids, 170–171.
  in oxygen cations, 48.
  in oxygen radicals, 48, 58.
  in radicals, 32.
  reaction mechanism and, 58.
  steric determination of, 123–125.
Mirror technique for radicals, 24.
Molecular complexes, of azulene, 140.
  of radicals and inhibitors, 62.
  solvation and, 62, 93.
Molecular orbitals, geometry and, 7, 8.
Multiple reactivity, resonance and, 19, 24, 68, 130, 214–216.
Mustard gas, 117.

N

Negative ion, effect on ionization equilibrium, 99.
Neighboring group effect, 116.
  carbanion analog of, 231.
Neophyl radical, rearrangement of, 32–34.
Nitric oxide, reaction with radicals, 18, 66, 67, 68.
Nitrobenzene, orientation of radical reaction, 30.
Nitrocyclohexane, oxidation of, 220.

V

Vinyl acetate, polymerization of, 243.
Vinyl lithium compounds, geometrical
stability of, 198.

W

Wieland rearrangement, 56, 57.
Wolf rearrangement, 45–46.
Wurster's salts, 36, 70–71.

X

Xanthene acidity of, 179.

Z

Zethrene, 141.
Zipper reaction, 38.